BRIAN WILLIAMS

Materials
Management
Handbook

Materials Management Handbook

Peter Baily and David Farmer

A Gower Handbook

Published by
Gower Publishing Company Limited
Aldershot, Hants, England

Reprinted 1984

British Library Cataloguing in Publication Data

Baily, Peter
　Materials management handbook.
　1. Materials management
　I. Title　　II. Farmer, David
　658.7　　　TS161

ISBN 0-566-02272-9

Printed and bound in Great Britain
at The Pitman Press, Bath

Contents

Preface

This handbook is written to be of use to anyone who is concerned with the management of materials, whether as buyer, production controller, stock controller, stores manager, systems analyst, consultant or general manager. The book originated in an attempt to revise *Managing Materials in Industry* (Gower, 1972) for a new edition. It was found that many chapters had to be omitted to make room for important new material, and most of the rest had to be rewritten because of the advances and changes which have occurred on so many fronts. Hence the new title, for what is substantially a new book.

We start with a brief discussion of the importance of materials and of how this has changed relative to other aspects of the management task, and go on in Chapter 2 to consider the general case for materials management. Chapter 3 examines the adoption in practice of various types of materials management organisation, and an attempt is made to isolate the key variables which influence the choice between specific types of organisation. It is hoped that this chapter will be of practical use to those who are considering the reorganisation of their materials-related activities.

The next four chapters provide a general introduction to production planning and control and inventory planning and control and some useful techniques are introduced. The concepts of dependent and independent demand are explained in Chapter 5. Systems for independent demand in the distributive environment are explained in Chapter 6, while Chapter 7 deals with MRP for dependent demand in the manufacturing environment. Major improvements in computer systems and their application to the materials area have occurred recently, and in real terms there have been significant reductions in cost; a selection of currently available computer systems for materials planning and control is reviewed in Chapter 8.

Two chapters on storing and moving materials are followed by two chapters on purchasing them. The important subject of negotiating comes up for consideration in Chapter 13, which suggests a number of guidelines for those who want to improve their negotiating ability.

A comprehensive account of quality control is given in Chapter 14; new methods such as quality circles as well as long established ones such as control charts and statistical sampling are explained.

The next three chapters deal with the vital topics connected with people in organisations: recruiting, training and developing, and motivating them. Under the latter heading there is an account of value analysis and of a proposal to treat a materials department as a profit centre, as well as a discussion of the human relations school. The last chapter deals with strategic planning and supply.

The twelve case studies at the end of the book can be used on in-company or business school courses, or by individual readers to consider the practical applications of matters considered in the text.

We thank P J A Herbert and T Patrick for their help with two of the case studies. We renew our thanks to J A Smith of the Polytechnic of Wales and to J I Hyam, formerly editor-in-chief of *Mechanical Handling*, for the original versions of Chapters 4, 9 and 10. We are particularly grateful to Rob Wagstaff for his treatment of quality control and for the first case study, and we thank John Read for his contribution on inventory control systems for retail distribution.

Peter Baily
David Farmer

Illustrations

Notes on contributors

New material for this edition has been contributed by R Wagstaff (Chapter 14 and the case study Eden Foods), R J Read (Chapter 6), and the co-authors D H Farmer and P J H Baily. The book was edited by P J H Baily.

PETER BAILY, BSc, ACIS, FInstPS, MBPICS, started off as a telecommunications mechanic and later worked in machine tool manufacturing and textile industries as a buyer, materials controller, chief buyer and assistant to company secretary. Has worked with the Business Education Council for several years as Board member, moderator, member of the Validating Committee and several working parties, and is a member of the Education and Training committee of the IPS. Author of several books and many articles, he has addressed conferences and contributed to courses in the USA, Ireland, Holland, Italy, Switzerland and the UK.

DAVID FARMER, MSc, PhD, FInstPS, has worked in heavy engineering, timber, refractories and aluminium industries and is now Professor of Management Studies at the Administrative Staff College, Henley. Co-author of several books and many articles, he has addressed conferences and contributed to courses in most European countries, South-east Asia, Australia and the United States, and is well-known as a consultant.

J I HYAM, entered journalism after graduating from Cambridge with a law degree. A fellow of the Institute of Materials Handling, Hyam is a well-known expert on materials handling and storage and has lectured in Italy, Switzerland, the UK and the USA. Formerly editor-in-chief of *Mechanical Handling*.

R JOHN READ has worked in the paper, industrial gas and food industries, mainly in the management services area. He is now research and development manager with the W H Smith & Son Ltd Retail Division. He is particularly concerned with business systems, especially POS systems at present.

J A SMITH, DIC, CEng, MIProdE, MIMechE, AMBIM, joined the staff of the Glamorgan College of Technology from the Steel Company of Wales Ltd, in 1963. Sabbatical year in 1966 to study and research in operational research and production engineering at Imperial College. Now Principal Lecturer in Industrial Engineering at the Polytechnic of Wales. Has written many papers and articles.

ROBIN WAGSTAFF, MBA, MBIM, FBPICS, qualified initially as a metallurgist and worked on metallurgical quality control and process control in the steel and engineering industries. In 1970 he joined the GKN group as a production manager with responsibilities which included production planning and control, quality control and transport. He gained an MBA from Cranfield Institute of Technology in 1976, and moved into education, first as a research associate in the Cranfield School of Management and then at the Polytechnic of North London where he is now Principal Lecturer. He retains close links with industry and commerce through in-company training and consultancy, mainly in the field of materials management, and is actively engaged in the development of specialist courses and teaching materials in this area.

Part One

Materials management and the organisation structure

Chapter 1

Materials matter more

Materials tend in many cases to account for an increasing proportion of product costs. Also, the problems encountered in connection with materials are tending to become more difficult and more numerous than was previously the case. In consequence, management needs to focus more attention, more talent and more time on the management of materials.

The term *materials* is used in a general sense and refers to the whole range of goods and services which are purchased or otherwise procured from sources outside the organisation, and are used or processed or distributed in order to provide finished products for sale. Such materials are often the finished products of other producers. In this general sense, energy and a variety of specialised services will be included under the heading of materials, as well as raw materials, component parts, processed and semi-manufactured materials, and merchandise for resale. Everything in fact which a trading organisation acquires from outside and then operates upon, using its human resources, its financial resources and its plant and equipment in order to produce its market offering, can be seen as materials in this sense.

Upward trend of material cost

Several tendencies can be identified which are contributing to an increasing emphasis by manufacturers on the management of materials. It is not suggested that the manufacturing processes themselves are not important; clearly they are of central importance, they are what makes a manufacturing business what it is. Nor would we wish to rank in order of importance such functional aspects of the management task as marketing, finance, product design, quality control, personnel, etc. The emphasis is rather on the need for cross-functional collaboration, and where conflicts exist on the sensible negotiation of trade-offs. To facilitate the better management of materials flow, many firms have reorganised their materials-related activities, along lines discussed in the next two chapters.

Immersed as most people are in the day-to-day problems of business, it is not always easy to detect a long-term trend or to distinguish it from a short-term fluctuation. But one trend is clear enough in manufacturing industries: the proportion of total revenue spent on the acquisition of materials has been gradually increasing until it has become four or five times as great as that required for the remuneration of direct labour. Similar developments seem to be occurring in retailing and other tertiary industries. The reduction in personal service and other labour-intensive aspects, the speed-up in distribution, and the automation of parts of the information collection and processing systems, have urged distributive industries along the same path as manufacturing industries, towards greater emphasis on the planning and control of the merchandise flow.

Downward trend of other costs

An upward trend of material cost is occurring at the same time as a downward trend of certain other costs. The gradual move towards mechanisation and automation in the manufacturing processes has for a century been progressively replacing the muscles of the labourer and the skills of the craftsman by materials handling equipment and machine tools of increasing sophistication; computer-aided manufacture (CAM) is the current catchword for one aspect of this, and robots appear to have made the breakthrough from science fiction to the shop floor. Recently, and much less gradually, a similar move has occurred in offices. Dazzling advances in electronic technology and its applications to information technology, informatics, the electronic office, will affect not only the drudgery but also the often undervalued skills of the clerk. Administrative work, like manufacturing work, is becoming less labour-intensive. Human effort is able to augment its effect while reducing the man-hours required. Inevitably this has led to unemployment, and some jobs which cannot have been very pleasant to perform have been tenaciously clung to by their holders. (Printers for instance fought many a doughty battle to retain obsolete technology around 1980). Although the jobs which survived these changes tended to be well paid, labour costs were significantly reduced, in relation not only to direct product cost but also to overhead cost.

While the proportion of operating costs which were due to labour was being reduced, thus indirectly increasing the proportion due to materials, other developments were directly increasing material costs. One of these is the fact that in an advanced and complex industrial economy, increasingly specialist suppliers offer services or products at prices and to standards which in-house provision could match only with the greatest difficulty. An ever increasing range of new manufacturing processes, products, materials, components and services are becoming available to the manufacturer. Any manufacturer would be at a considerable competitive disadvantage if these opportunities to improve the product or reduce the production cost were rejected in favour of making under its own roof all the components required. Some intermediate goods can be bought out at lower prices and to higher standards than they could be made internally; others can be bought at higher prices which lead nevertheless to lower product costs because internal machining or assembly processes are reduced or eliminated; and others lead to higher product costs and better product performance, so that customers get better value for money even though they pay more for the product than they would for an inferior product. But in all three cases, material costs increase relative to total product costs.

Another development is the increase in transport costs. Industry has become very dependent on fast reliable transport to move parts, materials, sub-assemblies and merchandise from producers to the factories at which the next stage of production is carried out and from factories to distribution centres and to customers. By 1981 almost all the transport services, whether by road, rail, air or water, depended on oil as the basis for their motive power. The very steep rises in oil prices imposed by the oil producer cartel made all forms of transport much more expensive. Close attention to transport planning and careful study of alternatives can materially reduce costs. Such study extends beyond transport modes and routes to policy matters such as the provision of intermediate stocking points, distribution centres and emergency ware-house stocks. Costs can be reduced relative to what they would otherwise have been, but will still be higher than they once were. High transport costs increase the costs of materials.

Oil is only one of the many gifts of nature on which all production is ultimately based, and nature's bounty is not inexhaustible. The subterranean pools of oil which power our ships, trucks, trains and aircraft, as well as many of our electricity generating stations, which run our motor cars and are the basis for many plastics and fertilisers, are not infinite in extent. If consumption continued to increase as it had done in the previous quarter of a century, known reserves would hardly last a lifetime. We are making rapidly increasing demands on the limited resources of a finite earth.

Many gloomy predictions have been made about the more or less imminent exhaustion of vital natural resources, and some have been excessively pessimistic. But as Dr Waterman has pointed out[1]:

> Over the past five years the selling prices of many materials, both metals and plastics, have been insufficient to generate the investment capital necessary for new processing plant; yet this plant when commissioned may reasonably be expected to have to process lower quality materials and leaner ores, conserving greater quantities of more expensive energy, under tougher legislative controls on pollution and safety, to produce the same tonnage of refined products.

Here we see a combination of three tendencies. While most raw materials still exist in abundance, the rich seams have already been exploited; leaner ores have to be processed to extract the mineral required. The processing demands energy, which is increasingly costly. And thirdly, people are insisting, through their legislative chan-nels, that the processing should cause less pollution to the environment and less danger to the population. All three add up to costlier materials; and more material problems, with the new long-term threat of permanent shortages looming behind the ever-present threat of temporary shortages.

Industrialisation in what is often called the Third World is also likely to add to the pressure on material resources, although it has of course a positive side which some would regard as more important. The so-called Third World comprises a large part of the world and many different countries in which people live mostly by farming, fishing, mining and other primary industries. To add to the wealth of the nations, and to increase a standard of living which, as conventionally measured, is much lower than that prevailing in the advanced industrial countries, secondary industries are being developed. This is also occurring in countries which are at present extremely rich, but owe their riches to the presence of a single natural resource such as oil which can be sold at a high price but will not last for long. These new secondary industries will make demands for energy far greater than is at present required for peasant farming, and will also consume materials. The resultant increase in world demand for energy and other materials seems likely to increase materials' costs as well as the threat of shortages.

It is also likely to increase enormously the search area for supply sources. Basic industries which are both materials-intensive and labour-intensive, such as steel, may perhaps be most competitively located where materials are locally available and labour is relatively inexpensive. At the other extreme, advanced electronic components are also being produced in places which electronics engineers had hardly heard of a few years ago.

These are some of the reasons why it seems likely that the historical tendency for materials to account for a gradually increasing proportion of the total cost of products will continue, and perhaps accelerate; and that the problems associated with the planning, procurement, transport and control of materials will become more challenging, wide-ranging and complex.

Need to improve performance

Turning from long-term trends to short-term problems one finds a similar emphasis. High interest rates have made managements even more conscious of the need for good, tight, flexible stock control. Must stocks swell up like a balloon as soon as there is a downturn in sales or a recession? Must they run out as soon as the order book starts to fill up? How can a better service level be achieved without worsening the stock turn rate?

Part of the answer to these questions lies in better stock control, with faster response to changes in market conditions. Part lies in better production planning and control, since work in progress accounts for a large part of manufacturing stocks, and another large part is held to cover for errors, changes and delays in scheduling production and estimating requirements. Part lies in better purchasing: short lead times, reliable on-time delivery from suppliers can substantially reduce the stock-holding which is necessary to give the required service. And part lies in better transport and stores arrangements.

Customers also have realised that shorter lead times and more reliable on-time deliveries by their suppliers can reduce their stock investment and improve their service. Management's need to provide shorter, more reliable deliveries and with greater flexibility in order to keep and to gain customers, increases the pressure for better stock control, possibly at least as much as the need to control working capital when the cost of money is high.

Better purchasing is concerned with finding and trading with better suppliers. But this should not be seen just in the context of stock control, or production control. The basic job of purchasing may be to deliver on time from outside suppliers the required quantities of materials as specified, with due regard to the price aspect which colleagues in other departments tend to ignore. But in addition to the basic job of supplying requirements, purchasing staff need to survey the whole world in search of better sources of supply. They operate in an increasingly turbulent environment.

One instance of this is the development of Third World sources mentioned above. Another is the availability of East European sources within the Soviet empire, which are obliged to make deals through some central government agency. Often some kind of barter deal is set up because they are in a different currency bloc. Counter-purchase transactions such as vodka for the USA in exchange for coca-cola for the USSR bring new complications involving trade-offs between purchasing and marketing.

Coordination

This example of the need for purchasing and marketing specialists to coordinate their efforts could be paralleled by a number of others. For instance fluctuations in the exchange rates of currencies bring new complications to buying (and selling) in other countries. Exchange rates used to remain constant for years at a time. Now they vary from day-to-day, and quite substantial changes can occur in periods of time comparable with the lead time on major contracts. For instance $2000 exchanged for £1143 in 1976 when the dollar-pound sterling rate was 1.75. The same sum in dollars exchanged for only £833 in 1980 when the dollar-sterling rate was 2.4. During the same period wages rose faster in Britain than in the USA and costs inflated at a substantially higher rate. The result was that in 1980 British factories were buying iron castings from foundries in Massachusetts at a time when British foundries were closing at the rate of one a week. Printing work was being carried out in America, and also in Hong Kong and Taiwan, while British printers were short of work. Similar developments occurred with other currencies, for instance the French franc—thousands of French people descended on London to do their shopping in 1976 then in 1980 cross channel ferry operators were organising special trips for British people to shop at supermarkets in France.

Buyers face an increasing range of choices and challenges in their efforts to supply requirements in a way which will enable their organisations to meet and beat the competition. There are no easy answers (as case study No. 5, XYZ Excavator makes clear). And purchasing needs to work in collaboration with finance to meet either the objective of reducing the risk of loss, or the objective of increasing the chance of profit, in connection with the currency exposure involved in these international contracts.

The need is to ensure the supply of materials, not necessarily at lower cost, but more profitably. When this involves the coordination of purchasing with non-materials-related activities such as finance or marketing, and when the potential contribution of purchasing to profitability is substantial, then perhaps purchasing should not be included in the materials management structure but should stand alone. When the main problem is to coordinate the materials-related activities, then purchasing should perhaps be part of the materials management structure. Coordination and cooperation between functional specialists is really what materials management is about.

References

1   Waterman, N A, *Facing up to a Future of Materials Shortages,* Design Engineering Conference, NEC Birmingham, October 1979.

Chapter 2

Why materials management?

The philosophical arguments for adopting materials management envisage an organisation as a whole rather than as a series of elements.[1] They promote the idea of effective collaboration between the various elements of a system towards the achievement of commonly agreed objectives. They indicate the problems caused by attempting to optimise at the "element" level rather than in respect of the enterprise as a whole. And they imply that many problems occur between departments (elements) rather than in them.

For and against

However, while the concept is appealing, the practicality of applying the ideas in medium to large firms has been questioned.[2] Two primary reasons are often quoted in support of this view. The first is that management methods/techniques are not sophisticated enough to allow one manager to handle the scope of the responsibility involved. Related to this is a second reason that computer software systems are not advanced enough to allow effective processing of a sufficient quantity of data of adequate quality. A third, more fundamental, argument sometimes used is that in many firms there is an executive (called general manager, or some similar title) who already performs an overall control function.

The latter argument would be dismissed by the proponents of materials management with the riposte that the orientation of a general manager would not normally result in the achievement of the objectives of the concept. No doubt they would also respond to both other "reasons" by citing examples of successful application of their concept in a wide variety of industries. The literature includes several references to support this argument.[3] In addition, there is some evidence that those who are promoting various other "systems" approaches are gradually widening the scope of their defined area of activity. Thus, for example, physical distribution management,[4] materials administration and materials management have each been defined by different writers as involving the total flow of materials from supplier to customer.

Indeed, the cynical reader of the supporting literature might be excused from feeling that each concept has proponents, all of whom are aiming for the wider acceptance of their "product". However, in widening their reference areas, by implication, each writer is supporting the feasibility of the total-flow management approach.

Admittedly, there are cases where a "system-wide" approach (whatever it might be called) has been applied successfully. However, the majority of organisations are not currently in a position, practically or philosophically, to apply these concepts across their systems as a whole. If this hypothesis is correct, and given that the concept of effective coordination is desirable (and it *is* difficult to refute), in which ways might the ensuing advantages be best achieved, having in mind the inadequacies of management control discussed earlier?

One approach involves the introduction of the philosophy and practice of coordination to a segment of the business as an initial step. At first glance this might appear to be a contradiction in terms, for it implies a separation of activity within the system. For example, an examination of the processes in a manufacturing concern, will illustrate that there are present two basic flows – input and output. While a management would be foolish to ignore the inter-relationship between these flows, each is a significant system in its own right. Further, each is complex in that it interfaces with a set of external systems (customers and suppliers). Consequently each area necessitates considerable attention in itself, particularly since effective coordination between functions is still far from common in industrial concerns.

Quite apart from any organisational implications, the systems approaches involve the acceptance of a basic philosophy by managements. They also necessitate commitment to the application of that philosophy as distinct from one of sectional interests. Very few organisations have succeeded in sublimating functional biases in the interests of total system effectiveness and efficiency.[5] It follows that there is a better chance that a philosophy can be developed in a recognisable segment of a business more easily than across the business as a whole. Further, that the concentration of management effort on applying the philosophy to that segment will help ensure that the potential benefits of the approach are recognised and realised more quickly than would otherwise be possible. In turn, successful application should prove to be a motivator for a similar drive in the other major segment of the business. The step to the integrated system-wide approach is then probably one of evolution.

The input segment will be referred to as "materials management", though, as was pointed out earlier, the area thus defined may well be narrower than that suggested by some definitions. This approach should serve several purposes. It should help to appraise managers concerned with the PDM area of the many implications of materials management which affect their own performance. It should help them to relate more effectively to the various aspects of the input systems of their own customers. It should provide those who are contemplating the development of a systems approach within their own organisation with an alternative starting point for the introduction of such a philosophy. Then it should provide the reader who is, as yet, uncommitted to the systems philosophy, with a view of its potential in an alternative environment. Apart from anything else it may also serve as a reminder of the importance of input management long and short-term, in strategic as well as operational terms, to the efficiency and effectiveness of, for example, the majority of firms engaged in manufacturing.

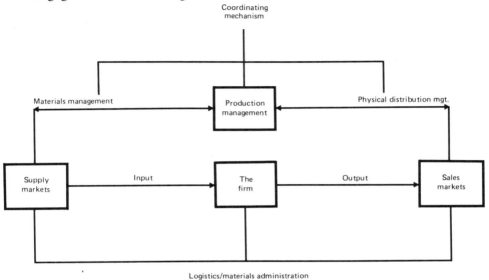

FIGURE 2:1   A CONCEPTUAL VIEW OF A MANUFACTURING FIRM

Materials management and PDM

Conceptually the relationship between materials management and the remainder of the system may be illustrated as in Figure 2.1.

The scope of materials management in this view embraces the management of the flow of materials from the supply market into the firm. It may be defined as:

The concept concerned with the management of the flow of materials into an organisation to the point where those materials are converted into the firm's end product(s). Responsibilities include collaboration with designers on material component specifications, purchasing – which includes the search for, and location of, suitable economic sources of supply, incoming traffic, goods receiving and inspection, supplier quality control, inventory control (raw materials and components and, possibly, work-in-progress) and material control. In some cases internal materials handling would also be included.

Clearly, if a systems approach has not been adopted, then the various functions which are embraced by the definition would generally be seen as separate departments, or as elements within more traditional departments, e.g. production control.

As with all systems approaches, the main thrust of the materials management concept is to avoid sub-optimisation; to look for system efficiency and effectiveness;

and to help ensure the achievement of common objectives rather than those which apply to elements within the system, which may be competing one with another. In addition, it should be concerned with "supply marketing", which implies an orientation towards the environment within which the firm operates as a buyer.

This latter part of the task may be seen as the linking mechanism with the many physical distribution systems with which it is in contact. This is suggested by Figure 2.2 which illustrates the mutuality of these relationships as regards efficiency and effectiveness. The scope of activity is, thus, considerable and, as has been argued elsewhere, it has important potential in terms of the efficiency and effectiveness of the total system. While many firms in the recent past tended to treat the supply segment of their business as mundane and strategically unimportant, things are changing fast. Firstly, the shortages and price escalation associated with 1973/4 have alerted many more managements to the importance of their supply markets. The demise of the pound in the mid-seventies and the resultant impact on the cost of imported materials and components emphasised that importance.[6] Then, the economic pressures in many markets, where the forecast upturn in trade has not transpired, are such that they tend to focus management attention on major costs. Since purchase costs typically account for more than fifty per cent of the total income of the average manufacturing concern, this enhanced attention is hardly surprising.

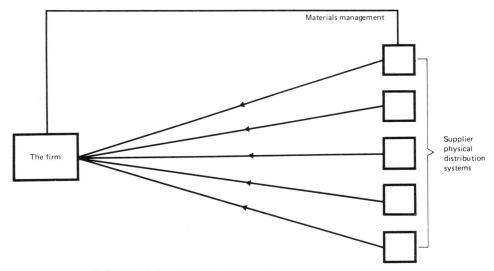

FIGURE 2:2   THE LINK WITH SUPPLIER SYSTEMS

Conflicts and trade-offs

Several studies have sought to explore the potential of the materials management approach. Zenz[7], for example, from an extensive research published in 1968 stated:

Materials Management provides concise delegation of responsibility and authority, eliminating the possibility that departments may have overlapping respon-sibilities. In so doing it recognises the importance of the management principle of accountability by providing a materials manager who is responsible for all aspects of materials decisions – a condition lacking in conventional organisation.

Ammer[8] had previously listed the possible conflicts and trade-offs between objec-tives relating to materials in a conventional departmental organisation (Figure 2.3) Ammer's thesis was that effective coordination through the adoption of the materials management approach would eliminate many of the problems associated with these conflicts.

Fearon,[9] reviewing the progress of materials management up to 1973, argues that:

> The Materials Manager, placed in a position to exercise direct control over all materials functions, can maintain the necessary overview and can assure that needed balance of functions is, in fact, achieved.

He goes on to argue that this balancing of functions results from two subsidiary objectives of materials management. The first of these is "To co-ordinate the performance of the materials function into a total materials system, in which the whole is greater than the sum of the parts". The second objective is: "To provide a communications network among the several materials functions that provides a quick, accurate, and comprehensive transfer of data, regarding demands occurring anywhere along the system."

Fearon's list of benefits which firms believed they had realised from adopting the materials management approach, includes elimination of buck passing; better inter-departmental cooperation; lower prices for materials and equipment; faster inven-tory turnover; continuity of supply; reduced material lead times; reduced transporta-tion costs; less duplication of effort; better morale; development of personnel; reduced materials obsolescence; improved supplier relationships and better records and information.

Market changes

Since Fearon's article appeared, the pressures on material supply, including cost and availability have escalated probably at a faster rate than ever before. In the UK the 1973 oil crisis with its aftermath of material shortages and frightening rates of inflation, forced managements to pay greater attention to supply factors. The area in many concerns which had been thought of in operational terms was now emphasised as of strategic concern. Inventory costs in the light of extremely expensive money became a focal point of activity in every organisation of any size. Purchase prices seemingly continued changing in an upward spiral as internal inflation was fuelled by the decline of the pound against other currencies. The importance of materials to the economy of manufacturing concerns was now not in question.

As has been argued elsewhere,[10] the measures taken to alleviate the problems which occurred most significantly in 1973/74 were of a defensive nature. Since that

Primary objective	Inter-related objectives that are adversely affected
1 Minimum prices for materials	High inventory turnover, continuity of supply, consistency of quality, low payroll costs, favourable relations with supply sources.
2 High inventory turnover	Minimum prices, low cost of acquisition and possession, continuity of supply, low payroll costs.
3 Low cost of acquisition and possession	High inventory turnover (sometimes), good records, continuity of supply, consistency of quality.
4 Continuity of supply	Minimum prices for materials, high inventory turnover, favourable relations with suppliers, consistency of quality.
5 Consistency of quality	Minimum prices for materials, high inventory turnover, continuity of supply, favourable relations with suppliers, low payroll costs, low costs of acquisition and possession.
6 Low payroll costs	Maximum achievement of this objective is possible only by sacrificing all other objectives.
7 Good suppliers relations	Low payroll costs, minimum prices, high inventory turnover.
8 Development of personnel	Low payroll costs (other objectives might also be affected).
9 Good records	Low payroll costs (other objectives might also be affected).

FIGURE 2:3   POSSIBLE CONFLICTS BETWEEN DEPARTMENTAL MATERIALS
OBJECTIVES

time the downturn in world trade has eased the majority of supply availability problems if not the financial implications. Consequently, many organisations have had the opportunity to reorganise themselves to take advantage of the lessons learned in 1973.

These pressures were significant in motivating changes in the market interface of materials systems in manufacturing concerns. A study undertaken by MacMillan and Farmer[11] showed that "raw materials shortages" and "the oil crisis" were the two most significant factors in causing buyers and sellers to work more closely together.

The advantages of this improved liaison cited by respondents were, not surprisingly, closely related to those suggested by Fearon. They included; "better liaison purchasing/production; better utilisation of own production facilities, better utilisation of stores, warehouses, and stockyards and better relationships with sources of supply". It would appear that improved liaison between parties in the total system is crucial to such benefits. However, there is little doubt that the advantages will accrue most readily and most quickly where the internal organisation is in a position to control its activities as it mates with those of its suppliers. The materials management approach would appear to offer a sound base from which to relate to supplier organisations. However, as has been suggested, materials management requires the commitment of top management to the concept involved and professional, capable management of the area if the objectives discussed earlier are to be achieved. The materials manager should be of a calibre commensurate with the importance of the task he has to undertake. He should be able to relate to colleagues within his own organisation and in those of suppliers, at the highest level. The objectives, goals and policies towards and within which he needs to work should be clearly defined. Like his marketing colleagues he needs to be consumer oriented but with the added responsibility of extending that orientation into his supplier's systems.

Ericsson,[12] writing about materials administration suggests that several other requirements need to be present in the company system if the approach is to be effective. He argues that management expertise should exist within the company to enable the approach to be adopted, and that management should have available to it the appropriate information processing equipment and techniques. Further that costs – especially those connected with the materials system – should be capable of being analysed and accounted for with a reasonable degree of accuracy. Then that top management, as well as those concerned with the materials system, should be wedded to the concept.

These requirements for system effectiveness are just as applicable to either PDM or material management. And while it is true that many current accounting arrangements, for example, are unsuitable for systems approaches there would appear to be a better chance for successful adaptation on a sub-system basis as a first step. Though it is probably true to say that the relevant deficiencies at the input end of many company systems are greater than in the majority of others. Nonetheless, the potential rewards – once recognised – are so great that the motivation to implement the materials management approach should ensure that these deficiencies are repaired relatively quickly

The significance of materials

The UK Census of Production for 1974 showed that the purchases of all UK manufacturing industries amounted to a total of £49,000 million. Direct labour costs, on the other hand totalled £10,500 million – a ratio of 4.7 to 1. The "average" manufacturing company thus disposed of more than four times the amount it paid for its direct labour on purchasing materials, components and services. Another relevant statistic relating to manufacturing costs is that the "average" company disposed of some 56 per cent of its income in buying materials and components. The impact of this statistic may be seen from the following illustration:

Company X has an annual turnover of £1 million, made a profit of 10% on its operations last year and spends £500,000 per annum on materials and components. If company X, through more effective and efficient materials management, was able to make a saving of 5% in its material costs it would *earn* a further £25,000, making a major contribution to the company's profit. Thus:

Income	*Profit*	
£1 million	at 10%	£100,000
Purchases £500,000 – saving 5% =		£25,000
	Total profit	£125,000

Assuming that at the same profit level the company wanted to make an equivalent profit without the contribution from the materials area, it would need to increase its turnover by 25%. In the light of this simple illustration, a 5% saving in material costs can equate in profit terms to a 25% increase in turnover. The converse is also true.

It may be argued that this is an over simplification of the situation. Such complications as utilisation of resources, additional marketing cost and possible effect of materials cost savings against larger volumes are ignored. Nonetheless, even when all are considered the basic fact remains that a £1 saved on materials costs is a £1 extra profit. A pound increase in turnover can only contribute a percentage of that sum to profit.

Implementing materials management

Given the commitment of management at all levels, an initial step in implementing a materials management approach frequently involves the formation of a project group. One of the group's initial tasks is to define the objectives of the materials system as related to corporate objectives. In so doing many anomalies of existing functional organisation will be uncovered, together with discrepancies in the information and control systems which are being applied. Existing systems most often reflect functional parameters and the project group has the opportunity to take a fresh view, orientating control towards the materials system as a whole. Ericsson[13] argues that such work should be undertaken in terms of decision-making points along the materials flow, not in existing departments. The task is then to locate these points, analyse what data are required at these centres and how to integrate them.

The reorganisation which inevitably follows such analysis needs to be dealt with carefully. Experience has shown that people who believe they have much to gain from such changes actively support the work in every way. Conversely those who feel exposed or threatened by the development take an opposite approach. Many of the latter fears are unfounded, but it requires skillful management to convince the people concerned. Nonetheless it is probably inevitable that the quality of the staff in the materials area will need to be scrutinised carefully if the concept is to achieve its potential. Traditional views of materials implying purely operational level management result in many cases, in a less than adequate quality of staff being employed in the area. As a result changes are often necessary.

In several organisations an early intiative in implementing the materials management concept has been a short series of workshops. As many relevant people as possible have been involved in discussions relating to implementation. Generally the workshop starts with a statement of reasons for the adoption of the concept. Then discussion groups examine, for example, problems associated with the current organisation in the materials area; the advantages and disadvantages which are believed to apply to the adoption of materials management; and the recommendations of participants as to ways of achieving those advantages while minimising the disadvantages.

Typical problems mentioned by materials staff include:

1   Poor communications with production and marketing.
2   Little influence on decisions taken by production and marketing.
3   No overall control in the materials area, with the various parts of the system working as if independent of each other.
4   Poor relationships with design engineering.

Frequent schedule changes, inadequate specifications, out of balance inventories and poor relationships with suppliers, are among the difficulties which have been suggested as resulting from the foregoing problems. Most groups have seen a materials management organisation as providing a broader, more influential base, from which they might collaborate more effectively with colleagues and suppliers. Typical initiatives which have been suggested include:

1   A formal link with design engineering in order to provide materials supply data to them. To collaborate with them (and with specialist suppliers) in order to meet their needs. And to promote rationalisation and standardisation of components and materials.
2   A closer link with marketing with similar objectives, again promoting, in conjunction with production, the advantages of range rationalisation on costs and pricing.
3   Improved forecasting and scheduling through more effective consultation within

the company with the considerable advantages which can accrue in terms of better data to suppliers.

4   More effective purchase specifications and greater discipline with purchase routines as a result.

5   More effective "Make" or "Buy" decision-making stemming from improved liaison with production and better cost data.

6   And a much better opportunity to measure performance in a materials management organisation as against a functional structure.

7   Better links with suppliers' PDM systems which have been suggested include:
    (a)   More careful consideration of the purchased component/material design-/packing/handling characteristics in order to minimise total costs *between* buyer and seller.
    (b)   Closer liaison between buyer and seller resulting in better data flow, more careful consideration of the interface problems of the two information systems.
    (c)   And better utilisation of transport resources through, for example, more efficient despatching and the use of return loading.

Typically, the last session of these materials management workshops has been devoted to "action plans", the basic idea behind these sessions being to ask participants to set themselves objectives based upon their discussions. Results, thus far, have been extremely encouraging in terms of the achievement of those objectives. The promise of materials management coupled with the involvement of those concerned in planning and implementation, appear to be key ingredients in this success.

Perhaps managers in the materials area, faced by a lack of enthusiasm for the concept, should seek the support of their colleagues in marketing. After all, the more effective and efficient the input system the lower the production cost and, thus, potentially the more competitive the company's end product in its market place. Materials management is no panacea for all ills, but as one marketing manager put it to the writer, "It can be a wonderful balm for my ulcers".

References

1   See, for example, Magee, John F *Industrial Logistics*, McGraw-Hill (1968)
2   Fearon, Harold E "Materials Management, A Synthesis and Current Review", *Journal of Purchasing*, volume 9, no 1 (February, 1973)
3   Op. cit. ref.1
4   See, for example, Bowersox, Donald J *Logistical Management*, MacMillan (1974)
5   The reasons are numerous; for example, accountancy systems frequently tend to focus attention on functional efficiency rather than organisational effectiveness.
6   This is true even of many companies which do not themselves import directly, in that, for example, their own purchases may be from organisations so affected.

7   Zenz, Gary J "Materials Management: Threat to Purchasing", *Journal of Purchasing*, volume 4, May 1969

8   Ammer, Dean "There are No 'Right' Answers in Materials Management", *Purchasing,* volume 46 (16 Feb 1959)

9   Op. cit. ref.2

10 Farmer, David H "Corporate Planning and Procurement in Multinational Firms", *Journal of Purchasing & Materials Management*, volume 10, no 2 (May 1974)

11 Farmer, David H and Macmillan, Keith "Voluntary Collaboration vs 'Disloyalty' ", *Journal of Purchasing and Materials Management*, volume 12, no 4 (Winter 1976)

12 Ericsson Dag "Materials Administration", in *The Scandinavian Journal of Materials Administration* Trial Issue (November 1975)

Chapter 3

Reorganising for materials management

The great majority of materials-related decisions have in the past been regarded as fairly low level decisions. The positioning of purchasing, production control, stock control, stores administration and transport staff in the organisation structure has in consequence tended to be relatively low. One reason for the reorganisation of materials-related activities into materials management departments has been to upgrade the organisational positioning of these interdependent activities which affect the flow of materials. This improves their visibility to top management, reflecting the increased leverage in relation to total costs which materials have acquired. It also makes materials manager posts more attractive to qualified people with general management capability.

Organisation structures

There are of course good reasons for the great variety of organisation structures which can be found in industry, and it is not intended in this chapter to recommend some unique pattern which should be adopted for materials-related activities.

There are differences in the type of organisation considered appropriate for job production, batch production, mass production and process production. Production processes differ very considerably in complexity and in the technology employed, and these differences lead to differences in organisation structure. Some manufacturers produce goods exclusively to the design and specification of customers; others to their own design and specification but not until a customer's order has been received; some manufacture for stock in anticipation of orders, and many manufacturers produce partly for stock and partly against customer's orders. Then there is the effect of size. Large firms are not organised along the same lines as small firms because there is a limit to the number of people one manager can manage effectively. Consequently large firms need to introduce additional tiers of management between the top and the bottom of the hierarchy. A hierarchy of managers implies a hierarchy of decisions. Typically, short-term decisions which are quickly reversible are taken at lower levels in the hierarchy, and long-term decisions which require major commitments of resources or determine the future direction of the business are taken at higher levels. More people also means more specialisation. Large firms can employ full-time specialists and set up specialist departments to deal with aspects of the management task which in a small firm would be part of general management.

Many firms are organised in a way which has developed gradually over the years in response to the problems of the past, and which could well be reshaped in the light of the problems of the present and future. However, it is not the intention in this chapter to recommend any blueprint of organisation structure as being universally applicable.

There is evidence that many companies have in fact reorganised their materials-related activities by bringing some of them, or all of them, under one head to constitute a materials management department, and we begin by reviewing this. Next, we consider attempts which have been made to identify some key variable which can be used to determine the most appropriate structure for the parts of the organisation which are concerned with the flow of materials. Finally, we refer to another trend which is also in evidence, towards the greater centralisation of purchasing decisions. Organisation structure problems are difficult to consider in the abstract, and the first of the case studies (p. 265) provides a concrete illustration of the difficulties of applying principles in practice. It is impossible to make any statement about organisations to which exceptions cannot be found, including this one.

Evidence of reorganisation

A typical materials management reorganisation is shown in Figure 3:1. The materials-related activities of production control, stores, stock control, purchasing and transport, which had previously come under three separate heads, are brought together under a single materials manager. Real life organisation charts rarely have the refreshing simplicity which can be achieved in books, and many variations on this typical structure can be found in practice.

American surveys show a striking increase in the number of manufacturing firms which have reorganised their materials activities in this sort of way: from 6 per cent in the later sixties (Schultz) to about 40 per cent in the early seventies (Ammer), to 50 per cent or more in the late seventies (Miller and Gilmour).

Dean Ammer's survey of 4000 American manufacturers, financed by the American Production and Inventory Control Society, showed that about 40 per cent had what Ammer regarded as materials managers, although not necessarily designated by that title.[1] Miller and Gilmour's more recent survey of a much smaller, but representative, sample found that nearly 50 per cent had materials managers designated as such. The proportion would have been 72 per cent if such titles as logistics manager, physical distribution manager, supply manager, etc. had been included.[2] There was no correlation with size; companies with annual sales over $200 million had the same proportion of materials managers as companies with annual sales below $20 million.

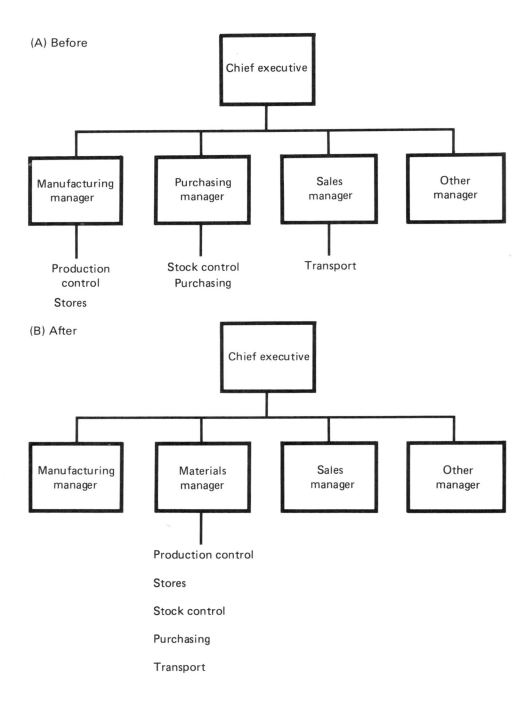

FIGURE 3:1   MATERIALS MANAGEMENT REORGANISATION

Was there any correlation with the use of computers? Here an interesting development seems to have occurred. Ammer found that the grouping of materials-related activities under a materials manager correlated with the use of computer systems for materials planning and control. Miller and Gilmour found the opposite. Some materials managers were in their posts mainly to implement the computer systems, but there was a much higher proportion of materials managers in the group of companies which made little use of computer systems. And of companies which made medium to high use of computer systems in this connection, over 70 per cent did not have a materials manager. This may well reflect the dramatic improvement in computer systems which occurred between the two surveys. It is possible that the sort of systems described in Chapter 7 can eliminate many of the inter-departmental hassles which are often given as a reason for combining the previously dispersed materials-related departments under one manager.

Comparable evidence does not seem to be available for the United Kingdom, although there is informal evidence that many British manufacturers have in fact appointed materials managers. Merchandising firms which distribute goods but do not manufacture them will not of course have a production planning and control activity as such, but many of these have grouped under one manager their inventory, warehousing, transport and reordering activities. An example of this is mentioned in Chapter 6. In any case, the differences between the USA and the UK, while greatly treasured by many of the inhabitants, seem unlikely to be great enough for significant differences to exist in the way materials-related activities are organised.

Clearly materials management, while it may or may not be the right answer for a particular firm, must in the light of these adoption rates be one of the options to be considered by those responsible for organisation design and development.

Activities affected

In the most recent survey it was found that the following functions or activities reported to the materials manager:

Production planning and control	77%
Purchasing	69%
Traffic	55%
Distribution	39%

Ammer's earlier survey obtained the results shown in Figure 3.2.

The various transport activities – shipping, traffic, distribution – can vary considerably in importance between different firms. It may involve little more than checking a supplier's quotation for delivering goods, sending for the goods in company transport or arranging for their collection by public carrier. Delivering the product to the customer is a minor problem, if it is a problem at all, in some firms such as building and construction firms, shipbuilders, etc. In other firms it is a major problem which may involve the appointment of a physical distribution manager, for instance those producing consumer durables with mass sales and using complex distribution systems

Percentage of materials managers responsible for the following job functions

Inventory control	95%
Purchasing	94%
Receiving	87%
Non-production stores	80%
Traffic	76%
Raw material stores	75%
Shipping	73%
Warehousing	72%
Materials handling	69%
Production control	68%
Physical distribution	48%

FIGURE 3:2   ACTIVITIES REPORTING TO THE MATERIALS MANAGER (from Dean Ammer, *op cit.*)

such as that shown in Figure 3.3. In many firms physical distribution lies somewhere between these extremes, and can form part of the material manager's responsibility. Miller and Gilmour report that distribution did not exist as a separate function in over half the companies in the sample.

Another problem is the place of purchasing. Ammer shows 94 per cent of materials managers are responsible for this activity, and 68 per cent are responsible for production control. The more recent survey shows 77 per cent are responsible for production control and 69 per cent responsible for purchasing.

The place of purchasing

It looks almost as if there are two views about this question of the materials

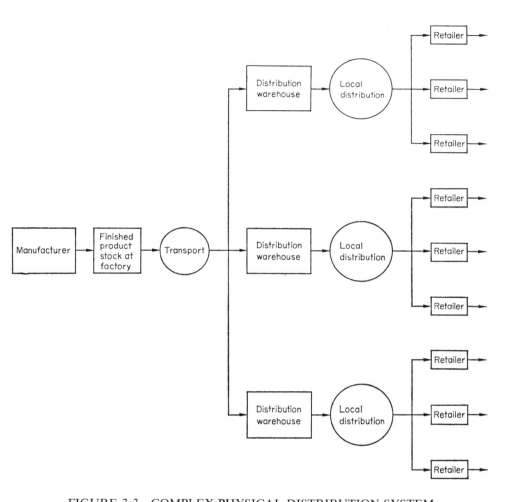

FIGURE 3:3   COMPLEX PHYSICAL DISTRIBUTION SYSTEM
Here products are shipped from stocks at one or more factories to several strategically sited distribution centres and then to local outlets. An extensive product range and movement across national frontiers and overseas might require an even more complex physical distribution system

manager's range of responsibility. In one, we add to purchasing a number of interfacing activities such as stores, stock control and transport, and perhaps, if it seems appropriate, production planning and control. In the other, we add to production planning and control a number of interfacing activities such as stores, stock control and transport, and perhaps, if it seems appropriate, purchasing. Physical distribution may be a separate department, or it may be a section within materials management, or it may not exist as a separate entity.

Certainly, despite the existence of the International Federation of Purchasing and

Materials Management, the Journal of Purchasing and Materials Management, etc., many purchasing experts do not look with favour on the incorporation of the purchasing function within a materials management structure. "Purchasing is about one thing and materials management is about something else", wrote Souster.[3] Purchasing in this view was about source marketing, and materials management was about materials flow. Different kinds of expertise were required: market knowledge, negotiating skills, and commercial flair on the one hand, technical skills in materials handling, inventory control, and shop scheduling on the other.

A similar view has been argued by Sheridan.[4] Buyers should concentrate on developing skills significantly different from those already available in other functions. They should concentrate in fact on buying: price, cost, commercial know-how, foreign exchange, commodity markets, contractual negotiation and the monetary aspects. They should avoid involvement, either personal or organisational, in matters which others in the organisation are well qualified to handle, such as specification. At the same time others in the organisation should stay out of buying and avoid giving any kind of commitment to outside sources.

One type of solution may be to split the purchasing function into two groups of activities: the source marketing part, which affects material flow only indirectly, and the ordering part, which affects it directly. The source marketing group might be located in a headquarters department, which would deal with supplier appraisal and development, negotiation and contracts. The second group might be located in the plant as part of a materials department, and would deal with timing and quantities of orders, delivery schedules and expediting.

Another type of solution is to look for some key variable to assist in positioning purchasing, and other activities.

The search for key variables

An early attempt to do this is due to S E Lauer Jr.[5] Noting that different types of materials organisation might be used in the different divisions of a large organisation, he identified three main key variables:

1   Purchasing cost reduction leverage: is it high or low?
2   Type of production: is it made for stock or made to customer order?
3   Profit centre: is the operation a single profit centre or does it include more than one?

Purchasing cost reduction leverage refers to the relationship between the cost reduction buyers might be able to achieve on purchases, and total product cost. A profit centre is a responsibility centre, the manager of which is accountable both for income and expenditure, and thus for the difference between them which is profit. A responsibility centre is a section of the organisation in charge of a manager who is held responsible for its performance: it may be either an expense centre in which the manager is accountable for expenditure but not income, or a profit centre in which he is responsible for both.

Lauer suggested three types of structure, shown in Figure 3.4 for the four cases

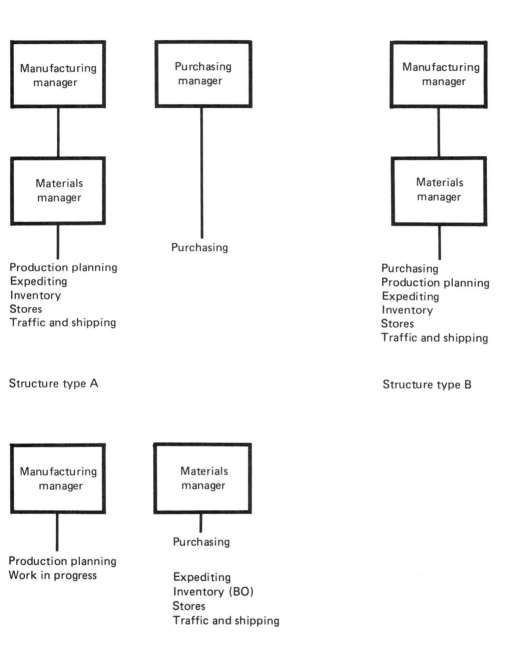

Manufacturing
manager

Purchasing
manager

Materials
manager

Purchasing

Production planning
Expediting
Inventory
Stores
Traffic and shipping

Structure type A

Manufacturing
manager

Materials
manager

Purchasing
Production planning
Expediting
Inventory
Stores
Traffic and shipping

Structure type B

Manufacturing
manager

Materials
manager

Production planning
Work in progress

Purchasing

Expediting
Inventory (BO)
Stores
Traffic and shipping

Structure type C

FIGURE 3:4   TYPES OF MATERIALS MANAGEMENT STRUCTURE (adapted from
Lauer)

arising in single-profit centre plants.

Type of operation	Purchasing cost reduction leverage	
	High	Low
Make to stock	Structure type A	Structure type B
Make to order	Structure type C	Structure type B

If the cost reduction leverage of the purchase department was low, then whether the operation was make-to-stock or make-to-order he considered that it should be included in the materials department reporting through the materials manager to the manufacturing manager. If on the other hand the cost reduction leverage of the purchase department was high, then two types of structure which we have shown as types A and C were suggested. Type A would be appropriate in a high production shop making for stock where considerable cost reduction potential existed relative to product cost. Here the purchasing function should be pulled out of materials and should report directly to the chief executive of the profit centre. Expediting and the rest of the materials activities should report to the materials manager, who would in turn report to the manufacturing manager (or works manager).

Type C would be appropriate in a plant making to customer order, where the cost reduction leverage of the purchase department was high, especially if purchase lead times were long. Here it is the whole materials function which is pulled out from manufacturing and reports direct to the chief executive of the profit centre. This would be a purchasing-centred materials department, because the purchasing function can contribute substantially to profits; and can probably do a better job of controlling stock of bought-out parts than the factory can, if production cycles are short and material lead times are long.

In the fifth case when there are several distinct profit centres in a single plant (by profit centre is meant an operation in which one manager is responsible for the three basic functions of manufacturing, engineering and sales, and for their total profitability), the best type of organisation structure was thought to depend largely on the extent of the overlap with respect to bought-out materials. Materials in common use were a strong reason for centralising purchasing and inventory control.

Trade-offs as key variables

A more recent proposal is to look for key variables in the trade-offs which seem of greatest importance.[2] The "classical" integrated materials management structure, said to account for 31 per cent of cases, is shown in Figure 3:5(A). Three partly integrated structures accounted for the rest: the supply-oriented structure, Figure 3:5(B), for 18 per cent, the distribution-oriented structure, Figure 3:5(C), for 23 per cent, and the manufacturing-oriented, Figure 3:5(D), for the remaining 28 per cent.

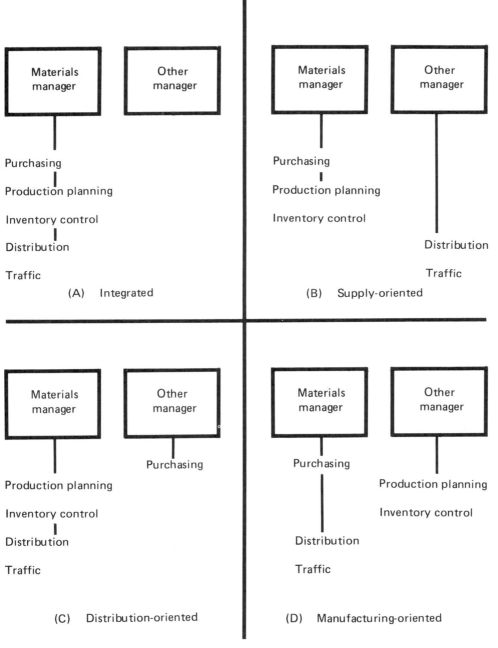

FIGURE 3:5 FOUR TYPES OF MATERIALS MANAGEMENT STRUCTURE
(adapted from Miller and Gilmour, *op cit.*)

Trade-offs (= exchanges, especially by way of compromise) could be between two of the materials activities, or between one or more of the materials activities and a non-materials activity. For instance the trade-off between inventory costs, reduced by frequent small orders, and purchase costs, reduced by infrequent large orders which qualify for quantity discounts, is a matter for discussion between two of the activities attributed to materials. But the trade-off between transport costs, reduced by infrequent bulk deliveries, and customer service, increased by small on-demand deliveries, is for discussion between a materials activity and a non-materials activity – sales.

A "traditional" organisation structure such as Figure 3:1 (A) can be used if most of the trade-offs which need to be made are between materials and other activities. A "classical" materials management structure such as Figure 3:5(A) is considered appropriate if most of the trade-offs need to be made within the materials department, between the various materials activities.

When the important trade-offs are both within materials, and between materials and other departments, then one or other of the partly integrated structures may be more appropriate than the fully integrated one. In one case, the authors relate, the most important trade-off was between inventory costs and purchase costs; so a materials manager was appointed. The second most important trade-off was between transport cost and customer service, so the supply-oriented model, Figure 3:5(B), was adopted.

Centralising purchasing

Alongside these developments, and not necessarily in conflict with them, there has been a tendency in large decentralised organisations to centralise purchasing policy making and the making of corporate purchase contracts. The British Gas Corporation and the National Coal Board are obvious examples of organisations which carry out basically similar activities at their various locations up and down the country, but a similar tendency can be seen in many large organisations where the operations are more diverse.

A key variable for this particular organisational question is the extent to which separate locations require the same things. If identical or closely related materials are called for at a number of establishments, then there is a *prima facie* case for buying them, or contracting for them, on a joint basis. This can be done by a central purchasing department, or through a central coordinator, or less formally still by periodic conferences between the heads of the decentralised departments, with the largest user acting as lead buyer perhaps for any item which has been designated as suitable for joint contracting at such a conference.

Commonality of requirement may be a necessary, but it is not a sufficient, condition for joint purchasing. If five separate establishments can buy an item at a unit cost of £5, it is not easy to justify a corporate contract which ties all five establishments to a single source at the same price of £5. In fact it would be hard to justify a joint contract for all five establishments which led to a lower price resulting in savings of

£2000 a year, if to obtain this saving a central office had to be established at a cost of £20,000 a year.

There may be other advantages in setting up a central purchasing organisation, whether it is a command organisation with line authority for the branch buying offices, or an advisory and consultative organisation which operates in a staff role. It may facilitate for instance the standardisation of requirements which makes possible the joint contracting leading to the economies of scale which provide the economic justification for its own existence. It may provide opportunities for the employment of specialist staff and for professional advancement. It may be able to organise on a company-wide basis the recruitment, training and development, and promotion of staff. It may be able to plan long-term availability and response to change in the business environment better than busy plant-level purchasing staff.

May should not be equated with *will*, or opportunity with achievement. This complicated question is considered in more detail elsewhere.[6] The point which needs to be made here is that this kind of centralisation of purchasing decisions, which is about source marketing and negotiation of contracts, should not be seen as involving any conflict with the ordering and expediting aspect of purchasing operations, which can still be integrated at plant level with other materials-related activities.

Most people find it difficult to consider organisational questions of this kind in the abstract. Many readers will have as their main interest the actual application of them in their own concrete situation. It is hoped that case studies 1 to 4 will serve as a useful halfway house between the general and the particular. These provide an opportunity to apply principles of the kind put forward in this chapter to simplified, but not unrealistic, situations.

References

1   Ammer, Dean, *Materials Management*, 3e, Richard D. Irwin 1974. We have also been authorised to quote material from the survey which may not appear in this book.
2   Miller, J G, and Gilmour, P, "Materials Managers: Who needs them?", *Harvard Business Review*, July–August 1979.
3   Souster, P, "The Materials Monster, Materials Management put in Place," *International Journal of Physical Distribution and Materials Management*, volume 10, no. 4, 1980.
4   Sheridan, David, in a talk at the BPICS 1980 conference, Blackpool.
5   Lauer, S E, Jr., in a contrubution to "*Managing Materials in Industry*", adapted from an earlier talk to the American Management Assocation
6   Baily, P J H, *Purchasing and Supply Management*, 4e, Chapman & Hall, 1978.

Part Two

Activities in managing materials

Chapter 4

Production planning and control

by *J A Smith*

This chapter provides a general treatment of production planning and control, and introduces a number of topics which are developed in greater detail in later chapters.

Production planning and control is defined as "the procedures and means by which manufacturing programmes and plans are determined, information issued for their execution, and data collected to control manufacture in accordance with the plans" (BS 5191:1975).

Although the terms production planning and control are widely used in industry, there is no universally recognised distinction between the two functions. Here the term production *planning* is taken to mean the technical aspects of production planning and involves the work that must be done before any product can be made. This information becomes the input to, and provides the basis for production *control*.

Production planning

Production planning is the link between design and manufacture. The planner's work begins on receipt of drawings and all relevant information from the design office. The planning department also requires information regarding quantities of production, labour costs, tooling costs and capital expenditure, and a complete inventory of existing production facilities, such as machine and manpower specifications.

There are many different terms used for the above function, the most common being "process planning", and "operational planning". This is the technical planning necessary to ensure the efficient processing of a particular product. Hence it covers a wide field of activity and it is unlikely that the approach to production planning will be the same in any two organisations. Differences are due to product differences, quantity considerations and perhaps even to the policies of the company. Although procedures may vary, all production planning departments should perform the following functions.

1 The precise sequence of operations to be followed for the manufacture of each component, subassembly and complete assembly has to be decided. Against each

operation the time required for its performance must be specified. This may be based on calculation, say for standard machining operation, or by the use of data supplied by the work study department, particularly for assembly operations, or perhaps from past data.

2   Having decided the sequence of operations required, the methods of manufacture for each operation will have to be specified. This will include process or machine tool selection. Break-even analyses are useful here to decide on economic grounds between competing processes. Techical considerations such as set-up, selection of appropriate machining conditions, speed, feed, depth of cut should be made, consistent with the size of the work piece, cutting tool material, surface finish and tolerance requirements.

3   It is at this stage that make-or-buy decisions may be made on component parts. Most manufacturers spend more than half their income buying materials and products from other companies. This is a decision that should be made on economic grounds but due account has to be given to plant capacity and reliability of suppliers, and special tooling and/or expertise requirements.

4   Aids to manufacture such as jigs and fixtures to be used, require consideration. This is decided by several factors, including the quantity of manufacture, complexity of components, grade of labour and tooling costs.

5   Material selection and material utilisation require very careful study. Materials are normally selected for their physical properties. When several materials are available, all of which are capable of functioning satisfactorily, then the cheapest is usually selected. However, there are numerous examples in industry where materials have been chosen without due consideration being given to functional economic or processing characteristics.

6   The grade of labour to be used for each operation has to be decided and specified. Due consideration must be given to any agreements between the company and trade unions.

7   Finally, decisions must be made regarding the stages of assembly; the number of assembly workers per stage should be specified at this point.

Although inspection is not a function of production, decisions must be made during the production planning stage about where inspection is to take place and what type of inspection will be used. This is acceptance of the fact that inspection is an integral part of manufacture.

The above information must be conveyed to all concerned and the process planner must complete a job instruction card for each component. Such cards may take two forms, one may be in skeleton form, often called a route card (Figure 4:1), this simply states the route of the work through the factory together with the machines and tools used for each operation. Such a card is also used by the progress department. This card would be of little use to the manufacturing department and so a job instruction card giving complete information and details of the methods of manufacture must be prepared (Figure 4:2). This often includes detail drawings of the machine set-up so

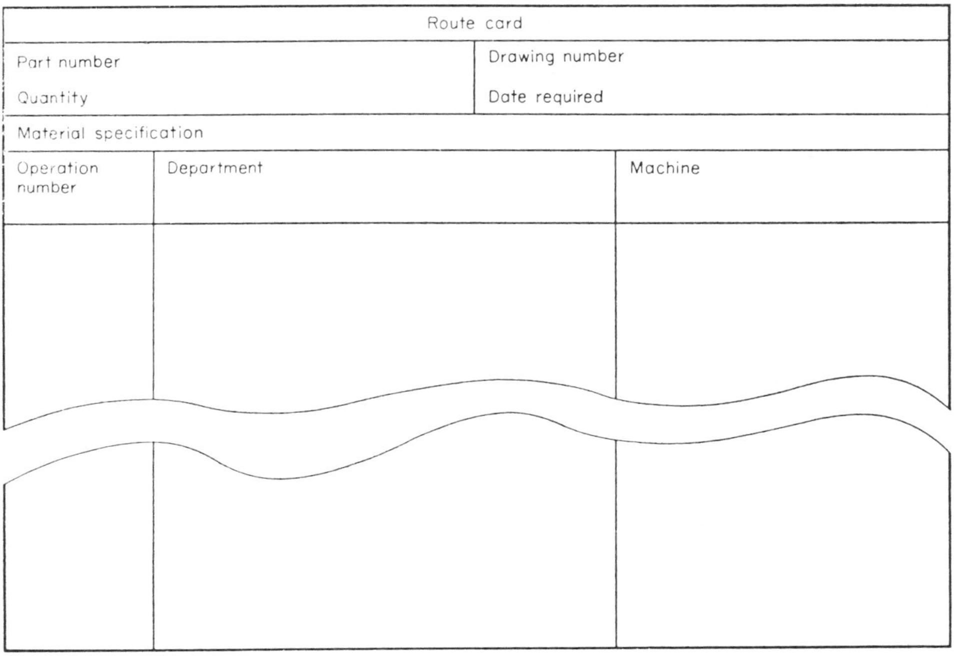

Route card		
Part number	Drawing number	
Quantity	Date required	
Material specification		
Operation number	Department	Machine

FIGURE 4:1   TYPICAL ROUTE CARD

that the operator would know exactly what to do, how to do it, and the machining conditions required.

Production control

A production control system should exhibit the following features, which are essential to all industrial control systems:

1   Prepare plan
2   Issue instructions
3   Measure performance
4   Compare performance with objectives
5   Report findings
6   Take corrective actions (when necessary)

Applied specifically to production control these elements of the control system are shown in Figure 4:3.

Stated simply, the purpose of production control is to match the available resources of production, men, machines, materials and money, with sales requirements. The flow diagram shown in Figure 4:3 suggests that establishing the produc-

Job card							
Date of issue		Date required			Quantity		
Part number			Drawing number				
Material specification							
Operation number	Operation details	Machine number	Jigs and tools gauge number	Set-up time	Operation time per unit		
						Hours	Minutes

FIGURE 4:2   TYPICAL JOB CARD

tion plan is a once-and-for-all exercise. This is rarely the case; sales levels, perhaps set by forecast, are continually changing. The availability of production facilities is also subject to constant variations due to machine tool breakdown, labour absenteeism, material shortages and the production of defective items. Hence we are involved in a highly dynamic situation in which the objectives of the system have to be constantly reviewed and restated. Whenever relevant parameters change, shop loading may require adjustment, or delivery dates modified. As the system has to be capable of responding rapidly to changes in important parameters, information regarding the state of the production system must be readily and quickly available.

In addition to the commonly recognised aspects of production control – namely, machine and labour loading, inventory control and progress – sales forecasting will also be considered, as this represents an integral part of producing the production plan.

It should be remembered that production control is only one aspect of the overall system of control in an industrial organisation. It is inextricably linked with quality control, financial control, purchasing control and sales control and should not be considered in isolation from these functions.

In discussing a production control system, consideration will first be given to the individual elements of the system and then to the integration of these elements into a cohesive system of control.

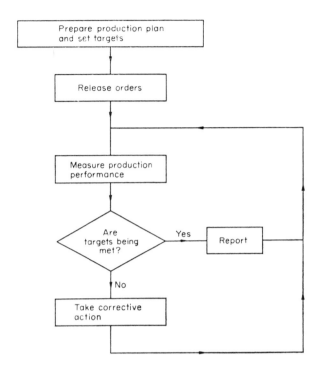

FIGURE 4:3   MAIN FEATURES OF A PRODUCTION CONTROL SYSTEM

Types of production

The system for production planning and control will vary greatly with the type of manufacture the company is engaged in. Although it is impossible to draw hard-and-fast demarcation lines, it is often convenient to divide manufacture into three categories, depending on the manufacturing quantities involved.

JOB PRODUCTION

Here the quantity involved is "one off" or very small numbers to meet the requirements of special customer orders. This type of manufacture is usually concerned with special-purpose machinery, prototypes and so on. Ship-building and capital equipment for process industries are typical examples. As orders are for one off or very small quantities, there is little scope for using refined production techniques. As orders are rarely repeated, past data is not available for planning and control purposes. For this reason the difficulties of production planning and control are greater here than for other types of production. Occasionally, the orders may be repeated in which case the problems of planning and control become easier. Consideration may then be given to manufacture of jigs and fixtures, special inspection equipment, the introduction of work-study methods and the application of other production techniques.

BATCH PRODUCTION

This is the most common form of production, accounting for approximately 60 per cent of British production. As the name implies, it is the production of small lots which can range from two or three to several thousand. These batches may be either manufactured to meet the requirements of specific orders, or to satisfy a continuous demand. This occurs when the rate of production of the component parts is higher than the consumption rate.

The problems of production planning and control are to decide the size of batch to be manufactured, and the integration of this batch into the overall manufacturing programme. In the case of batches manufactured to meet external orders the size of the batch is determined by the order. For batches manufactured to meet internal demand, the size of batch to be produced is an internal management decision. The size of the batch can be determined by calculating the economic batch size. Several formulas exist for this calculation, but all are based on balancing set-up costs against stockholding costs. Generally, if material cost is high, the batch size will be high. Other factors are, if labour cost is high and the operation long, the batch will be small, and if set-up times are long and expensive, then batches will be large.

MASS FLOW OR CONTINUOUS PRODUCTION

Continuous production covers production plant that runs 24 hours a day, seven day a week. The plant is highly specialised and often automated. Examples are such process industries as chemical, iron and steel, and oil refinery. The plant has been designed to manufacture only the product range in question, and is completely inflexible in that it is not possible to convert the plant to manufacture a different range of products.

Mass or flow production covers products which are manufactured in very large quantities and is associated with a high rate of demand. A shop of automatics is an example of mass production. Although the machines are engaged continuously in the manufacture of a particular product they can be changed over for the production of a different product.

As manufacture is of large volume, full advantage should be taken of such techniques as detailed production planning and control, careful design of jigs and fixtures, inspection equipment, mechanical handling equipment, plant layout and work-study investigation.

The characteristics of the above types of production are summarised in Figure 4:4.

Sales forecasting

Some industrial concerns are in the enviable position of manufacturing to firm advance orders. In this case, the problem of sales forecasting as a basis for production planning does not exist. However, even these firms face the problem of long-term forecasting to serve as a basis for future capital investment planning.

More commonly, the demand for the next production planning period will not be known. If the production level is set too high, high inventory-carrying costs will result. If the production level is set too low and demand cannot be satisfied, valuable sales orders are lost, which may not be recovered. Hence a fundamental question to be answered is how much to manufacture in the next period. This is a decision that has to be made under conditions of uncertainty.

Sales forecasting is not, and cannot be, an exact science. However, this does not excuse resorting to guesswork or relying entirely on intuition. Many quantitative methods are available to enable forecasts to be made in a more rational manner. Some of the more commonly used techniques are now considered.

MOVING AVERAGE TOTALS

The simplest form of forecasting would be a one-period total. The forecast for the current period would be identical to the demand of the previous period. This is obviously very simple to calculate, and the total forecast over a series of periods would not differ greatly from the total actual demand. However, the forecast would always lag behind the demand by one period and would be unsuitable under conditions of fluctuating demand.

More commonly, the moving average would be calculated from the demands of several previous periods, twelve-month moving average totals being extensively used. In the moving annual total method, the orders for the previous twelve months are summed, this being the twelve-monthly moving total. This total is divided by 12 to provide the forecast demand for the next month. The actual demand for that month is then added to the previous moving annual total and the demand for that month in the previous year subtracted to provide the new moving annual total. This can be used to calculate the forecast for the next period. Moving annual totals tend to be sluggish in following changing trends in sales patterns. To overcome this disadvantage, and to increase the sensitivity of the forecast to rapidly changing trends, the number of periods included in the moving total is reduced. Three-monthly or even three-weekly totals are widely used. The more periods included in the total, the smoother will be the final curve, the peaks and valleys in the demand pattern will be evened out. This means that twelve-monthly totals are best used to detect long-term trends, and three-weekly or three-monthly totals to detect seasonal or cyclic variations.

EXPONENTIAL SMOOTHING

The moving annual total and the three-week or three-month totals have severe limitations. The moving annual total gives equal importance to current and distant events whereas the three-month total gives equal importance to the previous three months' demand figures and does not consider demand patterns prior to this. A compromise between these two extremes is desirable. This can be achieved by using

	JOB	BATCH	MASS	CONTINUOUS
Characteristics	Small quantities or one off. Non-repetitive or intermittent demand. To agreed specification	Small or large quantity. Production rate greater than consumption. Repetitive demand may be regular or irregular	Large scale production of one or a limited range of products. Production geared to demand. Specialised equipment	Large scale production, long set up time. Plant completely inflexible, designed for production of one type of product
Demand	To order	To order or forecast	Forecast	Forecast
Layout	Fixed position, machines to work	Process layout, work to machines, like machines grouped	Product layout, work to machines. Machines arranged in order of operations	Depends on particular technology involved
Equipment	General purpose where possible, but some special purpose machines	General and special purpose machines, jigs, fixtures, special tooling	Specialised, a high degree of mechanisation	Highly specialised. Automatic methods of production and inspection
Equipment utilisation	Low	Medium, frequent set ups between runs	Medium to high	Very high
Labour	Highly skilled	Skilled and semi-skilled setters and operators	Semi-skilled and unskilled	Unskilled
Labour content	Very high	High to medium	Low	Very low

FIGURE 4:4 TYPES OF PRODUCTION
Comparison of job, batch, mass and continuous production

the exponential smoothing method of forecasting. With this method, it is possible to weight the importance to be attached to recent sales information and still give consideration to past data. This is achieved by using a smoothing constant, the numerical value of which can be varied to suit current demand patterns. The following equation is used to determine the required forecast.

New forecast of demand = old forecast of demand
                          + α (last month's demand – old forecast)

where α is the smoothing constant.

The main advantage of this type of forecasting is that it is "self-adaptive" in that it adjusts itself automatically to change in demand patterns. By changing the value of α, the forecast can be made to respond more or less rapidly to recent demands. The smoothing constant can vary between 0 and 1, but in practice takes a value between 0.1 and 0.8. The choice of the smoothing constant depends on the sensitivity required. If $\alpha = 1$, the total difference between the previous period forecast and actual demand is taken into account. This gives maximum sensitivity but minimum stability and amounts to using the last actual demand as the new forecast. If α is set at 0, the actual demands are completely ignored and this has the opposite effect – maximum stability but minimum sensitivity. The value selected for the smoothing constant is obviously of great importance and depends on the pattern of demand. A value of 0.1 to 0.2 represents a reasonable compromise between damping out random fluctuations in demand, and still detecting genuine trends in sales. If the demand is rapidly rising, a higher value of α should be used.

CORRELATION ANALYSIS

Correlation analysis is the mathematical study of cause and effect. Applied to sales forecasting, it requires the identification of indicators. An indicator is a factor that can be used to predict future sales of the product being forecast. Having determined suitable indicators, the relationship between changes in the indicator value and product sales has to be determined in mathematical terms, from past data. It is hoped that the established relationship will be projected into the future and that the equation derived can be used for predictive purposes. Some indicators are easy to identify – car sales would obviously be a good indicator for petrol sales – but most are often difficult to identify.

The application of these and other forecasting techniques need not be mutually exclusive, but can be complementary in obtaining the final forecast. Many companies prefer to rely on more than one method. The results obtained from using different techniques can be compared, and the value and reliability of each method can be assessed.

If a firm produces more than one product, then the forecasting exercise has to be applied to each product. This raises the question of how much effort to expend on the forecasting of each product. A graph constructed of cumulative percentage of sales income against cumulative percentage of products manufactured, would be as shown in Figure 4:5 and is known as the Pareto curve of unequal distribution. It is also

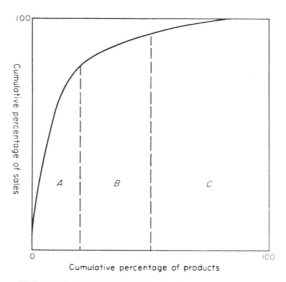

FIGURE 4:5   TYPICAL PARETO CURVE

commonly known as the 80/20 curve, because 20 per cent of the products account for 80 per cent of the sales income. When considering the amount of effort to be put into forecasting each product, it is far simpler to divide the products into groups before establishing the forecasting effort to be applied to each group. An *ABC* classification, as described in Chapter 6, is sometimes convenient. Group *A* products which are large-volume fast-moving items require maximum forecasting effort, group *B*, less stringent methods and group *C* the less-important, many requiring only cursory treatment.

As these forecasting methods are of a routine arithmetical nature, they can be readily programmed for computer calculation and are very economical in the use of computer facilities.

Product explosion

Products require to be exploded into final assembly parts and then to be further broken down into the various levels of subassemblies. A product specification will contain a complete list of all the materials and parts which go into it. Hence a detailed breakdown of the product structure is required. A typical product breakdown is shown in Figure 4:6. It can be seen that the product consists of ten individual parts with four levels of assembly. Large complicated products can contain thousands of piece parts with many stages of assembly. Information related to the product structure has to be filed or stored. For each component in the part list, information, such as identification number, purchase part number for bought-out parts, manufacturing

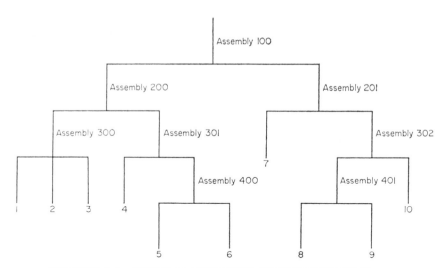

FIGURE 4:6   TYPICAL PRODUCT STRUCTURE FILE

details for made-in parts and number of parts required per assembly, requires filing and organising.

For products having simple structures – ones comprising only a few component parts – processing of this information can be handled efficiently by manual methods. But if product structures are complex and/or there are many products to consider, a total production plan explosion could take days or even weeks. In such cases, electronic data processing will not only reduce the processing time to a matter of minutes or hours, but will also help to reduce the frequency of errors.

In computerised production control systems, product structure files and the relevant information are stored on disc or tape, and programs are commercially available capable of loading, maintaining and reorganising these files.

Shop loading (or scheduling)

Scheduling involves the arrangement, coordination and planning the utilisation of the resources of production, to achieve some desired objective. We are concerned with the loading of jobs on machines, and manpower to jobs.

Management must define the objective of a scheduling system. Some practical objectives are:

1   Maximise machine utilisation
2   Maximise throughput
3   Minimise number of late jobs
4   Minimise in-process inventory
5   Minimum total manufacturing cost
6   Day-to-day stability

Unfortunately not all these objectives are consistent; for example, maximising machine utilisation would require continual rescheduling as new work arrives, this is inconsistent with day-to-day stability; maximum throughput requires a queue of jobs at each machine and is inconsistent with minimum in-process inventory.

Hence scheduling in practice becomes a compromise whereby no attempt is made to optimise any one criterion but rather to "satisfice" several.

Machine-shop scheduling is essentially a queueing problem. When a machine becomes free a decision has to be made; which of the jobs waiting to go on the machine is to be processed first? In a typical jobbing or small-batch production firm, there may be several thousand jobs on the shopfloor at any instant in time, and over a hundred production facilities. The number of possible schedules reaches astronomical proportions. To serve as an illustration, four jobs requiring processing on each of four different machines, in any order, would generate $(4!)^4$ or about 360×10^3 possible schedules. Hence the practical scheduler is involved in a combinatorial maze of possible schedules.

On the theoretical level, the scheduling problem has been tackled using linear programming, branch and bound methods and rigorous analysis but all of these approaches have succumbed to the enormity of the problem.

Simulation has provided the best approach to the problem to date. Computer models have been constructed of machine shops and have been used to test the effect of applying different loading rules to resolve conflicts when more than one job is waiting to be processed by one machine. The effectiveness of applying different loading rules – such as shortest operation rule, first come first served, and least float – have been tested under controlled conditions and this enables management to select priority rules that will be consistent with the objectives of the scheduling system.

The scheduler is faced with a multitude of practical problems such as machine breakdown, production of rejects, errors in time estimates and assemblies. These problems add to the complexity of the scheduling exercise. Practical loading systems are generally of two classes.

Minimum make span Typical criteria in this case are:

1　Finish last job as soon as possible
2　Finish each job as soon as possible
3　Minimise work-in-process inventory
4　Maximise machine utilisation

Due date

1　Minimise number of late jobs
2　Minimise total tardiness
3　Minimise cost of not meeting delivery dates.

A mixture of both classes is used to resolve conflicts when they arise.

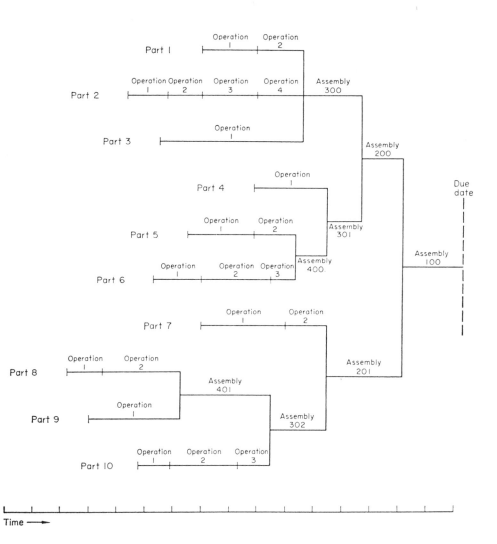

FIGURE 4:7 ASSEMBLY NETWORK DIAGRAM

Ideally, two schedules are required. A short-term schedule for, say, one or two weeks ahead, to plan the day-to-day loading of the shop, and a long-term schedule for as far into the foreseeable future as possible. This can be used as a basis for future capital investment planning, and making policy decisions regarding overtime working, subcontracting work and job discrimination.

The difficulty of assemblies can be seen from Figure 4:7. This is, in fact, a horizontal representation of Figure 4:6, the product breakdown structure. The manufacture of the individual component parts must be coordinated so that the parts arrive together at the right time for the assembly operation. This obviously imposes extra constraints on the scheduling system. This diagram is a divergent network, and network analysis methods (discussed elsewhere in this handbook) can be used to ensure manufacturing precedences and still hold the final completion date.

If scheduling is performed manually, visual aids are useful to chart the progress of work through the shop, gannt charts and loading boards are commonly used for this purpose. Loading racks, hook boards, pigeon-hole racks and box files are also used. All these devices are used to give assistance to the schedulers, and can work well in small machine shops. However, when scheduling is carried out in a highly dynamic situation where system parameters are constantly changing, the computer represents the only feasible way of rapidly processing the large volumes of data.

Progress control

The feedback link in the production control chain consists of measuring the actual performance of the system, comparing this performance with the present production targets and then initiating any corrective action that may be necessary. This is the responsibility of the progress department. The problem encountered here is the sheer volume of paperwork to be processed. This results in a time lag in the feedback mechanism which is often measured in days or even weeks before remedial action can be taken. This means that we may be tackling, today, last month's problem areas. Under this method of working, jobs that are running late are often expedited at the expense of overall shop efficiency because the overall effects of such changes in the production programme are not known – expediting one job might well put the delivery dates of several other jobs back.

For a production control system to function efficiently, feedback and corrective action should be carried out with a minimum amount of delay. In a computerised production control system, progress is usually disguised under the name of updating. The production plan has already been set with the aid of the computer. As actual production performance is fed back into the machine, comparison of performance with objectives is carried out. Adjustments can be made to the production programme to reflect any corrective action that may be required. These adjustments are made by considering not only jobs running late, but on the basis of balancing overall shop efficiency and operating costs.

Management information is readily available about the state of shop loading of manpower and machines, progress of jobs and levels of stock. Arrangements can be made for management exception reporting.

The frequency of updating will vary from firm to firm, common practice being weekly or fortnightly, provided that no serious deviations from the production programme have occurred.

Evaluation

If progress can be regarded as the short-term feedback link in the production control system, then evaluation can be regarded as long-term feedback. This is a very important part of the production control system and one which often receives little or no attention. This should be an important link between analysis of past performance, and future planning. During manufacture, large quantities of valuable data are recorded. Properly analysed, this can be used as a basis of reviewing and reforming system objectives. It also provides management with a quantitative basis on which to make future decisions.

Chapter 5

Inventory planning and control

Many manufacturers, if asked what were their biggest problems in connection with inventory, would immediately mention three areas:

1   Excessive stock investment
2   Inadequacy of stock to meet demand
3   Inaccuracy of stock records.

Record accuracy, as measured by physical count against quantity on record, is certainly important. Inaccurate records result both in shortages and in excess stocks. Plans based on incorrect information are inherently defective. Stock availability, as measured by service level or by line items filled against total line items, is fundamental; and for a variety of reasons planned levels of availability may often not be achieved. Stock investment, as measured by planned stocks against actual stocks in monetary terms, or average stock turn rate, has attracted much attention in recent years because of cash flow problems and the high rates of interest for borrowed money.

These are all aspects of stock control. Maintaining accurate records, achieving planned service levels and confining the amount of money invested in stock to target levels are part of the control process.

But deciding what level of availability to aim at and how much money to invest in stock are part of the planning process. Computer simulation facilities enabling management to look at the consequences of "what if we did so and so" before actually doing it have been useful additions to the planner's tool-kit. Stock planning also includes decisions as to what things to keep in stock and what lines to drop, a matter which often fails to receive enough attention in factories.

The distributive industries have similar problems, yet many retailers would give much higher priority to range problems: the introduction of new lines of merchandise, the discontinuance of old ones. Admittedly there is an obvious reason for this: the retailer sells what he stocks, the manufacturer sells products manufactured out of the parts and material he stocks. Demand for the retailer's merchandise comes direct from customers. Demand for the parts and material in factory stores comes only indirectly from customers: it is a derived demand.

But it should not be assumed that the manufacturer's product line decisions are just like the retailer's merchandising decisions and the stocks in store result inevitably from them. As product ranges alter and designs are modified, yesterday's fast movers become today's slow movers, last year's bread and butter items become this year's surplus stocks. Mistakes also are inevitable. Things are procured for needs which do not materialise, requirements are over-estimated, plans change. Unwanted or excessive stocks pile up in odd corners as well as in the main stores. Regular identification and elimination is necessary to keep the stock range appropriate for current requirements. It is not enough to do this only for the basis of records, although the records should certainly be used, and computerised records normally have a facility to identify slow movers and non-movers. Physical count procedures also need to be used to locate surplus stock which has disappeared from the record but is still cluttering up the store.

A determined attempt to standardise and simplify requirements by cutting out needless duplications in the range can considerably increase efficiency. Gifted design engineers have been able to increase the choice of end-products while actually reducing the range of parts and material from which end-products are fabricated.

Stock planning and control comprises policies and procedures which systematically determine and regulate which items are held in stock and what quantities of them are held.

Dependent and independent demand

Having decided on a range of stock items, stock control needs to produce for each item answers to the questions:

1 What quantities will be required?
2 When should we order more?
3 What quantity should we order?

There is a significant difference in the way the first question is answered between items the demand for which is independent, and items the demand for which is derived from the quantities required for some other item. Sales of the various different lines in a variety chain may fluctuate up and down with the fortunes of the particular retailer concerned and with the state of the economy, but in no way are sales of one line such as a video recorder dependent on the demand for another item such as a wristwatch or a man's shirt. These are cases of independent demand.

But most of the stock held by a manufacturer is of a different kind; Figure 5:1 illustrates this. Sales of the various end-products may move to some extent in step with the state of the order book and of the economy generally, but they are cases of independent demand. This is not the case with the other stocks shown. Purchased parts are acquired for assembly into the finished product; raw materials are acquired for machining or processing to produce parts and sub-assemblies for assembly into the finished products; work-in-progress includes all the items which have undergone

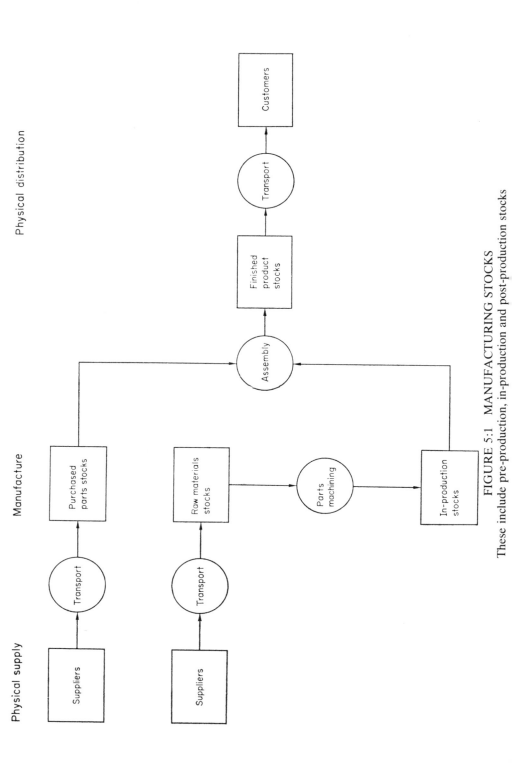

FIGURE 5:1 MANUFACTURING STOCKS

These include pre-production, in-production and post-production stocks

some processing and are no longer in the same condition as when bought, but which are not yet finished products. Some of the latter items may be on machines being processed, some on the shop floor waiting for the next operation, and some may be in an intermediate parts store where they can properly be regarded as stocks, although it is also correct to regard them as work in progress. Requirements for all these parts and materials is dependent on the demand for the products into which they are manufactured. This is the case not only for complex engineering products, but also for relatively simple products: chemical products, such as Battersby's example in *A Guide to Stock Control*, (Pitman), of a manufacturer buying and stocking chocolic acid and garlium oxide to make garlic chocolate! Demand for the ingredients is dependent on demand for the product. Or a lamp filament factory which makes 200 different filaments out of a range of wires and mandrils, the demand for which is dependent on sales of the filaments.

For these, dependent demand items, the question "What quantities will be required?" is best answered by materials requirement planning, dealt with in detail in Chapter 7. It is a process of working back from the timed program for the production of end-products to timed programs for the production or purchase of parts and materials. Requirements for stock are determined from future requirements for products.

With independent demand items, future requirements cannot be calculated in this way, but must be forecast. These may include, in the case of manufacturers, any finished products which they stock, including stocks of spare parts held for direct sales to customers. It may also be convenient to treat in the same way stocks of materials which are used on many products. The raw materials from which a foundry produces castings, or a plastics manufacturer mouldings, can be treated as cases of independent demand because the various dependent demands for different products add up to a fluctuating but continuous demand. All manufacturers also carry non-production stocks, which are needed to keep the business going but are not incorporated directly into products. These include maintenance, repair and operating supplies, often referred to as MRO. In some cases spares for plant and machinery can be a large and costly element, as with an airline or a chemical process plant. These are again independent demands.

Forecasting demand

Forecasting techniques are based on the assumption that future demand can be deduced from past demand, and much effort has gone into finding better techniques which can detect a trend early and distinguish it from random fluctuations or statistical noise.

The most popular forecasting techniques are probably exponential smoothing and moving averages. Exponential smoothing has many variants, such as double smoothing, triple smoothing, adjustment for lag and trend and deseasonalisation. Adaptive smoothing is itself a variant of exponential smoothing in which the smoothing constant is automatically adjusted to adapt to the size of the forecast error, and also has a number of versions. Methods developed by Box and Jenkins are quite sophisticated and in one version the forecast can be correlated with other variables which may be relevant to demand. Unfortunately, it appears that the more elaborate techniques, while they perform better than the simple ones with simulated figures derived from statistical distributions, do not always perform better with real life figures and sometimes yield a less accurate forecast than the simple moving average or exponential smoothing technique.

Computers are widely used for stock control, and all the above forecasting techniques are available as packages. Computers can quickly compute forecast demand for each item and as part of the same routine can compute and smooth forecast error (the difference between actual demand and forecast demand).

None of these techniques give accurate forecasts. Human judgment can be used to improve them in the case of major items. In the case of minor items, buffer stocks can be provided to reduce the incidence of shortages due to forecast errors.

Given some idea of future demand, we next need to decide when to replenish items held in stock to meet continuing demands by ordering further supplies as necessary. The question, when should we order more, so as to keep shortages down to an acceptably low level without resulting in an unacceptably high level of stock, depends on a number of considerations. Two basic approaches can be distinguished: in one approach each item is considered separately and is reordered when the stock on hand falls to a certain level (known as order point, order level, or reorder level). In the other, groups of items are reviewed periodically to see which needs to be ordered.

Continuous systems

The first approach results in orders being placed continuously, since in a range of stocks there is usually some item which has just reached its reorder level. Consideration of whether or not to order items also takes place continuously; in principle each item is reviewed after each transaction to see if it needs to be ordered. Such systems are consequently known as continuous systems.

The order point or reorder level in a continuous system is based on the maximum quantity likely to be used during the lead time. The lead time is the total time it takes to get things, and it may be thought of as the average time taken plus a margin to allow for variations. The maximum quantity likely to be used during this time may also be thought of as the average requirement per period multiplied by the number of periods in the lead time, plus a margin to allow for variations. These margins to cover variations are known as buffer stock.

Buffer stock (or safety stock, as it is sometimes called) is shown in Figure 5:2. Here the quantity in stock is shown as reducing, at a constant rate in the first instance, until a new order arrives. Halfway through the next cycle the demand increases, and only the buffer stock prevents a shortage. A new order is delivered, and halfway through the third cycle the demand falls off, restoring buffer stock to its initial level. In the lower part of the diagram demand is shown at a constant rate throughout. But in the second cycle the order arrives late, and again the buffer stock prevents a shortage

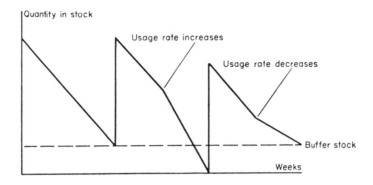

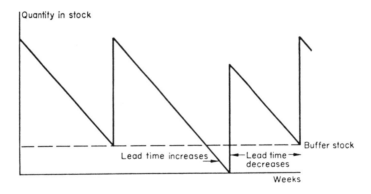

FIGURE 5:2   BUFFER STOCK

resulting from this increase in lead time. In the third cycle an early delivery restores buffer stock to its initial level.

For example if item YB is required at a rate of about 100 a week and if lead time is 4 weeks, would it be sensible to set the order point at 400? A shortage would occur whenever actual delivery took longer than 4 weeks, and whenever actual requirement exceeded 400 in four weeks. Suppose records show that in the past requirements have varied from 75 to 125 a week, averaging 100; and that deliveries have taken from 3 to 5 weeks, averaging 4. If we are pessimistic (and many people think that pessimism pays, with stock control) we would set the order point at 5 × 125, i.e. 625. That should prevent shortages. If we analyse it, clearly it is based on the following equation:

Order point   = av. weekly usage × av. lead time in weeks +   buffer stock
        625   =   100   ×   4   +   225

Although this rule is used in practice, a statistician would regard it as over estimating the need for buffer stock. It is unlikely that usage would stay at its top value of 125 for five successive weeks. Better methods are given in most books on stock control and in many books on quantitative methods or applied statistics, but they will not be reproduced here because there is little point in knowing methods which are better in principle if they cannot be applied in practice. It is theoretically possible to find a least-cost solution for buffer stock if the cost of a shortage is known and if the forecast error distribution is also known – that is, the difference between actual usage during lead time and forecast usage during lead time. Unfortunately, the cost of a shortage varies not only from item to item but also from time to time, and forecast error distributions are hardly ever known with sufficient accuracy in the area which matters most for shortage prevention: the tail of the distribution, the infrequent large discrepancy which leads to a stockout.

Buffer stock and shortages

Whatever the theoretical difficulties, decisions must be taken in practice as to what buffer stock should be carried or what emergency action should be taken to fend off shortages. A common approach is to divide stock into three classes: vital, important, and routine.

Vital items are the very few items which should always be in stock at whatever cost, because a major hold-up of factory operations or severe blow to customer relations would be the result of a shortage; lives even might be endangered, as in the case of some pharmaceutical products.

Important items comprise the broad range of stocks on which shortages must be kept down to an acceptable level. What level is acceptable is not something to be calculated from a formula. Too many variables or unquantifiable parameters are involved in the manufacturing situation. It is something to be developed by the management as part of a continual evaluation of the consequences of shortages and the cost of preventing them. Of course managers would prefer never to be short of anything, and not only managers if Burbridge's suggestion on page 79 is right, but in practice it pays to make do with a service level somewhat below 99 per cent.

Routine items are those on which shortages do not matter much because they can be quickly put right without much inconvenience. Every shortage causes some inconvenience and wastes some time, but the cost of prevention has to be kept in line with the cost of *not* preventing a shortage. If shortage cost is slight for some item, perhaps just the cost of a phone call to a local distributor, surveillance of stocks can be less strict and reserves small or non-existent.

Order quantity and EOQ

The quantity which should be reordered of a stock item in regular use could depend on a number of considerations. There may be special purchasing considerations to do with price, lead time, availability, market structure. In the case of made-in parts there may be special production considerations. But when appropriate arrangements have been made for all these special cases a wide range of stock items to which no special considerations apply is usually left.

There are broad limits: order too much and the risk of obsolescence or deterioration becomes unacceptably high; order too little, and unit cost is disproportionately inflated by small-quantity extras and other such costs. Within these limits the stock controller is free to vary order quantities. Small order quantities keep stocks low, but they mean that a large number of orders are placed. Large order quantities reduce the number of orders and deliveries, thus saving on administrative cost, but they lead to high stocks.

It was to provide the optimum solution in this situation that economic order quantity (EOQ) formulas were developed many years ago. These are most useful for items with stable prices, short lead times and which can properly be treated independently – that is, decisions about order quantity for one item do not act as constraints on decisions about order quantities for another item.

Traditionally the approach is to express in symbolic form three cost elements:

1   The annual usage value of the item A: this is the quantity we expect to use in a year multiplied by unit cost or price
2   The expense of ordering, P per order: for wide ranges of items this will be a constant amount, covering paperwork, cheques, postage and variable labour costs
3   The expense of carrying stock: only variable or direct cost should be taken into account, not fixed overhead, and this can be expressed as a constant fraction S of the monetary value of stock

It is then quite simple to show that the order quantity which gives the lowest total cost is given by some version of the well-known square-root formula:

order quantity (in monetary value) $= \sqrt{(2AP/S)}$

It is also simple to transform the formula so as to give direct solutions in terms of number of months supply to order, number of parts to order, or optimum frequency of order if these versions are more convenient in use. For instance if we write u for the quantity used in a year, and c for unit cost (so that $uc = A$), then:

order quantity (in physical units) $= \sqrt{(2Pu/Sc)}$

For example if we take the stockholding cost as 20 per cent per annum, so that $S = 0.2$, and if we take ordering cost as £10, so that $P = 10$, then we can calculate the EOQ for an item costing £2 each of which we use 800 a year.

The first formula gives the value of order as £400. The second formula gives the quantity to order as 200 – which at £2 each gives the value of order as £400 of course.

We should order this item four times a year if we are to minimise the joint costs of ordering and stockholding.

Let us consider another item costing 10p each, of which we use a thousand a year. The second formula gives the economic order quantity as 1000. We should order this item only once a year. This illustrates the point that we can minimise costs by ordering high usage value items frequently so as to reduce stockholdings, and low usage value items infrequently so as to reduce ordering costs.

This may be regarded as intuitively obvious. Many purchasers apply it in practice without giving much thought to the theory behind it. What is less obvious is the square root relationship between demand and order for continuous independent demands. For instance, why, in the two examples just considered, should we order the first item four times as often as the second item? Because the annual usage value is sixteen times as high, and the square root of 16 is 4.

No formula is a substitute for commonsense. This is not a reason to reject the use of formulas; it is an argument for confining their use to conditions which are reasonably approximated by the assumptions underlying the formula, and modifying their application where other relevant considerations need to be taken into account.

For instance if demand is very seasonable the formula should not be used. If price varies considerably or there is a large variation in lead time, again other considerations are much more important than the balancing of internal costs at which the formula aims, and it should not be used.

Actual calculation of the EOQ can be done in seconds on a programmable calculator costing a few pounds, or as part of a computer stock control system. But no formula is a substitute for commonsense, and it is desirable to include a number of modifers.

The formula may suggest that we order six years supply, based on the assumption that we will continue to require the item at the same rate for the next six years. The modifier is a 'maximum' limit: not more than one year's supply, or two year's supply perhaps. It may suggest that we order one week's supply. But surely there is no need to place a separate order every week; for these volumes we would adopt a different ordering method. It may suggest that we order very small quantities, unacceptable to the supplier or penalised by small quantity extras. The modifer here would be a "minimum" limit. Some items are best ordered jointly from a single source, if they are bought-out, or ordered at the same time from the works in the case of made-in items to save on set-up time or for some other reason. "Order with" would be the modifier.

Quantity discounts, rebates, and other forms of reducing the price for larger quantities are sometimes available. It is easy to calculate when it will pay to order larger quantities to qualify for a lower price. For instance, with an ordering cost of £10, a stockholding cost of 20 per cent, an annual requirement of 10,000 and a unit cost of £1, the economic order quantity is 1000 units. Now suppose a 10 per cent discount is available if 5000 is ordered for delivery in one lot. The annual saving on purchase cost is 10 per cent of £10,000: i.e. £1000. There is a further small saving of £80 because we would be placing two orders a year instead of ten. On the other hand average stock would go up from £500 to £2250, an increase of £1750, and at 20 per cent this would cost £350. Since this is much less than £1080 it would pay to accept the offer.

If on the other hand the discount offered is 5 per cent for 10,000 delivered in one lot, the annual saving on purchase cost is £500, plus a further saving in ordering cost of £90. On the other hand average stock would increase from £500 to £4750, an addition of £4250, and at 20 per cent this would add £850 to annual cost. Since this is much more than £590 it would not pay to accept the offer.

Exchange curves

In many organisations the range of stock items for which the EOQ is adopted may be very restricted – just stationery, for instance. But if it is proposed to adopt it more widely for a broad central range of routine stock items, some preliminary evaluation might be advisable. Financial resources could be stretched or storage accommodation may need to be extended if substantial increases in stockholdings turned out to be required. Increases in staff might be called for if the proposal led to substantial increases in the number of orders placed. A simulation of the probable results of the proposal, carried out on a reasonable sample of the stock range will be well worthwhile.

In particular such simulations can be used to experiment with the effect of changing the value of the constant k. The first formula given for the EOQ was:

order quantity (in monetary value) $= \sqrt{(2AP/S)}$

This can alternatively be written as:

EOQ (in £) $= k\sqrt{(A)}$

The second formula was:

order quantity (in physical units) $= \sqrt{(2Pu/Sc)}$

This can alternatively be written as:

EOQ (in physical units) $= k\sqrt{(u/c)}$

In terms of the discussion so far, the value of k is given by:

$k = \sqrt{(2P/S)}$

The factor 2 appears here because average stock is order quantity divided by two. The two other factors are there because the aim of the formula is to balance stockholding costs (S) against ordering costs (P). Sometimes management may find it easier to decide if the results of adopting a particular value of k are desirable, than to decide what values of P and S should be adopted to calculate the value of k.

The effect of using a series of different values of k with the sample of stocks can be calculated and plotted as an exchange curve, as shown in Figure 5:3. In effect this shows the rate of exchange between varying the order frequency and varying the stock investment. Locations to the left of the curve are out of bounds; there is no way to get there. Locations to the right of the curve are common enough, but it is easy to improve on them. Points on the curve represent a series of different optima corresponding to different assumed values of stockholding cost and ordering cost. The only way to improve on them is to assume different values, which would lead to a different point on the curve.

Production quantities and EBQ

The EOQ formula has proved particularly attractive to operations research workers, no doubt because of its refreshing mathematical simplicity, so different from the human complexities before which they often find themselves standing glumly. A lot of effort has been put into devising more elaborate versions of the EOQ for use in determining production quantities. In this connection it is often called the EBQ formula, or Economic Batch Quantity.

The ordering cost P will usually include the cost of setting up or changing over a machine or process. This set-up cost can be quite high, and consequently this method of minimising the combined total of set-up/ordering costs and of stockholding costs may appear attractive. In practice its adoption has led in many cases to serious production control problems and to excessive stocks.

Some of the complications may be mentioned. Suppose a factory uses 12 000 parts a year which are machined out of castings. The purchase ordering cost is £10 and the stockholding cost is 24 per cent per annum. Unit cost for the casting is £1, and application of the EOQ formula gives an order quantity of 1000. So the purchase department orders a thousand castings once a month. Meanwhile the production control people are working out what batch quantities to release. The production ordering cost including set-up time is £100. Unit cost for the machined part is £2.50. The formula tells them to release 2000 castings for machining at a time, every two months. Purchasing were clearly wrong to apply a formula based on the assumption of continuous demand when demand for the castings occurs discontinuously six times a year; joint planning was called for.

Many production parts go through several operations, each with its own set-up cost; but it does not seem sensible to fix different order quantities for each operation. Furthermore the assumption that order quantity can be decided independently for each production part is not valid when orders have to be produced on the same set of limited resources. It is more important to optimise the use of plant, machinery and production workers than to minimise the joint total of set-up costs and stockholding costs. We will return to this theme in Chapter 7.

Periodic review systems

An alternative to the continuous systems in which an order is placed for any item when stock level falls to an action level called the order point, is the periodic systems in which large groups of stock items are reviewed periodically – every day, week or month for instance. These are sometimes called constant cycle systems. They lead to orders of varying size at fixed intervals, instead of orders of fixed size at varying intervals as with continuous systems (although this may not apply to some hybrid systems used in practice). In principle they lead to higher stocks because of the need to carry enough stock to last until the next review, plus lead time. In effect the review interval is added to the lead time. But in practice they can often result in lower costs, both for made-in parts because of more efficient production planning and for bought-out parts where parts can be aggregated to obtain quantity discounts, or transport costs can be saved by delivering different items at the same time. They are widely used by retailers and have obvious advantages when many items are obtained from one source.

One method for deciding order quantities is to forecast future demand for one review period plus the lead time, add a margin for safety or buffer stock, and call this the target stock. The order quantity is then given by: target stock minus stock on hand. For instance if the interval between reviews is four weeks, lead time is six weeks, forecast demand for ten weeks is 1000, and buffer stock is two weeks' supply, the target stock would be 1200. If on review the stock level for this item is 200, the quantity to order would be 1000.

Another method, sometimes called the s,S system, differs in that it does not lead to orders for every item being reviewed. Instead an order is only placed if stock level for an item is below the order point s. Order quantity is the target stock, S, minus the quantity on hand, so that the smallest order that can be placed is given by $S - s$.

ABC analysis

Efficient procedures allow for the very large difference between stock items both in unit cost and in rate of requirement. Shops have top sellers and slow movers. Factories stock some very costly items as well as some very cheap ones, and require some of them perhaps once a year while others may be used at a rate of hundreds a day. An invaluable method of sorting the wheat from the chaff in this connection is known as ABC or Pareto analysis.

It is not efficient to put as much effort into the control of ten-a-penny nails as into the control of vital and costly production components. We learned as children that for want of a nail a battle was lost; but in the case of nails the answer is not tight control but ample stocks. For want of an engine, a car assembly line could be stopped; but in this case the answer is not ample stocks but tight control.

Usually about ten per cent of the items in stock account for over three quarters of the expenditure on stock purchases. These are called Class A items. Certain other items may call for close attention because they are perishable, or very bulky, or so vital that the risk of being out of stock has to be made minimal and these can be included under the same heading as Class A.

At the other extreme, about half the items in the stock range usually account for only 5 to 10 per cent of total usage value. These are called Class C. The intermediate

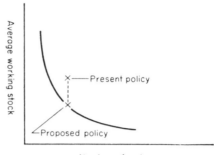

FIGURE 5:3   STOCK/ORDER EXCHANGE CURVE

group, Class B, could include from 10 per cent to 30 per cent of the range.

ABC analysis is based on usage value classification: all stock items can be listed in order of usage value (monetary value of a year's estimated demand), with the largest at the top of the list and the smallest at the bottom. A typical distribution is shown in Figure 4:5. (These curves are usually called Pareto curves or Lorenz curves, after investigators who studied how incomes and wealth were distributed among the inhabitants of various countries during the early part of this century.)

SYSTEMS FOR C ITEMS
Since the large group of *C* items only accounts for 10 per cent or less of the money spent it does not warrant more than 10 per cent of the control effort. To cut down accounting effort, class *C* goods can be written off to expense accounts or production jobs on delivery rather than charged to a stock account. Many of them are held in open racks, where people can help themselves, and no stock records are kept. Instead, sealed-minimum or visual-control or ruled-bin methods are used: with all these, stock is reordered when the reserve or order level supply is broken into. A travelling requisition or order card attached to the order level stock can be written up, dated, and sent to the buyer for review and reorder. The card shows order quantities and dates, and stock count figures; the essential minimum data enabling usage rate to be checked and order quantities selected. These are all versions of *two-bin systems,* where each item stock is physically segregated into two lots: working stock and order level stock.

Alternatively, imprest or topping-up periodic systems can be very suitable for class *C* items, especially when small stocks are kept so that stock counts can be made visually.

What is wanted is some routine system which will maintain adequate stocks without management attention. Unit cost being low, it is usually cheaper to carry ample buffer stock to cover errors and variations than it would be to spend time eliminating errors and calculating probabilities.

SYSTEMS FOR *A* AND *B* ITEMS

The small but important group of class *A* items is where the money goes, and often where most of the problems occur. These are the stocks that call for time and administrative effort. Purchases will be phased closely with actual requirements. Frequent checks of stock against orders and commitments will be made. Unit cost is high and it is cheaper to allocate considerable administrative time to eliminating stocks than it would be to carry the stocks.

If a continuous system is used, order level will be set after careful consideration of average demand and of likely changes in it, as well as of the probabilities of demand exceeding average by various amounts: order quantity is calculated by the EOQ formula to keep the costs both of holding and of procuring the stocks down. But periodic systems are more usual for class *A* items, and, where possible, period contracts should be placed with call-offs or scheduled deliveries at frequent intervals.

The EOQ approach is particularly favoured for the intermediate class *B* group of items, and a fair amount of care is justifiable in checking demand and recording usage. Buffer stock can also be calculated to give a specified percentage of stockouts.

Allocation systems are sometimes favoured for *A* and *B* items when advance notice of requirements is available, from manufacturing programmes or customers' orders.

Stock records

It is not necessary to have an accurate stock record in order to find out what is in stock. The alternative is to go and count. This method is very widely used by retailers, both in small establishments and in branch stores operated by major chains. Stock replenishment orders can be based on regular counts, or they can be triggered by "two-bin" and "visual control" systems such as are used in many factories.

For materials requirement planning it is of course convenient to have an accurate stock record available so that planned requirements can be substracted from available stock and orders due, for the calculation of orders which need to be placed. For forecasting future requirements by extrapolation it is necessary to have details of past usage upon which the forecasts can be based.

Details of past usage can be extracted from stock records, whether clerically processed or computer processed; alternatively they can be derived from records of orders placed and deliveries received, in conjunction with stock on hand as determined by physical count. If stock records are used, transactions must be posted promptly and accurately to provide the up-to-date information which is needed, and regular stock counts are required to correct the inevitable errors which occur in records.

A straightforward clerically processed stock record is shown in Figure 5:4. Such

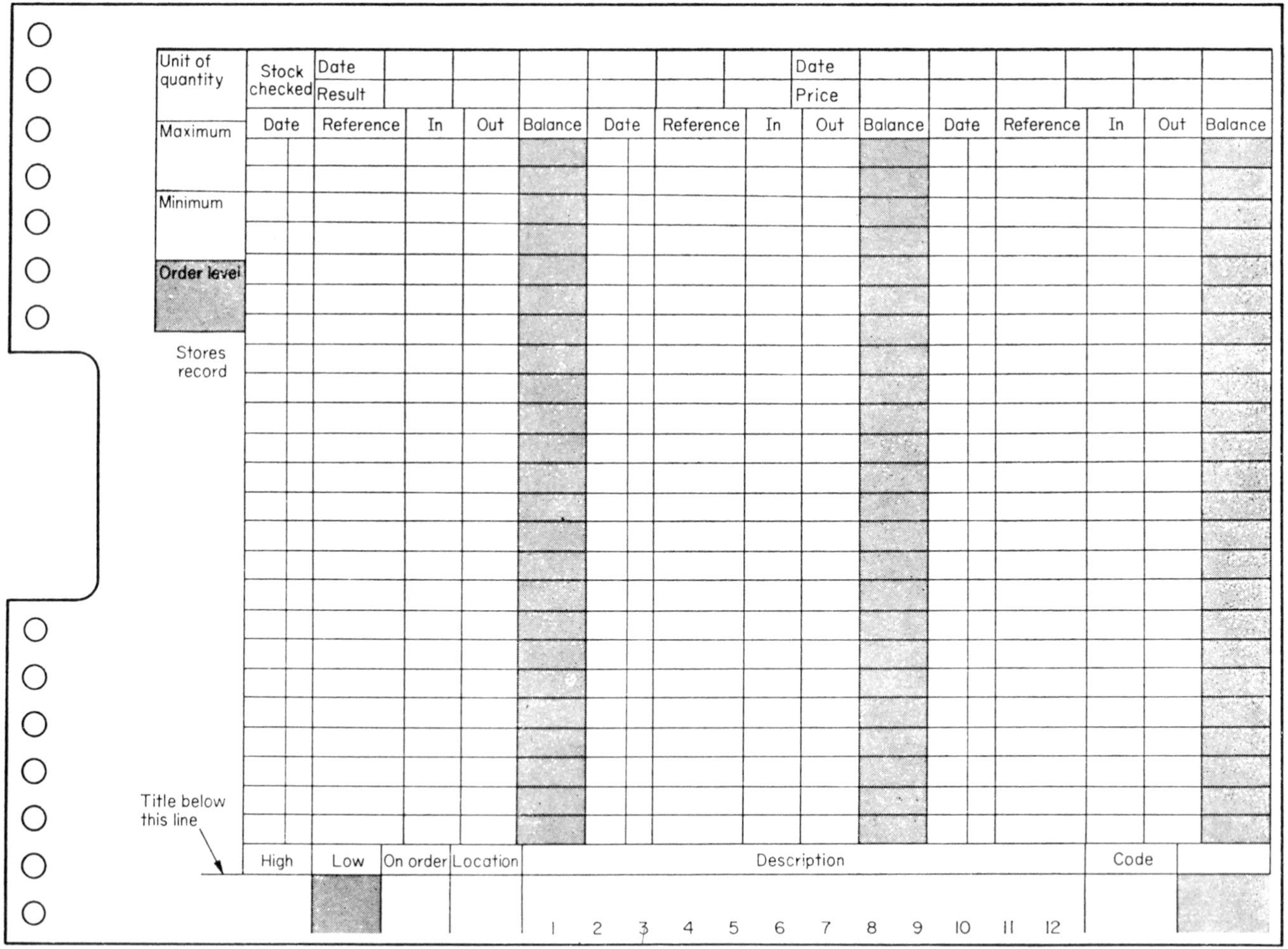

FIGURE 5:4 MANUAL STOCK RECORD

records are becoming less and less common. Computerised stock recording which was so disappointing in the early days is at last becoming a practical proposition, even for the smaller firm. Although clerically processed records are still common in small firms, microcomputers and minicomputers now offer a practical alternative. These devices are increasing in power and complexity, and for around £10,000 in 1981 could provide the equivalent of a main frame computer costing twenty times as much a decade earlier. They also provide interactive on-line question and answer facilities; this is what is required with stock records, and the fact that it was not available on the older batch-processing serial access machines is the main reason for the disappointment many organisations formerly felt with their computerised stock record systems. The information stored on the computer stock record usually includes:

1   Stock code/description
2   Reorder level
3   Reorder quantity
4   Quantity in stock
5   Record of quantity issued or sold to date
6   Goods received to date
7   Quantity on order
8   Supplier and purchase price

There may also be provision for allocations and free stock balance, stock location, and other data.

Systems usually provide a facility to list all items which have fallen below reorder level. Other facilities often provided include ABC analysis, EOQ calculation, inactive stock list, stock movements, stock valuation, and partial lists for continuous stocktaking. Reorder levels may be dynamically determined using current monthly usage or sales for each item instead of predetermined quantities. About two dozen standard packages are currently available for stock control on microcomputers, and these are normally cheaper than developing a tailormade system for individual requirements, because development costs can be spread over a number of customers. Prices range from about £50 to over £1000.

In selecting a system the first time user would be well advised to concentrate on the software: is it easy to use, clear, unambiguous, foolproof; and how does it react when a nonsense input is made? The hardware is a secondary consideration because most systems are machine-specific: that is, they are written for one particular make of machine. These machines are nowadays very reliable, but it is still necessary to check on the type, quality and cost of maintenance available from the supplier. How long before a service engineer arrives; what level of spare parts are held locally? It is also a good idea to contact someone who is already using the system for an opinion on it.

Performance measures

The total retail trade obtained a stock turn rate of 7.4 in 1980. There were, however, wide variations between different types of retailer, with confectionery, tobacco and newsagencies averaging 11.1 and household goods down to 5.1. Large multiples averaged 11.1 and some did still better, for instance Marks and Spencer. There is usually a conflict between carrying a wide stock range including slow movers and thus providing a comprehensive service to customers, and improving stock turn rate and thus getting a better return on capital employed.

Few manufacturers can manage stock turn rates as high as these. One machine tool manufacturer (since gone bankrupt) had a stock turn rate of 1. Leading the field are the mass producers whose 'stocks' are in the pipeline, in transit between supplier and assembly line rather than in the stores.

Stock turn rate is a convenient and popular ratio which relates the amount of money invested in stock to the rate at which stock is turned over, thus indicating the velocity with which materials move through the business. Changes in aggregate inventory value, while relevant of course to cash flow and other matters, are not meaningful in terms of stock control performance until related to demand. An increase in total inventory could be a response to increased demand for the products sold by the business, but it could also be the result of a fall in demand.

Stock turn rate is the ratio of average stock over a period to demand for stock in that period. For instance if a business carried an average stock of £0.5m over a year in which issues from stock totalled £2.5m, the stock turn rate would be 5 (2.5/0.5). The reciprocal of the stock turn rate shows how long the stock will last: a fifth of a year in this example.

The way to get a faster stock turn rate is firstly to clear out surplus and cut down slow moving stock; and secondly to concentrate on rapid turnover of the big-money A items. Do not worry about the C items; it is often cheaper to order a year's supply at a time than to try and keep down stocks which amount to very little in cash terms.

Service level is the other common measure. It is the percentage of demands on stock which are met off the shelf.

Chapter 6

Inventory control systems for retail distribution§

by *R J Read*

The compilers of the *Oxford Dictionary of Quotations* obviously did not believe that either inventory control or retailing were very interesting topics because there is no entry under either retailing or inventory. There is of course the famous Napoleonic description of the British as a nation of shopkeepers, but that is as near as they get. Perhaps this means that both inventory control and retailing are relatively new subjects and have not yet found their way into the literary world. Let us make the assumption that there is something worth saying about stock control and about running shops and see how we go about things in W H Smith, compare this with other well known high street names such as Marks & Spencer and Sainsburys, and then at the end sketch out what the future holds for us, in particular the development of point of sale systems.

Organisation structure

However, before we do any of that, we ought to have a look at the way W H Smith is organised. The Retail Group is headed by a managing director, three directors responsible for the line operations of buying, distribution and retail shop administration. The group has its own management executive comprising the four directors and certain senior managers and they form the most senior decision making body within the retail group.

The buying division is responsible for initial buying, product development and promotional plans.

The retail division selects sites and builds new or resited shops and controls the

§ This is an amended & updated version of a talk given at the 1979 BPICS Conference in Birmingham.

staffs and administers them. There are some 319 W H Smith shops and 89 bookstalls divided into 21 retail areas. The shops are located throughout England, Wales and Scotland.

The distribution division has large warehouses at Swindon and Dunstable which between them stock some 31,000 lines to meet approximately 60 per cent of the volume demand. The balance of 40 per cent is supplied directly by the manufacturer. The departments within the distribution division are staff services, operations and inventory.

The operations manager controls the efficient running of the warehouses, transport and engineering and negotiates the cost of contracted distribution.

The inventory department is responsible for retail group inventory. Its task is to provide the right amount of stock (in financial and volume terms) to meet the needs of the group. It must do this at pre-determined service levels and at acceptable costs.

Each line manager has a small development department which is responsible for providing industrial engineering, operational research and materials handling systems as appropriate. Their work includes stockroom design at branches, stock control systems both at Swindon and in branches, and economic modelling.

The distributing director is also responsible for the development of business systems throughout the retail group and I as retail group R & D manager report to him.

Inventory Control

The buying division is responsible for choosing lines, fixing margins and making the initial purchases of items. The inventory department at Swindon is then responsible for stocking and replenishing these lines at the central warehouses. With the exception of about 200 lines, the branch manager or his departmental managers are free to order stock from a catalogue which is tailored to their size and turnover. Naturally, the branch manager makes use of stock control systems devised by the inventory department and works to stock budgets also determined by them.

Let us look now in a little more detail at how the inventory department manages the stock held in the central warehouses. As we have already seen, goods are supplied to branches by one of two channels.

1   Directly by the manufacturer, or
2   From the central warehouses at Swindon and Dunstable

The choice of channel is usually the one which produces the best margin for the company and this decision ultimately rests with the distribution director. He has at his disposal a mathematical model which calculates the marginal costs of going direct from manufacturer to branch or from manufacturer to warehouse to branch and he uses this to help him with his decision making. I say "help" here because as with any model, we cannot programme in all the constraints.

The channel supply having been determined, further economies may be achieved in examining:

Pack size
Delivery methods

Once the buyer has placed the initial order, the setting of the first and subsequent review levels and all future purchasing is done by the inventory department which seeks to minimise the costs of distribution while maintaining stocks at economic levels to produce the service levels required.

The inventory manager who is ultimately responsible for stock levels in the group has the task of directly controlling the stock and service levels from the warehouse to the branch and sets the target levels and systems for all branch stock. He also has a considerable influence on the buying decisions made by buying division.

The Purchasing Cycle

Once a year, members of the retail group devote considerable time and effort to producing a corporate strategy and sales and profit plan taking into account as many factors as possible. These include:

Market share
Market growth
Price and volume analyses
Development of product range
Additional selling space
Re-allocation of space per product range

THE EXTENT TO WHICH ADDITIONAL SALES MAY BE GENERATED BY ADVERTISING AND SALES PROMOTION

The corporate strategy is converted from a sales and profit plan into a purchasing estimate of what is required to meet stockholding budgets set throughout the distribution pipeline.

The first stage of determining the provisioning estimate is to calculate the sales requirements, and the ideal supporting stock. Predictions of the stock holding levels of the year end are deducted from the provisioning estimate to establish the purchasing requirements. Having established how much stock is needed, we have to schedule its delivery to the warehouses and determine the rate at which it should be ordered, delivered to warehouse and to branch. Stock budgets are therefore provided to branch management enabling them to interpret the rate of supply for each merchandise range. The branch stock level budgets are expressed in number of weeks forward sales and value and are compiled taking account of the following factors:

1 The effect of operating stock control systems allowing for order review periods.
2 Manufacturers lead times and pack size limitations.
3 The value of display stock required.
4 Whichever is the greater of 1 or 2 above plus additional values of stock delivered

in anticipation of the selling peaks at Christmas and other times throughout the year. This avoids undue pressures on the central warehouse or manufacturers transport.

Warehouse stock levels depend on the characteristics of the merchandise. For example own brand products produced in this country are usually readily available whereas imported products have long and unpredictable lead times.

Ideally the current month's deliveries to warehouse become the next month's deliveries to branch, though of course this rapid turn round of stock is not always achieved.

A prediction of the demands for cash is made at the same time based on the pre-determined flow of merchandise through the least cost channel of supply.

Naturally, we aim to reduce the cost of holding inventory as much as possible by trying to make the number of weeks stock held less than or equal to the number of weeks credit. There are some types of merchandise in which we do very well, for example, newspapers and magazines where the turn round is measurable in hours rather than weeks. On the other hand, some of our slower selling lines such as the less familiar book titles are held for much longer periods but this is essential for maintaining a service to our customers.

Naturally, the credit period which we enjoy with our suppliers – the time taken in between receipt of their invoice and our payment of it – also has to take into account any settlement discounts.

Branch managers receive a regular statement of sales, stocks and the number of weeks forward supply that these represent. Decisions to alter the rate of stock intake, are taken by comparing actual performance to budgets. The aim in using this stock control system is to reduce branch stock to a minimum consistent with reasonable service levels and to hold any stock which is required to meet unpredictable supplies from the manufacturer at the centre rather than at the branch. This management control system is backed up by line by line branch stock control systems for all types of merchandise.

We can play tunes on the way in which we store stock and pay for it in that we smooth the peaks and troughs of the distribution workload without incurring a financial disadvantage. For example, we will often arrange with manufacturers to receive in stock early if they have too little warehouse space. In return, we defer payment to them. This helps both the manufacturer and ourselves.

Stock budgets are applied to total stocks of a range of merchandise or to stocks in a single branch. The detailed processes involved in translating these plans into actions on a day-to-day or item-by-item basis are carried out by replenishment purchasing staff and these comprise the main activity of the inventory department.

Replenishment purchasing

We have already seen that the channel of supply is one of the first distribution decisions to be made. The initial order is placed by the buyer and the responsibility is then passed to the replenishment purchasing manager. He has to find out how the line is likely to behave in conjunction with the buyer. He determines the lead time of supply, the review level at which the line will be considered for replenishment, the pack size, the pallet quantities and order multiples and any expected change in normal demand rates (to take account of promotions, or supplier closedowns etc).

A computer print-out shows the state of the line at intervals which are either regular – where the line falls below the review level – or where the line goes out of stock. The replenishment purchasing manager receives these two reports every day. He also gets a print-out of the behaviour of all his lines every 5, 10 or 20 days depending on the stability of the line.

As orders are created, so they are sent to suppliers with precise delivery instructions on them. They are entered onto the computer file so that at regular intervals a statement of the due deliveries can be given to goods-inwards staff to estimate forward workload. In addition, progress chasing has to take place on key lines and poor performing suppliers and short-term forecasts of cash requirements prepared for the accounts department.

The life blood of the replenishing purchasing section is of course the information which it obtains from the computer. Let us look in very broad outline at the computer system in use at W H Smith in 1980.

The core of the system is the central suite of programs which updates the master file and produces picking lists for the warehouse. History reports are produced at the same time for use in stock control, stock valuation, and in planning future requirements. The output of the central processing system is also fed into retail branch accounts – all branches are charged for goods they receive from the warehouse at retail price.

The central system is fed with input from the branch stock control systems, which we will look at in more detail below, and by centrally determined allocations of warehouse stock to branches. In addition, we should also mention that backorders are kept if no stock is available at the centre. Stock is then supplied when this becomes available. In addition, the computer system is used to manage the volumes to be handled through the warehouse and by the transport system. This is done by holding or releasing backorders as appropriate.

The central processing system has to be updated for goods received and any amendments which need to be made to the masterfile such as price changes via a transaction processing system which is on line to the master stock file.

What we have seen so far is a very simplified description of the way central stock control is carried out at two levels – the control level and the day to day. Of course, like any progressive company, we are always looking at ways of improving our methods and currently we are examining the whole of our inventory procedures with this in mind. We are hoping to build in some form of automatic stock replenishment for our slower selling lines although we expect that we will still need to keep a closer (human) eye on our top selling lines and those which are subject to variations in supply and demand. We are also looking at information systems which should give us much more detailed information of sales and stock levels for the branches which should enable us to further reduce our stock levels and increase our service levels.

Branch Stock Control Systems

Let us take a look now at the way the branch manager controls his stock and the ordering of stock in his branch. I think if you were to come into our organisation and look at the different types of merchandise and outlets that we have you would quickly realise that there is no one stock control system which will cope with all of these. In fact, we have quite a large number of separate systems. For example, the retail shops have one batch of systems whilst the airport stalls have another and Bowes & Bowes chain of our speciality bookshops have a quite separate one.

For simplicity, let us look at the ordinary retail branches which I am sure you are familiar with. These branches sell a wide range of goods including stationery, books, periodicals, records, confectionery and tobacco. We organize our stock control procedures on A, B, C lines – that is the A lines are the top 1 per cent accounting for 30 per cent of the volume, the C lines are 85 per cent lines accounting for 20 per cent of the volume and B lie somewhere inbetween. The figures are not precise.

Our A lines – the top one per cent – are partly controlled by a top sellers system. This looks after about 80 lines. Branches report the stock level of each of these lines at weekly intervals and from this we calculate rates of sale. This combined with an estimate of how long it takes to get goods from the warehouse to the branches and previous history of the way lines behave allow us to calculate an order at the centre. This is then fed into the central computer system, which generates picking lists. The system has been highly successful in keeping down stock levels to very acceptable figures whilst maintaining service levels to the branches in the region of 94 per cent.

Our top sellers system is one of two central branch stock control systems – the other is our central allocation system for high value goods. Here we need a separate system because these are delivered to the branch by Securicor and require special handling and accounting and it is essential that for such expensive items we maintain stock levels at the lowest possible levels. Stock levels are therefore counted on a fortnightly cycle and in this case the branch work out their sales and their next order which is advised to the centre who will vary it according to the stock available and their special knowledge of any changes in range which may take place. This system is currently being merged with top sellers.

Our books are mainly C items in stock control terms, that is they are 85 per cent of the lines which account for 20 per cent of the volume. For example, we hold 31,000 lines at Swindon of which 25,000 are books. For our really slow selling books, we use a system called SABRE which stands for Sales Activated Book Re-Ordering. This is in effect a primitive point of sale system. A stock card is inserted in each book and removed when the sale is made by the assistant and the book re-ordered provided its sales have achieved certain target levels.

Our stationery and toys and games lines are controlled by a system known as the BSOB – branch stock order book system. This is a re-order level system. The sales assistant counts the stock every three weeks and provided this is in excess of the re-order level no order is made. If the stock count is below this figure, a standard order quantity is ordered – the standard order quantity being determined centrally from computer history files. The system is simple to operate and relies on computer produced stock books which are themselves a spin off from our master stock files. The system is also geared to take account of the size of the shop and the amount of its display stock and its turnover of any particular type of merchandise. We have up to six different catalogues depending on the size of the shop.

It has been our experience over the last five years of installing branch stock control systems that these are some of the more difficult things to do well. We find that we need really effective teams of people to train our shop assistants and branch management in the way that these systems should be operated. Bear in mind, that with over 300 shops it is very difficult to police a stock control system particularly as we have quite a number of these. However, we have been able to demonstrate quite convincingly that the BSOB system for general merchandise as we call it – mostly stationery lines – has been effective at the branch in maintaining service levels and reducing stock levels. Of course, stock and service levels for a central warehouse to the branch vary according to the nature of the merchandise. They also vary quite dramatically throughout the year but as you probably realise our selling patterns, and therefore our stock levels, are heavily influenced by the Christmas selling peak.

One very real problem is that we know a good deal less about the service levels between the branch and the customer. What we do know, however, is that our centrally controlled branch stock systems seem to give a very much higher service level than the ones which are operated by the branch. That is, there are many fewer stockouts. We are therefore looking at systems which will allow us to control stock centrally. However, you will realise that with 300 plus branches and perhaps 60,000 product lines in total, only half of which are supplied centrally, this is no easy matter.

Comparison with other retail companies

Let us now compare W H Smith with other high street retailers. You will probably know that in the case of British Home Stores, Marks & Spencers and Mothercare, they are characterised by a relatively small number of product lines, tight margins, high sales per square foot and a high degree of central control. At the other end of the scale W H Smith, Boots and Halfords, all have a very large number of lines, lower sales per square foot, lower stock turns and much less central control. It is also true to say that British Home Stores, Marks & Spencer and Mothercare tend to have very many high fashion items particularly in clothes and these require, as in the case of our central allocation system, a high degree of central control.

As already mentioned British Home Stores, Marks & Spencers and Mothercare all have very tightly controlled central stock systems, in some cases based on the Kimbal tag system, in others on simple stock counts. For those of you unfamiliar with the Kimbal tag, this is a small punched card which is attached to the item by the manufacturer. At the point of sale the tag is detached, later to be punch read at the central computer. This system can be remarkably effective in determining sales rates of individual lines. Obviously, the fewer lines the better when operating such a system. We probably could not afford it because of the cost of producing the tags.

We in W H Smith, and our colleagues in Boots and Halfords, are all looking at the new point of sale data capture systems. For the system to work each item has to have a bar code on it. This bar code can be scanned by a light wand and the unique number of the product (and the fact that it has been sold) transferred to the central computer via cassette storage, floppy disc storage, or bubble memory. The sales data can then be integrated with other data about receipts and distribution from warehouse and transfers between the stores to arrive at an accurate figure for sales of each line item. This information can then be built up into a picture for the whole group of merchandise within a branch and within all branches.

There are great potential benefits to be reaped particularly in reducing stock levels, increasing sales, reducing what we euphemistically call "shrinkage" – that is theft – and for the first time it makes possible a high degree of central control in W H Smith's kind of business. Of course these systems are expensive – their costs run to many millions of pounds – but we would expect to see prices come tumbling down over the next few years and at the same time the facilities and storage offered by the manufacturers of the point of sale terminals greatly increased.

The problem, however, is not so much a technical one of design of systems but in making sure that we know how to use the information and that we have the kind of organisation which is geared to this very sophisticated type of information system. We are currently looking at the whole problem of defining key information requirements for the retail group and of course point of sale is one of the things we are looking at very closely. We are already running an experiment in our Portsmouth shop which looks very encouraging but each step along the way has to be seen to pay for itself.

We see one of the major hurdles being that of getting the manufacturers to put bar codes on their products. This is not a very costly exercise for them but it is for us. You can imagine that labelling every product – which we already do for pricing purposes – with a bar code in addition would be expensive in terms of labelling equipment and time. We are therefore making strenuous efforts to persuade the manufacturers of records, books, periodicals and stationery to put European Article Number bar codes on their products. From their point of view they will have access to a great deal of marketing information which could prove extremely useful. We, for our part, will have to bear a large proportion of the costs of point of sale though we expect that this will be greatly outweighed by the benefits. It may well take us four to five years to get the necessary 90 per cent of our items coded. However, next year should see the first bar codes appearing on books and some stationery products.

Of course, we recognise that these systems will all have an effect on our staff and indeed on our customers but the effects are likely to be beneficial to both these groups. The sales assistants will be spared the task of stock counting at frequent intervals – though they will still have to count stock for reconciliation purposes every so often – and the customer will have an itemised bill which will say in clear English what he has bought – for example, a pencil or a ruler and its price. This of course is only possible because the POS tills will have what is called Computer Price Lookup –

the wanding of the EAN number causes the till software and hardware to look up the price and item description and then instantly flashes this to a display in front of the cashier and customer.

I think you can see that these are exciting times for retailers. Perhaps the most recent revolution in retailing was the move towards self service with its considerable benefits in terms of cost reduction which have been passed on to the consumer. Point of sale could have just as far reaching benefits. The most obvious conclusion is that retailing like other areas of industry must have good, tight information and control systems operating at the right levels of detail. At the same time our systems must be capable of being understood and operated by the people under our control and we must be able to take advantage of the micro processor revolution which is just around the corner, if not already with us.

It is an exciting world to be involved with and perhaps one day we may even see something about the inventory control and retailing finally appearing in that Oxford Dictionary of Quotations. I'm sure the day is not too far off.

Chapter 7

Materials requirement planning for manufacture

This chapter considers in detail the use of materials requirement planning (MRP) systems, which were mentioned in outline in Chapter 5. These are appropriate when the demand for an item is not independent of the demand for other items, but instead is dependent on the demand for an end product.

Traditional assumptions in stock control

Traditional stock control theory starts with the consideration of a single item in isolation. It is assumed:

1 That the demand for this item is independent of the demand for any other item;
2 That the demand is continuous and in the simplest case fluctuates about a constant mean;
3 That these fluctuations can be represented with reasonable accuracy by some standard statistical distribution (the binomial, Poisson, normal, etc.) which can then be used to derive buffer stocks to prevent shortages;
4 That a standard forecasting technique such as moving average or exponential smoothing will give reasonably accurate forecasts in the simplest case where demand fluctuates about a mean, and more elaborate statistical techniques can be used in cases where there is a seasonal variation or a trend upwards or downwards;
5 That the supply of this item is independent of orders placed for the supply of other items, and consequently there is no need to coordinate orders for different items, and the order quantity can be worked out in isolation using some mathematical approach such as the EOQ.

These assumptions are not unrealistic and do in fact apply reasonably well to many of the things held in stock by organisations. They lead to an idealised picture of stock as shown in Figure 7:1A. This is idealised by making the rate of requirement perfectly continuous and constant and the lead time for replenishment constant too, giving the sawtooth curve shown. Quantity in stock falls smoothly until the order point (or reorder level) triggers an order, which arrives exactly when due; and quantity on hand increases by the order quantity. It is however, not unrepresentative of the situation for many items, for instance the merchandise lines carried by a retailer. It also applies to some of the items held by manufacturers, for instance MRO items, and materials which are used on many products, so that the demand for them is, in practice, fairly continuous.

But if we consider a part which is used on one product made in batches at intervals corresponding to the stock cycle shown in Figure 7:1A, we find the pattern shown in Figure 7:1B. Stock stays at its maximum level until the batch requirement is called for. It then falls to its minimum, triggering a new order, which when it arrives again lies idle in the stores until the time comes round for a new batch to be issued. Average stocks are higher than intended. The remedy is to use MRP, which leads to the stock pattern shown in Figure 7:1C. Here the quantity required arrives shortly before the time at which it is required. Average stock is much lower, rather than higher, than the average stock envisaged in Figure 7:1A.

Dependent demand

In fact for such items all the traditional assumptions given above are invalid:

1   Demand is dependent on the demand for the end-product
2   Demand is discontinuous and occurs at intervals
3   Demand does not fluctuate about a mean, although buffer stocks may be needed to provide some slack
4   Standard forecasting techniques do not apply, since they try to smooth out discontinuous demands into a continuous demand
5   Orders for items dependent on a single end product should be coordinated and the order quantities should not be decided by using the EOQ formula.

Inappropriate application of order point – order quantity systems to such items leads to consequences described by Burbidge.[1]

Using a conventional simple inventory control system for the control of finished product stocks, or stocks of components produced internally, can lead to chaos in the machine shops where they are manufactured. Simple stock control systems of the continuous or reorder level type arrange for each stock item to be reordered when stock on hand falls to a trigger level intended to be equal to the average amount required during lead time plus a margin for variations. The quantity ordered is usually either:

1   Enough to cover a fixed period such as three months, or
2   An economic order quantity, calculated to balance set-up and ordering costs on the one hand against stockholding costs on the other hand and to give order quantities varying with usage value.

In theory the latter approach should minimise total operating costs, but simplifying

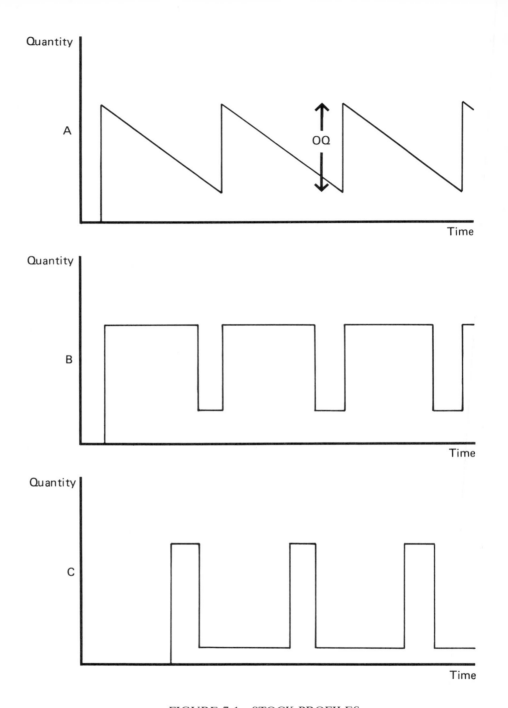

FIGURE 7:1   STOCK PROFILES
(A) independent demand with OP/OQ control; (B) dependent demand with OP/OQ control;
(C) dependent demand with MRP

assumptions are made which are so sweeping that in practice the result is far from optimal. The main simplifying assumption is that no interaction occurs between items: all or none of the items can be in progress at any time without affecting costs. This could be true for bought-out items. It cannot be true for made-in items, where ordering means initiating a manufacturing batch. Here the flow of work through the factory should be considered. As steady a load on the factory as possible is desirable, and batches of similar items should be initiated in sequence so that machine set-up times can be reduced. Yet many batch production manufacturers have used the stock-controlled production approach despite its inherent instability and the crisis management it leads to. A typical stock control system has the following characteristics:

1   Each component is treated individually
2   The order quantity is generally fixed for each item
3   The interval between orders is varied to regulate materials flow
4   The system generates multi-cycle multi-phase materials flow
5   New orders are released when the stock of any part drops to a predetermined reorder level ("order point")

This ordering system has been used for centuries by merchants. It sees each item as an entirely separate problem. It does not distinguish between maintaining a flow of materials and maintaining stocks of materials. It tends to believe that the only way to improve the service is to increase the stock. Our acceptance of these ideas may go deeper than reason. To our ancient ancestors, winter stocks of food meant survival. It is possible that we may be already programmed at birth to associate high stocks with peace of mind.

A typical materials requirement planning (MRP) system used in conjunction with period batch control would on the other hand have the following characteristics, which are the exact opposite of those quoted above for stock control:

1   Components are ordered in balanced product sets
2   The order interval is fixed
3   The order quantity is varied to regulate materials flow
4   The system generates single-cycle single-phased materials flow
5   New orders are released in accordance with a master schedule which may be used over and over again in each cycle

In an engineering company making a wide range of assembled pumps, compressors, or complex valves for instance, a high level of management skill is required to achieve a stock turn rate of $2\frac{1}{2}$ times a year with functional layout and stock-controlled production. With functional layout and period batch control using a four week cycle, the rate of stock turn can be increased to, say, $3\frac{1}{2}$. With group layout and period batch control using a two week cycle, a stock turn rate of five times per year has been achieved, and it is probable that this figure could be further improved, to six or better. Stocks are much higher with stock-controlled production than with period batch control for one main reason. A simple system which generates an order when

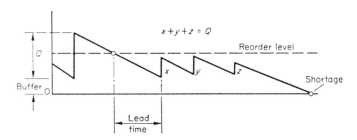

FIGURE 7:2   SPLIT DELIVERIES
These can cause a shortage, as shown in the diagram, or may cause double ordering

stock falls to an order level, will only work if the time it takes to replace a batch is less than the time it takes to use it up. If the lead time is longer than the consumption time, the reorder level will be a fictitious level never reached by the stock. In practice the lead time must generally be at least one-third shorter than the consumption time to reduce the risk of errors due to short, split or delayed deliveries, as shown in Figure 7:2

The limitation that the lead time must be less than the consumption time can be overcome by using more complicated systems. The order level can be based on physical stock plus replenishment orders outstanding. This is more complicated than simple stock control and in practice often does not lead to any less stock.

Substantial savings can also be made in setting time, and in effective plant capacity, by bringing together parts which use similar tooling for machining one after the other. Substantial savings in direct material cost are often available if the blanks for all parts made from the same general material are cut at the same time. Cutting can be planned for minimum wastage when all blanks are cut together. With the stock control system of ordering in which orders arrive at random, it is impossible to take advantage of this family processing. In the Perfect Flow simulation at the Turin International Centre for Advanced Technical and Vocational Training, ten parts out of the 229 parts in the sample were assumed to be in the same tooling family and capable of being processed on the same set-up. On average only 2.7 of these parts were on order together. With the same average batch frequency, stock control required nearly four times as many set-ups as period batch control.

When used to control the ordering of parts for assembled products, the stock control ordering system also induces heavy material obsolescence losses. Because the different parts are ordered in different quantities at different times, they are never in balanced product sets.

All product changes or design modifications, therefore, tend to leave a remnant of components which can no longer be used. With complicated mechanical products few of these components have any reasonable sale as spare parts. Most of them must be scrapped as obsolete material. With period batch control, obsolescence is easier to avoid because parts are ordered in balanced product sets.

Thus, the system of production control in which production orders are initiated from stock records with preset order levels has the following main deficiencies in assembled product manufacture:

1 It requires a very high investment in stock
2 It generates highly variable and unpredictable changes in both finished stock and work in progress
3 It generates a variable and unpredictable load of work on the machine tools which it feeds with orders
4 It make it impossible to achieve the significant savings possible from family processing
5 When demand is transmitted back down a series of inventories, the system tends to magnify at each succeeding inventory stage the demand variation about the mean
6 It leads to materials obsolescence
7 It is particularly unreliable under conditions of varying demand.

MRP without computers

Although the term MRP (for Materials Requirement Planning) came into use after computers had become commonplace for production and inventory control applications, the basis of the system is quite simple. Long before computers appeared on the scene, clerical versions of what would now be called MRP had been implemented by batch production manufacturers such as machine tool makers and by mass production manufacturers such as vehicle makers.

The process is outlined in Figure 7:3 which shows the planning process for cycle 8 in a firm which starts a new cycle each month and takes four months to complete a cycle. Cycle 8 is due for despatch to customers in November, and the planning therefore needs to be done in August. At the beginning of August consideration is given to the November sales plan for the three products A, B and C. The October assembly program to meet this plan is decided after adjusting for available stock and planned increases in stock. The net requirement for parts to be made in September is obtained by exploding the October production program through parts lists (bills of material) to get gross requirements for parts and adjusting for stock and orders due in, and adding spares and scrap or shrinkage allowance. Works orders are released in August calling for the manufacture of parts in September and the assembly of products in October for despatch to customers in November.

This example illustrates the way in which MRP converts a timed schedule of due dates for end products into timed schedules of due dates for parts and material, and offsets the due dates by lead times to arrive at the latest release dates for works orders and purchase orders.

A further example is given in Figure 7:4, and here it is assumed that no orders are outstanding and no stock is available. The end product X is sold from stock at between 60 and 70 per period. Assuming an initial stock of 250, an order point of 50 and an order quantity of 200, the three batches of 200 shown on the second line

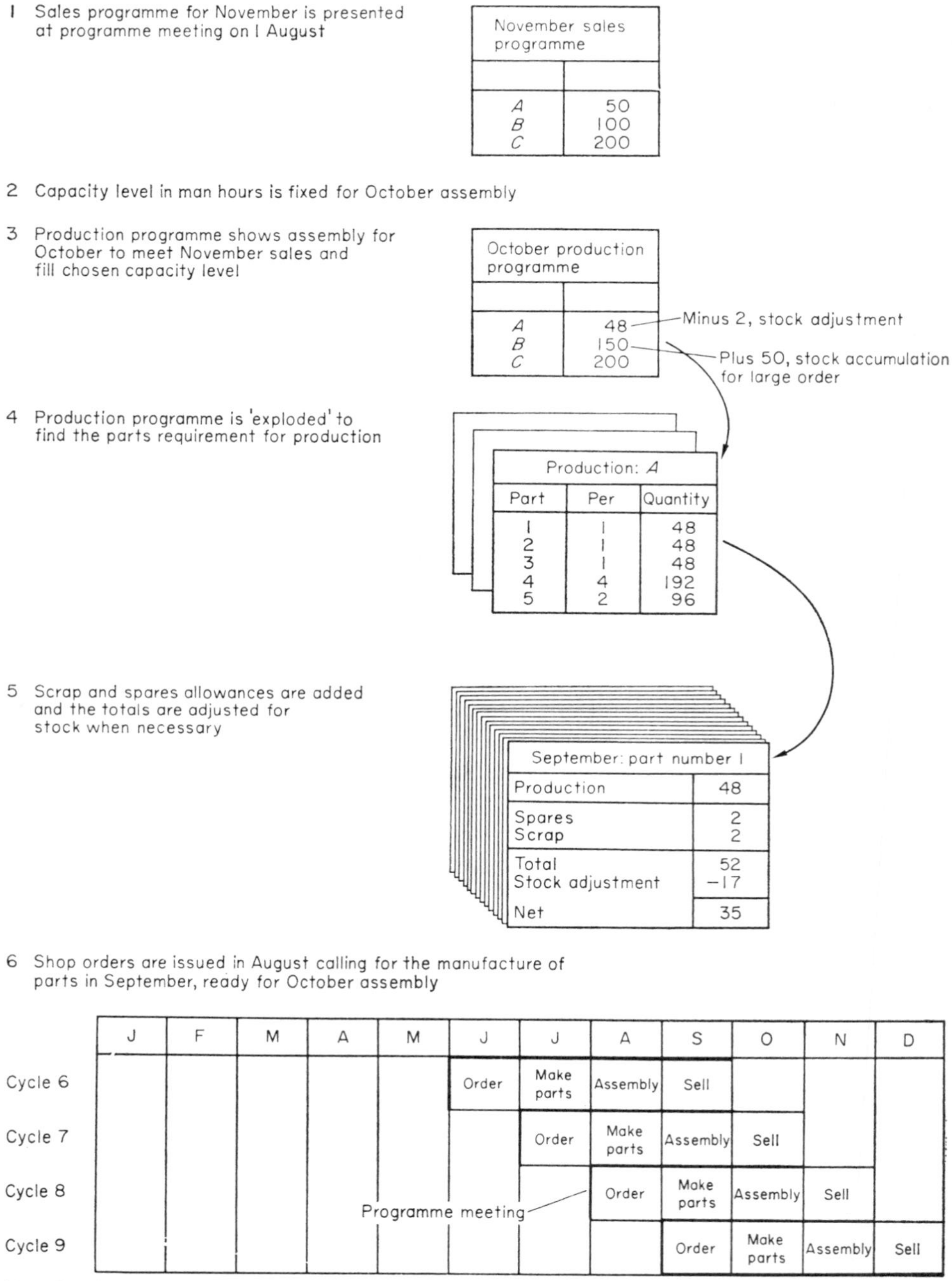

1   Sales programme for November is presented at programme meeting on 1 August

November sales programme	
A	50
B	100
C	200

2   Capacity level in man hours is fixed for October assembly

3   Production programme shows assembly for October to meet November sales and fill chosen capacity level

October production programme	
A	48
B	150
C	200

—Minus 2, stock adjustment

—Plus 50, stock accumulation for large order

4   Production programme is 'exploded' to find the parts requirement for production

Production: A		
Part	Per	Quantity
1	1	48
2	1	48
3	1	48
4	4	192
5	2	96

5   Scrap and spares allowances are added and the totals are adjusted for stock when necessary

September: part number 1	
Production	48
Spares	2
Scrap	2
Total	52
Stock adjustment	−17
Net	35

6   Shop orders are issued in August calling for the manufacture of parts in September, ready for October assembly

	J	F	M	A	M	J	J	A	S	O	N	D
Cycle 6						Order	Make parts	Assembly	Sell			
Cycle 7							Order	Make parts	Assembly	Sell		
Cycle 8								Order	Make parts	Assembly	Sell	
Cycle 9									Order	Make parts	Assembly	Sell

Programme meeting

Note: In this case a new cycle starts each month and each cycle takes four months. In most cases it is possible to use shorter cycles of one or two weeks

FIGURE 7:3   PERIOD BATCH CONTROL
Process of ordering for cycle 8

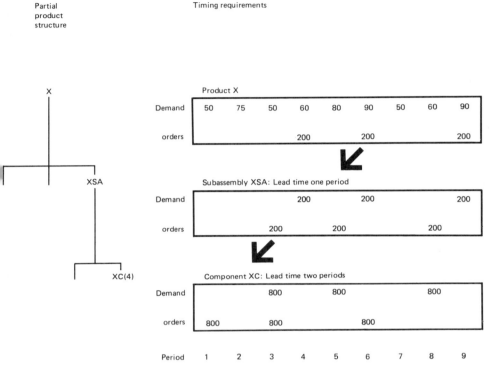

FIGURE 7:4   TIME-PHASING REQUIREMENTS
Determining release dates for parts and sub-assemblies using lead times and due dates

(under timing requirements, Product X) would be triggered by the sales forecast shown on the first line. Everything after this is arithmetic. Consequently it is very suitable for computer processing, and it would be very unusual for a computer to make a mistake in the arithmetic. But it would still come up with the wrong answers if the sales forecast is wrong. Garbage in, garbage out!

Fundamental to the whole materials requirements planning process is the master production schedule on line 2: which products are due for completion in which periods. The product structure diagram shown in partial form at the left of Figure 7:4 shows that product X incorporates one sub-assembly XSA. Consequently the batch of 200 of product X due for completion in period 4 requires 200 sub-assemblies XSA to be available at the beginning of period 4. As the lead time is one period, a works order for 200 XSA needs to be released at the beginning of period 3, as shown.

The product structure diagram also shows that each sub-assembly XSA incorporates 4 components XC. Therefore 800 of these parts are needed at the beginning of period 3, and as the lead time is two periods the order needs to be released at the beginning of period 1.

MRP thus requires the following:

1 Master production schedule – a schedule showing what quantities of what pro
   ducts are due to be completed in which periods.
2 Product structures and parts lists – details of the parts and material required to
   make those products
3 Lead times for all the products, parts and material
4 Details of uncommitted stock and orders due for parts and material.

Given this information, which can be carried on cards and files for clerical processing
but is now more usually held on disks as a materials database, it is straightforward to
work out net requirements level by level for each time period.

Master production schedule

The master production schedule is a detailed statement of the quantities of each end
product which are due to be completed each week or other time period in order to
meet customer orders or management plans. The schedule should be realistic, that is
capable of being achieved in the real world where 100 per cent capacity utilisation
often figures on the "wish list" but never appears to apply to last month's output.

In the short term, capacity can be increased by overtime, weekend working,
additional shifts or subcontracting. Long-term increases require investment in additional plant or the employment of additional people. Computer systems usually have
facilities for simulating the effect of alternative plans on capacity and the effect of
capacity increases on potential output. "Rough-cut" capacity planning gives a quick
approximation which is useful at the planning stage. This can aid management
judgment, but management judgment still needs to be exercised.

Supply of bought-out parts and material is also increasingly subject to supply
capacity constraints. In the short term these can be overcome by capable purchasing
staff. They may persuade existing suppliers to give priority or to increase their
short-term capacity, or they may succeed in finding new suppliers. Before buying
parts from suppliers they may buy capacity; this can appreciably increase short-term
flexibility at relatively low cost. Long-term planning inputs from purchasing may
include supply industry capacity, supply market share, preferred supplier capacity,
and proportion of preferred suppliers' output which it is proposed to take, in the case
of key materials. This raises the question: how far ahead should the master production schedule extend? The planning horizon clearly needs to extend at least as far
ahead as the longest purchase lead time. But this is still not far enough, since buyers
need to decide on order quantities even when ordering a year ahead and so they need
some idea of probable production requirements further ahead than that.

Setting the planning horizon far enough in the future to cover the longest procurement lead time plus manufacturing lead time for products made from purchased
materials plus in some cases a further period to enable suitable order quantities to be
determined will often take the scheduler into areas of uncertainty where forecasts are
clouded by fog. One approach to this is to prepare production schedules in three
parts. Output in the near future is scheduled week by week. The second part

schedules probable output month by month so that short-term capacity plans can be made and purchase orders placed. The third part outlines projected output by quarters for use in connection with long lead time purchases and the acquisition of additional permanent capacity.

Managers often try to reduce the gap between what is thought to be achievable and what is actually achieved by scheduling quarts out of pint pots. One firm actually conducted an experiment on this. When the system had been in operation for about a year, the master production schedule was deliberately overloaded. "Plans to develop additional capacity failed, inventory escalated, output declined, and a cash flow crisis developed. The master schedule was then loaded to historically viable throughput rates, whereupon inventory and cash flow were quickly brought under control and factory output rose to record levels".[2]

Computer systems, as at present designed, take statements literally and do not apply "pinches of salt". It is, for instance, pointless to carry forward at the beginning of a new planning period a backlog of overdue orders from previous periods, and schedule them on top of plans for the new period which commit available resources to the limit. The result is a plan which cannot be achieved. The only person to be blamed for failure to achieve it is the planner.

It follows that planners need to be very capable people. "An effective master scheduler needs to have a wide spread of attributes, being both numerate and a lateral thinker, a wise negotiator and able to give much attention to detail". Rather unusual graduates with shop floor experience would be a possible choice.

Product structure and parts list

To explode the master production schedule, which shows what end products are due to be completed in each period of time, into lists of parts and material required to complete them, we need details of the product structure as shown in Figure 7:5 and we need parts lists as shown in Figure 7:6.

The product structure file shows for instance how product X is assembled from one part XD and one each of sub-assemblies XSA and XSB. It shows also how sub-assembly XSA is put together from 4 parts XC and one part XD, and how sub-assembly XSB is put together from one part XD and 2 parts XE. Part XC is made from material M1, part XE from material M2, and part XD must be bought out. Computer systems can display or print out exploded requirements in a number of alternative formats. A *single level* explosion would be similar to the left side of Figure 7:6 for level one, or to the right side with the addition of requirements for sub-assembly XSB for level two. An *indented explosion* shows all the parts and material required to make the product, parts used on more than one level being shown separately for each level as shown in Figure 7:7.

A summarised explosion is similar except that each item is shown once only, at the

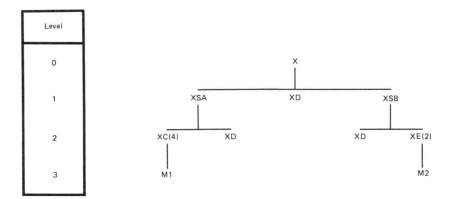

FIGURE 7:5   OUTLINE PRODUCT STRUCTURE

Parts list: Product X	
XSA	1
XSB	1
XD	1

Parts list: Sub-assembly XSA	
XC	4
XD	1

FIGURE 7:6   OUTLINE PARTS LISTS

lowest level at which it occurs, but with total quantity required shown. The lowest level would be shown as the low level code for the item. The only item in Figure 7:7 which appears at more than one level is XD, which might be shown as follows:

Level	Item	Quantity	Gross requirement
2	XD	3	150

An "implosion" or "where used" facility is also provided, which enables any part or materials to be traced to the parts, sub-assemblies or products on which it is used. This is useful in considering the effect of a strike at a supplier or a late delivery. It is also useful in connection with the introduction of modifications and engineering changes. If we want to use up existing stocks before introducing the change we need to attach a "date effective" both to new and old versions of the item in product structure and part master files.

Level		Item	Quantity	Gross requirement
0		X	1	50
1		XSA	1	50
1		XSB	1	50
2		XC	4	200
2		XE	2	100
2		XD	2	100
1		XD	1	50
	3	M1	1 ft	200 ft
	3	M2	1.5 ft	150 ft

FIGURE 7:7   INDENTED EXPLOSION

Lead times

Lead time can be defined as the total time it takes to get things. In the case of bought-out parts it may include internal delay in producing and authorising documents; delay in the post; supplier's delivery period; transit time from supplier to customer; and delay in inspection. Thus, a quoted delivery period of four weeks might correspond to a lead time of six weeks. In the case of made-in parts it will normally include allowances for waiting time. It might take twenty standard minutes to weld four parts XC together to make sub-assembly XSA, but because there would normally be a queue of parts awaiting welding the lead time might be stated as one week so as to give some shop floor flexibility.

Complex products naturally have complex lead times. Thousands of parts are put together to make a motor car, but they are not all required at the same moment in time. The gearbox needs to be assembled before the car; gears need to be ready before the gearbox is assembled; raw materials such as forgings or alloy steel bar need to be available before the gears are machined, etc. Product X in Figure 7:4 could be completed in the same period as it was ordered, provided that the parts and sub-assemblies required were available. But if the lead time for sub-assembly XSA is one period, and for part XC is two periods, the composite lead time for product X is at least three periods. ("At least" because we have not yet considered lead times for other parts and materials).

Stock and orders

Exploding the master production schedule through the bills of material or parts lists gives the gross requirement. Offsetting the results by lead times gives the gross requirements per period. To obtain the net requirements per period we need to make adjustments for the stock on hand which is not committed to other orders, and also for any orders which are due in. Thus, if the gross requirement for period 6 is 100, and we have 20 in stock and 40 due in, the net requirement for period 6 is 40. Should we release for production or purchase just that quantity? Or should we try to save

money by covering additional future requirements in the same production or purchase lot?

Lot sizing rules

Several methods can be used to decide order quantities: for instance lot for lot,
part-periods balancing, and the EOQ.

LOT FOR LOT

This is particularly suitable for costly items required infrequently, for jobs where no
unallocated stock is wanted, and for many items used only on one product. Just the
quantity required to complete the batch is ordered, after adjustment for scrap
allowance, shrinkage, spares orders, and stock.

PART-PERIODS BALANCING

Part-period balancing, or the least total cost algorithm, is used when parts are
required more frequently, and it is desired to balance the cost of holding parts in
stock against the savings obtained by spreading set-up costs over a larger quantity.
First we need the cost of holding one part in stock for one period. If stockholding cost
is $\frac{1}{2}$ per cent per period, and unit cost of an item is £10, then the cost of holding it in
stock for one period is £0.05. This is divided into the ordering cost to obtain the
part-period value. For instance if for this item the ordering cost, consisting largely of
set-up or changeover cost in the works, amounts to £25, the part-periods value is 500.
This means that we can carry 500 parts for one period, or 50 parts for ten periods, or
5 parts for 100 periods, before the increased stockholding cost outweighs the cost
reduction due to spreading ordering cost over more parts.

If an item is used still more frequently, so that the requirement can be regarded as
more or less continuous, a version of the EOQ formula can be used, and the resulting
order quantity rounded up or down to the nearest whole number of periods'
requirements.

Other lot sizing rules include *fixed quantity,* and *fixed period* of supply. Various
modifiers can be provided, for instance "order with" to enable related items to be
ordered together, "minimum" to ensure that orders are not issued for quantities too
small to make or buy, "maximum" to put an upper limit on order quantities,
"multiple" to make the order quantity a multiple of some predetermined quantity.
Allowances for shrinkage or scrap can also be incorporated.

Computer systems usually allow for "pegging" and "allocation". Pegging creates a
link between a particular customer order and the various items required to fill it;
allocation is a process of reserving material for specific orders.

It used to be common to prepare a revised plan, when this became necessary
because of changed circumstances or the passage of time, by "regeneration": the
whole process would be repeated, starting with the revised master production
schedule, exploding it, offsetting and netting. Net change systems are now increasingly used: these process only the actual changes in the master schedule, for instance

new customer orders, amendments or cancellations. Run time is very much shorter than for regeneration, so the plan can be kept up-to-date more easily. In some cases the plan could be updated each evening.

A selection of off-the-shelf computer systems is considered in the next chapter.

Finally, in this chapter, we would mention that MRP is really a simple and sensible technique. People are sometimes disappointed to find how simple it really is, after all the publicity and the "crusade" which APICS ran in the 1970s. This may be the reason for the attempts sometimes made to let the initials stand for something less simple and more comprehensive: Manufacturing Resource Planning, More Real Progress, for instance. We must welcome anything which helps the manufacturer of complex products in the difficult task of planning and controlling operations so as to efficiently produce the right goods on time. But it seems preferable to let MRP continue to denote materials requirement planning and to adopt some new term for any new technique.

References

1   Burbidge, J L "The Case for Flow Control", in *Managing Materials in Industry*, Baily and Farmer, Gower, 1972.
2   Winfield, D E "MRP – an In-house Approach", in *More than Just Techniques*, conference proceedings, BPICS, 1980.
3   Ibid.

Further reading

Two books by Colin New provide a very clear account of materials requirement planning in greater detail than can be given here:

Requirement Planning, Gower, 1973, and *Managing the Manufacture of Complex Products*, Business Books, 1977.

Chapter 8

Computer systems for materials planning and control

Review of some off-the-shelf systems

Computer systems of the kind described in this chapter began to be developed in the 1960s, but significant improvements in computer technology and hardware occurred during the 1970s, and are still of course going on. These in turn made possible the development of ready-made systems, most of which can be modified to meet individual user requirements more quickly and at less expense than starting from scratch and developing internally a tailor-made system.

Such systems are available from IBM and from many other manufacturers, and from consultants. A selection of the systems currently on offer is reviewed in this chapter. Some are intended for large manufacturers and some for small; some need a large mainframe processor and others a small computer or a microcomputer. These are quite sophisticated systems in comparison with what was available a few years previously, and internally developed systems have become much less common.

After briefly outlining a selection of the systems on offer, we draw some conclusions about the current state of the art, and end with a note on implementation.

PHILIPS DATA SYSTEMS
Philips Data Systems offered what they described as a total production management system for the small and medium size manufacturer. With software written by Safe Computing Ltd in conjunction with Philips, and operating on the Philips P430 computer, the P430 PMS system did not need qualified operators but was intended to be operated by materials staff in their normal working environment. An instance was quoted in which a 150 employee firm had used the system to derive standard costs for any Bill of Material in less than two hours. Previously 12 man-weeks had been required to do this clerically.

Users communicated with the system by VDU. Accurate, up-to-date answers could be obtained immediately to such questions as:

What is sub-assembly X used on and how many of our products use it?
What is the current stock level?
Where is it located in the warehouse?
What does it cost to make?
When is the next delivery due?
Can we accept an order for 100 for delivery 3rd March?
If we accept the order, which parts are required, by what dates?
Is it possible to produce 20 today?
What is the current position on works order AZ493?

Modules available comprised: bill of materials processor, stock control, product costing, requirements planning, and work in progress.

Bill of materials processor stored all data about specific characteristics of each part relevant to planning, scheduling and purchasing, together with the information needed to control the flow of products through fabrication and assembly.

Stock control provided detailed information on stock levels and reports on stock movements, shortages and valuations, accepting existing cost codes.

Product costing maintained data for use in calculating standard costs and actual costs for all parts and assemblies. It included a "what if" facility for testing cost changes.

Requirements planning calculated net requirements for future production periods, based on available stock and forecast demand.

Work in progress provided all information needed to control changes in routing, timing and plant capacity.

PACS/VS

PA Computers and Telecommunications Ltd had a revised version of their PACS Planning and Control System, using a Wang VS computer. Minimum configuration required was 256KB of main memory on the CPU, 30MB disk storage, a line printer and VDU's as required. Like all these systems it was on-line, real time, interactive, with an integrated database and a number of modules which could be installed in a variety of sequences and adapted to suit user requirements.

Modules 1 and 2 comprised the database as shown in Figure 8:1. Module 1, described as the planning database, maintained data on what was required to build a product: part number, bill of material, work centres, routing, operation descriptions, drawings, tooling. Module 2, described as the control database, comprised four main sub-modules: customer orders, inventory, manufacturing orders, and purchase orders.

Customer order sub-module recorded sales orders with line item detail and scheduled despatch date, and could report on sales per customer, value of order book, and overdue orders.

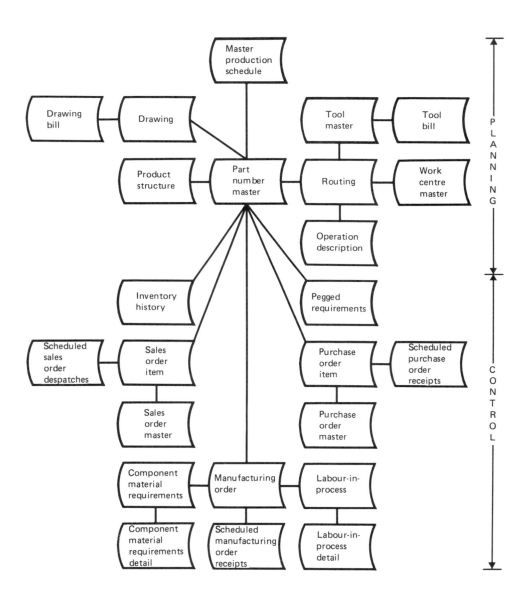

FIGURE 8:1   MATERIALS DATABASE

Inventory sub-module recorded stock (in stores, receiving, despatch, work in progress, and loaned to production) and stock history. It could provide ABC analysis, prompt cycle counts, include stock location, analyse inventory profiles or delivery periods (set-up, run and queue time). Component lead times could be displayed in Gannt chart format.

Manufacturing orders sub-module recorded manufacturing orders, component material requirements, allocation and operation-by-operation labour-in-progress, with a variety of screen displays and reports.

Purchase orders sub-module recorded purchase orders (pending, firm, released and closed), with due dates and purchase history. Reports included: orders per supplier, orders per buyer, and time-phased commitments in terms of value.

Other modules available were:
3   Master production schedule
4   Materials requirement planning
5   Capacity management
6   Priority control
7   Standard cost generation
8   Standard job order costing.

Module (4), materials requirement planning, exploded the master production schedule through all levels using the bills of materials and summarised the component material requirements for each time period. These gross requirements were netted against on-hand and on-order inventory. Order action messages were then produced which took account of order policies, lead times and batching rules to show: order start dates, order due dates, and recommended quantities. Order policies provided were: as required, EOQ, fixed quantity, least unit cost, periods order quantity, order with, non-MRP. Order quantity modifiers were: minimum, maximum, multiple, order shrinkage, component scrap.

Features included a 52 period planning horizon. Reports could be provided on: gross requirements, on-hand and scheduled receipts, available, planned order starts, exceptions, material action (order, expedite, defer, cancel), and pegged requirements, all by time period. Part by part single level pegging, and a multiple level pegging option using order numbers, were available. Firm planned orders could be specified. Order lead times could be fixed or variable. Order critical path and safety lead times were provided for.

Level by level gross to net explosion could be shown. A variety of run options were available, including: gross only, gross/offset, net on-hand, net on-hand/offset, net on-hand/on-order/planned orders/offset.

KEWILL SYSTEMS – MICROSS
Kewill Systems Ltd claimed that their Micross system for workshop production control, developed under the auspices of the National Computing Centre with financial support from the Department of Industry, was the first to be based on a

microcomputer. No doubt this decade will see many more. Hardware required was a Zilog Z80 processor with 64KB memory, Shugart dual floppy disks with 1000KB storage, a matrix printer and a VDU.

Intended for engineering firms employing 30 to 300 people, or for operations of comparable size in larger organisations, the system was capable of handling up to 2000 jobs in progress, up to 5000 operations in progress, 100 work centres and 200 days of forward scheduling. Small batch manufacture of a wide variety of end products, or jobbing production to customer's order, were said to be suitable applications.

The system provided:

1   work in progress reporting and control: detailed up-to-date information on the status of works orders and loads at work centres
2   machine and factory loading
3   work schedules per work centre
4   forecast job finish dates
5   overdue orders report

Work scheduling could be by predetermined week number, or according to priorities set by management or calculated by the computer. Finite or infinite loading could be used, and a PERT-type network planning facility was available. As with all these systems, customers could either take the complete system or parts of it, for instance just the work in progress reporting facility.

In addition to workshop production control, a material control system was offered on the same hardware. This included a materials requirement planning module and a stock control module. The material requirement planning module exploded orders through the bill of material system to give a gross cumulative requirement for sub-assemblies, components and raw materials. Bill of materials explosions could be shown at highest or lowest level or at all levels. "Where used" lists could be produced for all components and materials. Bills of material could be costed at selling price, average cost or standard cost. Gross cumulative requirements could be compared with available stock and outstanding works or purchase orders, and with earlier allocations, to show up shortages. Requirements could then be allocated.

The stock control module maintained stock records and adjusted them for issues, receipts and allocations. Reports available: stock on-hand, stock reorder report, shortages, redundant stock, stock valuation, ABC analysis, items for checking, stock check variance, parts costs listing, works orders, purchase orders by supplier, order number or stock number, etc.

NCR (IMCS and Mission)
NCR were offering two systems, IMCS ('Interactive Manufacturing Control System') and Mission.

Aimed at the medium size manufacturer, IMCS comprised a number of modules which could be installed one at a time or in groups. A menu system allowed selection of the desired display or report, and the menu processor had multi-level access security provision. Modules available included: bill of material, material requirements planning, routing, order processing, work in progress, and capacity planning.

Bill of material maintained current and historical data on product structure, which could be exploded into components. Single level, indented, summarised, costed and extended explosions were available. Where used or implosion facility was also provided.

Inventory management maintained current and historical stock data. Features included automatic prompting of cycle counts for continuous stock check, ABC analysis, stock status and material variance (planned versus actual issues) reports. Safety stocks and other parameters could be specified.

Materials requirement planning converted marketing forecasts, product demands, and master schedules into complete time phased lists of requirements. Planning periods could be daily, weekly or monthly as required.

Routing recorded all the operations and associated resources required to manufacture or assemble an end product, and the sequence in which they occurred. Set-up time, queue time, production time, shrinkage and work centre capacity could be recorded, lead time calculated, and details of routing, cost and time data for any item displayed.

Work in progress continually updated the status of works orders as they progressed through manufacturing; provided travel and works documentation to accompany workpieces; maintained and reported costs, cost variances, and scrap loss.

Capacity planning provided data for short range planning such as authorising overtime, shifting work between machines and adjusting schedules, and also for long range planning involving the adjustment of capacity or production plans or both to meet management requirements.

Mission was a similar system aimed at the larger manufacturers, including those with several factories or warehouses. Modules similar to those in IMCS were available with some additional features. Some additional modules were also available, for instance master production scheduling, purchasing/receiving, and costing.

POWELL-DUFFRYN PROTOS
Powell Duffryn Computer Services had a system called Protos 2000, comprising a database maintained on-line by VDU, plus six major modules. The database recorded details of products, orders, stocks, work in progress, manufacturing methods, machine and labour resources, etc. *Help* facilities were provided to assist in getting the hang of the system, and an *Education* mode enabled users to experiment without corrupting production data.

Modules included sales order processing, engineering data control, requirements planning inventory control, and production planning.

Sales order processing recorded customer orders and provided comprehensive enquiry facilities. Customers could be given accurate delivery dates during the course of a telephone conversation by means of the on-line interrogation of uncommitted stock position at component level. Delivery dates requested could be checked for feasibility, orders received compared with forecast, sales accounting data and picking and despatch documentation provided.

Engineering data control recorded details of product assembly, component manufacture and machine and labour resources. Planned engineering changes and planned changes in machine capacity or routing could be maintained alongside current data, becoming effective at predetermined dates, or as otherwise specified.

Production Planning included facilities for capacity planning and for shop scheduling.

Requirements planning inventory control provided a variety of facilities, including bill of materials explosion, allocation, current stock status of any item, and forecasting routines based on exponential smoothing which could be used as the basis for calculating EOQ, safety stock and reorder point.

VENTEK DATAMAKE

Ventek Ltd stressed particularly the net change feature of their requirements planning system. This started, as do regenerative systems, with a forward program, by time period, of customer orders, stock orders, and spares requirement. To these would be added detailed sales forecasts of the orders which the sales department expect to receive for as far forward as they can see with any confidence. The system calculated raw material and manufacturing requirements, net of available stock and work in progress, to fill the output program. Release dates would also be worked out on the basis of supplier's delivery periods and average factory lead times. The results would be a comprehensive schedule of purchase orders and manufacturing orders required to meet the firm demand schedule, plus also the sales forecasts. Depending on the confidence management felt in the forecasts the latter part might or might not be actioned.

Such a statement of what needed to be made or bought to meet the whole of the forward order book or master production schedule, scheduled by week number, is the normal output of any good requirements planning system. Where the net change differs from the regenerative system is that the statement can be amended for changes in the order position or in the status of any item without recalculating the whole schedule from scratch. Instead only the items affected by the change are recalculated, a process which can often be completed on-line in minutes instead of hours.

New orders could be entered individually as received, and the effect of changes simulated without altering existing records or works documentation. On-line enquiry facilities provided information on current position of any order or stock item, current work load, forward work load and capacity for each cost centre, also which customer orders would be affected by late deliveries or machine breakdown. Full multi-level pegging facilities were provided.

Preset batching rules could be used to merge the demand for like items into suitable batch sizes; minimum stocks and minimum order quantities could be specified; set-up costs could be balanced against inventory costs in a least cost algorithm. Manufacturing programs could be frozen for any specified number of weeks forward as "it is maddening for a foreman to find that next week's manufacturing program has altered significantly between Friday night and Monday morning". This facility also allowed works documentation to be prepared in advance, and made time available to assess the implications of a schedule of new works orders before they were released.

Start dates and due dates were calculated for every purchase or manufacture of piece parts, sub-assemblies or finished products. Progress was automatically monitored against these dates, printouts could be provided of all transactions which were later than any specified period, and the pegging facility would display how delivery dates were affected.

The Ventek Datamake system was said to comprise, in addition to system support programs, the following modules: bill of materials, materials requirement planning, work in progress control, inventory control, product costing, sales and purchase order processing.

Bill of materials maintained the part master file, part costing file, product structure file and operation routing file. It could provide indented components list, including single level only or purchased part only; indented where used list; single level or finished parts only; bill of materials report by components or operations; cumulative lead time, etc.

Materials requirement planning exploded the master production schedule of firm and tentative planned production for up to a year ahead, by means of the bill of materials module, into gross requirement allowing for shrinkage. This in turn was reduced to net requirements, using the inventory module, by deducting available stock, and incoming orders at their due dates. Net requirements were converted into orders using any lot sizing rules specified, and starting dates worked out for each order taking account of days of factory closure. The proposed order pattern could be studied, customer orders likely to be late traced through the pegging facility, and amendments made as required, before release, to the work in progress module, and printing of shop floor documentation.

Work in progress kept track of works orders released by the MRP module, providing a variety of reports and enquiry facilities.

Inventory control posted goods in and goods out to item records to maintain stock on hand balances. All transactions were logged to provide an audit trial. ABC analysis, shortage reports, kitting lists and weekly cycle count prompts could be provided.

HEWLETT-PACKARD MATERIALS MANAGEMENT 3000

Hewlett-Packard claimed the advantages both of off-the-shelf packages and of internally developed software for their Materials Management 3000, stating that materials people without programming knowledge could modify and "customise" it. It was described as a comprehensive materials requirements planning and control system designed for use on HP 3000 computer systems.

Major functions were described as follows:

Master production scheduling provides the capability for on-line production schedule development and on-line "what if" simulation.

Rough cut resource planning provides the capability to test the master schedule against known resource "bottlenecks" to determine possible resource constraints.

Parts and bills of material maintains descriptive, cost and planning information about each part and how they relate to one another in product structures.

Routings and workcentres maintains descriptive, cost, and planning information about each workcentre in a manufacturer's production facility and the routing sequence necessary to build each assembled or fabricated part.

Material issues and receipts provides the facility for issues and receipts of materials and also maintains the audit trail.

Inventory balance management maintains information about inventory balances and provides control of cycle counting and management of inventory locations.

Work order control tracks scheduled receipts and monitors planned issues (allocations) required for assembly. Also maintains and tracks backorders.

Purchase order tracking monitors scheduled receipts of purchased materials and maintains vendor information. Provides purchase order commitment information.

Material requirements planning generates the materials plan with recommendations about what and how much material to order and when to order it.

Standard product costing provides the capability to roll-up current costs and to accurately set standard costs.

BURROUGHS PCS

Burroughs Machines Ltd were also demonstrating their PCS system, intended to help manufacturers to generate and control production and purchasing plans and to manage inventory. Their literature described a generalised version of the system, with a variety of facilities which could be implemented in various ways. Three "functions" were described as follows:

Master production schedule maintained all requirements, including customer orders, sales forecasts, branch warehouse orders, interplant orders, stock orders, spares orders, and production orders, where applicable.

It was the source of all requirements to be exploded through the bill of material. It included a rough-cut capacity planning facility to determine whether the master schedule was achievable or should be amended before input to MRP.

Materials requirement planning accepted as input the master production schedule and also the definition of a number of parameters, such as:

Reorder level
Shrinkage factor
Purchase lead time
Manufacturing lead time if routing not available
Parts classification
Ordering policy – EOQ, time bucket, make to order

It calculated gross requirements for finished products, net requirements for products after allowing for inventory and ordering parameters, gross and net requirement for components, shop and purchase order quantities based on ordering policy for each item and modifiers such as shrinkage factor.

Release dates for finished products were computed by off-setting lead times against due dates, and release dates for components were computed by off-setting component lead times against product release dates. Firm orders, whether planned or released, could be flagged in such a way that the system did not reschedule them.

Reports included: planned orders – all items; firm planned orders – by planner; overdue firm orders; firm planned orders by time period; customer order backlog; and customer service.

Capacity planning would forward schedule all orders by period, assuming infinite capacity, and accumulate loads and capacities required, period by period, for each work centre and for the whole plant. Reports would compare load and capacity by periods, indicating overloaded work centres and orders likely to be overdue. Various load levelling possibilities could then be simulated until a satisfactory match between load and capacity emerged.

Reports included: work centre profile and load; plant profile and load; work centres overloaded and underloaded; parts and orders schedule; late orders; work centre operation schedule.

State of the art

There is evidently a strong family resemblance between these systems. Indeed it may be stronger than may appear from the brief outlines given above, since to avoid repetition these have been cut short.

A typical system uses a database rather than sets of separate files. There is a great deal of duplication when separate files are kept, because of the complex relationships between the data used in sales forecasts, customer orders, works orders, purchase orders, stock, work in progress, etc. This is largely avoided when all these operations use a common database which can be updated or amended by a single entry. A database contains a mass of information which is continually being retrieved, displayed, updated and manipulated possibly by several people at once, in different departments, and for different purposes. Clearly it is important to emphasise security. Precautions need to be taken against unauthorised access, and corruption of or tampering with the data. Provision also needs to be made for system recovery in the event of mishap, which could have much more serious consequences than when sets of separate overlapping records are maintained.

The system is on-line: users can contact the system at any time and quickly obtain the required information. It is interactive: users can select displays or reports from menus or contents pages and can usually engage in a sort of dialogue with the system. Transaction data fed in by VDU keyboard or by other form of data collection device normally updates the database immediately, although sometimes it is accumulated for later batch processing (for instance overnight). The system is then said to be operating in real time. An on-line interactive real time system should be able to display up-to-date information on demand, without delays of more than a minute or two.

The system comprises a number of modules which can be installed separately, and which can add up to a "closed-loop" system.

Suppliers were confident that their hardware was now robust and reliable, and claimed that the software could readily be adapted to the special needs of customers. But the effort required to install even an off-the-shelf system which proves appropriate to the need, should not be underestimated.

Implementation

Before such a system becomes operational, an awesome amount of information in the form of product structures, bills of material, stock records, etc., covering thousands of items even in a relatively small manufacturing operation, may need to be transferred to the database. It is often found that parts lists are not in suitable format and are incomplete or otherwise inaccurate. It seems to be found, almost invariably, that stock records contain many errors, which will continue to occur after the system is implemented unless suitable action is taken. Computer processing eliminates only one of the sources of error – mistakes in the arithmetic. It is necessary to keep the stores locked and count the contents regularly, and most current systems have a facility to prompt or suggest cycle count items for continuous stocktaking.

Many organisations have had trouble installing these systems through lack of organisational readiness. The system depends crucially on the people who operate it. In fact, this may be putting things the wrong way round. It is people who run the business, not the computer. The system is there to help them, and they need to be convinced of this.

Stage by stage implementation is recommended. Involve those who will use the system; build up a core group whose familiarisation with the system in the first stage of implementation will enable them to train others who will be involved at later stages.

Chapter 9

Storing materials

by *J I Hyam*

Storage systems have to accommodate the inflow of goods and materials bought from outside, in-process stocks, and the outflow of goods to customers. Storage systems may be compared and their efficiency assessed in terms of the unit cost (per volume or weight unit) of moving goods through a storage building or storage area over a given period. This method of assessment takes into account the efficient use of storage space as well as the speed and frequency of order picking. It is usually based on the cost elements of labour, equipment and space.

In any specific system, there may be advantages in sacrificing the accessibility of stock in favour of getting more stock into less space, or vice versa. Thus while it is not possible to arrive at absolute criteria for the efficiency of one storage system or another, the selection of the right system does depend upon assessing and evaluating materials handling requirements in terms of distribution strategy or, in the case of works stores, of manufacturing strategy.

Warehouse design

The design, size and location of a warehouse or store must in fact be an integral part of a wider management strategy. What happens in a warehouse affects and is directly affected by a whole range of other management activities. The most important of those activities are: purchasing, marketing, transport and production.

PURCHASING

The form in which goods or materials are delivered, the quantities in which they are delivered, the frequency of their delivery, the degree of reliability needed for a store or warehouse to provide a satisfactory service, are all important factors in choosing the right type of building and the most suitable handling system for use inside it. Factors like the number, importance and geographical distribution of sources of goods and of ultimate delivery points, affect the location of a warehouse and to some extent its size and type.

MARKETING

A company's marketing policy should interact with its warehousing policy. The number of product lines stocked and the quantity, form and frequency of delivery to retail outlets are warehousing problems influenced by marketing objectives and by a company's overall marketing strategy.

TRANSPORT

Frequency of delivery and despatch and the speed and efficiency with which the reception, checking, packaging and despatch of stock are effected are important factors in the handling system employed in a storage building. It is quite common to find intensive storage and order-picking systems alongside slow, untidy and space-consuming reception and dispatch arrangements. Serious delays in vehicle turn-round are the result.

PRODUCTION

Most finished goods storage occurs because goods are produced faster than they can be taken away from their place of manufacture. Storage thus becomes necessary as a buffer between production and distribution or as a stage in the distribution/sorting operation which brings the right goods to the right places in the quantities required. The speed at which goods are produced, their shape and the quantities in which they are produced usually result from economic and commercial decisions far removed from the storage problem. But it is nevertheless of value to consider storage requirements when designing production systems and even when designing a product. A few inches off a component or a product's dimensions can add up to a great deal of space saved in an intensive warehouse (and incidentally in transport) without seriously affecting the finished product.

Warehouse siting

Because storage is, or should be, part of a company's overall strategy, the choice of one type of building rather than another, or between a new building and an existing one usually depends upon factors other than merely what is going to be stored and how it is going to be stored.

It is the same with a building's location. There are operational research techniques and computer programmes which can find the optimum position for a central warehouse in terms of the receipt and despatch of goods from a given number of sources to a given number of outlets. Methods of transport with their alternative costs can be built into such programmes and the results can be of practical value.

Important points to look out for when choosing a site for a warehouse are: labour costs in the area, future planning proposals, legal and other restrictions which could be applied, ground load-bearing capacity, effluent disposal and future road patterns.

Sufficient space should be allowed for expansion and for essential services such as road access, vehicle parking, boiler houses, administrative blocks and transfer repair shops.

New buildings

There are two schools of thought about warehouse design. One says: "A warehouse is no more than a sorting machine. Goods go in in one sequence and out in another. The building should therefore be designed round the sorting process and the product which has to be sorted." Take that philosophy to its extreme and you get the pallet silo type of store where the building such as it is consists of a skin supported by the framework of a huge block of racking served by stacker cranes.

The other school of thought says: "Buildings last longer than products and sometimes last longer than the companies which inhabit them. A warehouse which is too specialised is therefore likely to become a white elephant if things go wrong, whereas a general-purpose building designed with storage in mind becomes an investment in its own right."

General-purpose warehouses should have: good heavy-duty floor surfaces, good clear heights, a minimum interference from stanchions and pillars. The choice may be between portal types of buildings and flat-roofed, box-construction buildings. Though the latter are more expensive, some architects prefer them because they provide simpler service routes through the lattice roof which can also carry pipe runs for the removal of rainwater and because they allow more headroom near the eaves than the portal type. Stanchions in portal buildings can get in the way of a handling system.

Some architects, aware of the intended use of a storage building, recommend artificial lighting in preference to natural lighting. Sunlight can adversely affect stock by fading carton design and increasing the temperature to the detriment of products. Keeping a building at the right temperature in winter and summer is therefore best achieved without windows. Insulation and the strategic siting of dispatch and receiving areas are important factors for conserving heat in winter. In some cases it is desirable for loading and unloading to be performed inside the building in an airlock.

Stores layout and type of storage

Choosing the most suitable storage systems means dealing with a number of interacting, and sometimes conflicting, factors. Inevitably the degree of mechanisation affects layout while scarcity of space affects the height to which racking is erected. The need for rapid, intensive order picking means a need for rapid and easy access to stock. But accessibility weighs against space economy. A satisfactory storage system is therefore a compromise between the use of space and the use of time. The way in which stock is located helps make the compromise a satisfactory one.

There are three basic ways of locating stock: fixed location, random location and zoned location.

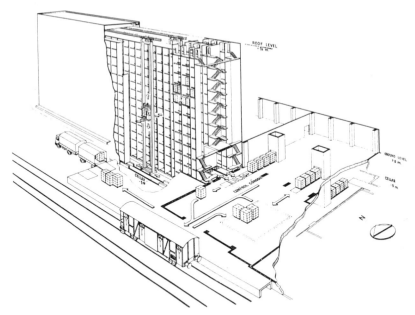

FIGURE 9:1   A HIGH BAY AUTOMATED STORE
Pallets are positioned and retrieved automatically by stacker crane (Viscosuisse)

Fixed location means that goods of a particular type have a position in the store assigned to them exclusively. That means that while stock can be found immediately without a complex system for recording its position, there can be considerable waste of space, because when stocks of any one item are low the space left vacant cannot be filled.

Random location means that items can be stored in any storage position which is available. Space is thus better utilised but, particularly where there are a large number of product lines, a record has to be kept of where goods are and frequently of when they entered the storage area.

Zoned location means that goods of a particular product group are kept in a given area. They may be random stored in a zoned location or stored according to fixed locations.

A common form of zoning, particularly in large, highly mechanised or automated warehouse, is to group fast-moving, or high-turnover goods, and sometimes medium and slow movers. The object is to assign the most suitable types of storage and mechanical handling equipment to the different kind of stock movement. Fast-moving lines are usually positioned near the input and output end of a store with the object of reducing the travel time for order-picking staff and thus speeding up throughput. (This of course only makes sense when reception and dispatch are in the same area or in adjoining areas.)

Another important distinction frequently made in large sophisticated systems and

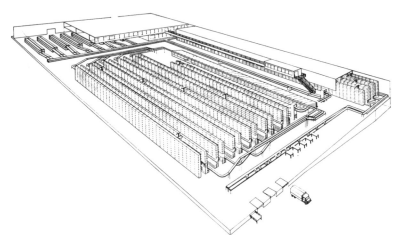

FIGURE 9:2   A HIGHLY MECHANISED SPECIAL PURPOSE STORE DESIGNED
FOR INTENSIVE ORDER PICKING
Goods are stored in bulk in the racking on the right and transferred to reserve storage racks in
aisles which are interspersed with picking aisles. Conveyors at waist height in the picking aisles
take away the picked orders. The racks from which the goods are picked are fed from the
reserve storage aisles by means of chutes. (Drawing by courtesy of Demag)

sometimes applicable in less complex systems is between bulk stock, back-up or
reserve stock and picking stock. Goods zoned in this way are moved from one to the
other on their way through the system. The object of breaking down stock into bulk,
back-up and picking stock is to make better use of space where accessibility is no
problem and to give maximum access where accessibility is needed. Thus in a typical
automated warehouse (such as is shown, in part, in Figure 9:1), bulk stock might be
stored in racking 70ft high, and reserve and picking stock in lower parts of the
building. Picking by hand might be performed at two levels of a 12ft high racking
system in alternate racking aisles. The remaining aisles would be used for "backing
up" the picking stock, goods gravitating through to both levels of the picking racks.
Figure 9:2 depicts a highly mechanised special purpose store designed for intensive
order picking and in which the zoning of bulk storage and reserve storage goods is
apparent.

In some non-automated systems back-up stock is kept in the upper levels of pallet
racking, and picking stock in the lower levels, where their contents can easily be
reached by order-picking staff. When a pallet is empty one of the forklifts, which
replenish the racking, removes the empty pallet and replaces it with one from the
upper levels of the racking.

Storage methods – the equipment

The method used to retain stock depends on the form in which stock is received and to some extent upon the degree of accessibility required. The following broad headings covering types of stock may help in describing the main types of equipment available to handle them:

1   Loose stock items (small components etc.)
2   Discrete units without pallets (cartons, sacks etc.)
3   Palletised and stillaged goods (almost anything that fits on or in a pallet)

Loose items are generally stored in special containers of varying sizes and modular design which fit economically into shelving. They are shaped to allow their contents to be easily removed by hand, and are intended to be used on work benches as well as in intensive storage. Various trolleys, racks, louvred plates from which boxes can be suspended, and other accessories are available to make the system as flexible as possible. Sizes range from a minimum of $3\frac{1}{2} \times 4 \times 2''$ to a maximum of $28 \times 18 \times 12''$. The larger sizes are generally determined by the ease with which the containers can be lifted by hand when filled with heavy items. Dividers are available to allow maximum use to be made of the space inside the containers. With small, slow-moving components it is thus possible to avoid wasting space when stocks begin to run low. Tote boxes are made of plastic or galvanised metal. They are often supplied in conjunction with special shelving or may be used with conventional or slotted angle-supported shelving.

For items like tools which do not have to be moved continuously, modular drawer systems are made, which, with the help of dividers, can be extremely economical of space.

Discrete items (sacks or cartons, for example, stored without pallets or stillages) are sometimes free stacked. The two main problems with free stacking are:

1   Accessibility – you can't get at items at the bottom or in the inside of stock without removing the top or outside items: first in, first out sequences are totally impracticable
2   Stability – special stacking patterns are often required and care has to be taken with slippery items like plastic sacks

The main advantage of free stacking is space economy. Theoretically this is the only way of making full use of available stacking space.

Discrete items can also be stacked on shelving. Shelving gives much better access than free stacking but is more space-consuming. Live storage systems (see below) are suitable for discrete items which are not too heavy. Light cartons, for example, are well suited to gravitate down channels of roller or wheel conveyors supported by a racking structure.

Goods in unit loads – flat or box pallets or stillages – can be free stacked, stored in pallet racking, or in certain kinds of live storage racking. Unit loads, as far as stores are concerned, have the advantage of good potential movement – they are designed to be lifted and transported by forklifts and other mechanical handling equipment and for transport operations at other stages of the distribution cycle, but they take up more space than is generally realised. In one recent book warehouse it was found that the use of pallets in one area of the store would have meant a loss of 15 per cent of the 402 000ft³ space available. It was in fact found more economical to transfer packs from pallets into shelving rather than to store on pallets. The cost of space in this instance was in fact greater than the cost of movement.

Racking and shelving

Static shelves. Until recently most shelving was of the conventional adjustable type. Slotted angle is frequently used as a support for shelves. Access to fixed shelving may be at two levels if mezzanine floors are used.

Mobile shelving. This is becoming increasingly popular with space-conscious companies. Complete blocks of shelving mounted on rollers set in the floor are movable so that space for only one aisle is necessary in a block of several shelf units. The disadvantage of mobile shelving is its limited accessibility. Items can be reached in only one aisle at a time. Mobile shelving is thus unsuitable for intensive and order-picking. Smaller units can be moved manually while heavier united may be powered. Powered mobile racking is illustrated in Figure 9:3

Pallet racking. This is a skeletal framework designed to support pallets. It is usually adjustable, partly because it is more useful if it is adjustable but also because it is easier and cheaper to erect. Intensive purpose-built racking systems (as in automated high-bay warehouses) are usually of the fixed type being made from structural steel or reinforced concrete.

Adjustable pallet racking usually consists of standard lengths of slotted steel members which are designed to bolt together or to interlock without the need for bolts. Other types can be built up from steel tubing of the kind used for scaffolding.

Mobile pallet racking. This works like mobile shelving but is nearly always powered. Recent installations have been more than 30ft high and cover considerable areas. Special safety precautions using interlocks and photoelectric cells as well as automatic mechanical cut-out devices are essential when personnel enter the racking for order-picking. Again, limited accessibility is a disadvantage which has to be weighed against the advantage of space economy.

Live storage racking. The simplest form of live storage consists of lengths of wheel or roller conveyor supported by racking at an angle sufficient to allow cartons or similar items to move from one end to another by means of gravity. The drawback of this type of system is that the lighter the goods handled, the steeper the angle of inclination has to be and the more space is consumed by the slanting arrangement of the block of racking. The heavier an item is, on the other hand, the greater the problem of braking it as it gathers speed in its journey from one face of the racking to the other. Various methods of braking have been tried but none has been proved really successful with really heavy loads.

For loads weighing more than about 150 kilograms, powered live storage is

FIGURE 9:3   POWERED MOBILE RACKING
The blocks of racking close up leaving only one aisle per block open at a time. This is a way of
getting most out of limited storage space. The one drawback is limited access. You can only get
to one aisle in a block at a time

therefore a better solution. Various methods are available. Some power the rollers.
Others drive dogs which engage with pallets in certain positions so as to move them
forward when required and pass under them once they are in position. One system
uses a mobile motor-powered transporter with a hydraulic platform which passes
under pallets already in position, stops under pallets which have to be moved, picks
them up, transports them and sets them down where required.

Another drawback of live storage is that it generally excludes random storage.
While it has the advantage of providing a first-in, first-out sequence, only one type of
product can usually be stored in one racking lane and that will mean wasted space
when there is a run on a particular product. Live storage in its conventional form is
thus best suited to fast-moving stock of a small number of different lines where full
advantage can be taken of the first-in, first-out facility (one example is perishable
goods).

A recent development of the powered live storage concept, however, does make
random storage possible. This concept allows pallets moved in powered live storage
racking to be transferred from lane to lane by a transporter moving in a single central
racking aisle or along the input or output faces of a block of live storage racking. By
using the pallet-transfer transporter in conjunction with an in-racking transport – the
one carries the other – pallets can be moved from aisle to aisle and random storage
becomes possible. With a digital memory unit controlling the system, pallets can be

shuffled in any permutation and the quickest possible job can be made of the slow business of extracting pallets from inner positions in the storage lanes. Vertical movement between storage levels can be provided by fork-lift truck, stacker crane or elevators.

Another system consists of a transporter which also acts as a winch. The transporter moves down a central racking aisle, but in this case also provides the motive power for pallets ranged several deep in the racking lanes. Here the pallets, which are specially designed for the job, are linked together and move on wheels. The transporter pulls a whole train forward, separating the leading pallet from the others. The transporter can then remove the pallet to another pallet position or deliver it to a despatch station.

Mechanisation in order-picking and internal transport

Fuller details of the mechanical handling equipment used in stores and warehouses are given in Chapter 10. The equipment is referred to here only in the context of its storage applications.

NON-MECHANISED HANDLING

Where there is a great variety of stock items, where retrieval of stock is occasional rather than intensive and where space is not scarce and there is no great pressure on time, there is usually no case for mechanising stock-picking. A variety of steps, mobile ladders and trolleys are available as order-picking aids in these circumstances.

MECHANICAL HANDLING

Unit load handling equipment consists of:

Pallet trucks. Both powered and non-powered types are used for transporting pallets but not for stacking them.

Stacker trucks, which are primarily used for lifting or stacking pallets, but which have the disadvantage of being able to handle only certain types of pallet.

Counterbalanced forklift trucks, which are suitable for transporting and stacking pallets.

Reach trucks, which are also used for transporting pallets and which are more compact than counterbalanced forklifts. The term "reach" is used because the forks reach forward within the wheel base of the truck, allowing it to operate in narrower storage aisles than counterbalanced machines.

Rotating-fork reach trucks, in which the fork carriage rotates through 180 degrees, allowing pallets to be stacked on either side of a racking aisle without the truck having to turn. This type of truck can be designed to pick up pallets from the front as well as from either side.

Sideloaders, which load to the side and which transport long loads on the platforms between which the fork reaches forward for picking up and depositing a load. One type of sideloader rotates its mast to stack on either side of an aisle and may be equipped with a separate elevating platform for order-picking.

Stacker cranes, or rigid-mast fork cranes, which are designed to handle pallets on either side of very narrow aisles (little more than a pallet's width) in very high racking. They may run on rails set into the floor, on rails suspended from the racking or they may be suspended from beams moving on gantries like overhead travelling cranes. Such cranes can be rider controlled or manually remote controlled from consoles. They can be controlled by means of punched cards or "on-line" by a computer.

If a platform is provided which allows an operator to reach into racking on either side of an aisle in order to assemble orders on the pallet-cum-platform, stacker cranes can be used for order-picking. When designed with this purpose in mind, they are often referred to as high-level order-pickers.

Stacker cranes usually operate one to an aisle but it is possible to transfer a machine from aisle to aisle by means of a transporter which moves along the end of the racking at right-angles to the aisles.

Figure 9:4 shows trucks designed for narrow aisle operation.

Free-path order-picking trucks. These are forklift trucks with the addition of a platform which lifts the operator to heights of twelve feet and sometimes substantially more, allowing him to collect goods from pallets on either side of a racking aisle and assemble them on a pallet which the truck is carrying. The operator can steer and drive the truck with the platform raised.

Figure 9:5 illustrates free-path order picking as well as fixed-path and gathering tower systems.

DIFFERENT TYPES OF STORAGE SYSTEM
The different types of system which are built round the equipment mentioned above are basically industrial truck systems (forklift and pallet trucks used sometimes in conjunction with free-path order-picking trucks) and high-bay stacker crane systems. Though in some labour-intensive situations, order-picking staff may work entirely with hand trolleys. In some cases, where there is a very large variety of product lines, as for example in a mail order store, conveyors fed by staff working on foot are the main method of collecting stock and delivery to packaging and despatch areas. Tilt tray or tilted band conveyors may be used to deliver stock to specific packing areas.

The main advantage of industrial truck systems is their adaptability. They can easily and inexpensively be adapted to changing circumstances and if appropriate machines are used they can produce an economical balance between the use of space and time. Where space is short, reach trunks and rotating mast trucks come into their own. Where pallets have to be taken comparatively long distances, counterbalanced machines may be more appropriate. In some systems a combination of the two may be used and in others pallet trucks may be used for the horizontal movement of

Fig. 9:4a

Fig. 9:4b

FIGURE 9:4 TRUCKS FOR NARROW AISLE OPERATION

The trend in forklift truck design is towards narrow aisle operation. The reach truck (a) evolved from the counter-balance forklift in order to save storage space. Now a new type of truck, the 180 deg stacker, is proving increasingly popular. This represents a further stage of evolution towards higher stacking and narrower aisle operation. The Lansing Bagnall turrett truck (b) can rotate its forks so as to be able to reach into the racking to left or right. It can operate in an aisle only fractionally wider than itself. This type of truck can stack as high as 40 ft

(a) An order picking truck which can move freely from aisle to aisle. The operator goes up with the forks and can operate the truck when his platform is in the raised position. (b) A fixed path order picking platform in use at the Rieter store in Switzerland. The platform rises while the mast, which is fixed to the racking, moves horizontally down the aisle

Fig. 9:5a

Fig. 9:5b

pallets as order-picking aids. Because they are cheaper and more flexible in their use, industrial trucks generally have the advantage over stacker cranes except where great heights are involved.

It is only when racking reaches heights approaching 40ft that stacker cranes take over from forklifts. When dire space shortage forces racking up in the air, the stacker crane becomes almost the only means of handling pallets. When stacker cranes are used, the question of automation nearly always arises. A great deal has been learnt in recent years about controlling stacker cranes automatically and the first lesson is: don't, unless it is economically justified. The on-line computer control of stacker cranes is possible but it has been shown to be expensive. A very rapid picking cycle and a large number of pallet positions are needed before full automation can be justified.

When it comes to picking less than pallet loads for small-order delivery the problem immediately becomes more complex. Here full automation may be used for bulk storage but so far as order-picking systems are concerned automation has never been more than an aid to manual handling.

Chapter 10

Moving materials – transport and materials handling

by *J I Hyam*

Any account of the manner in which materials are moved should be set in the context of the management responsibility and functional demarcation in the organisation or organisations through which the goods and materials move. The problem is to get a balanced interaction between the departments and functions involved. The acquisition of raw materials and components by manufacturing concerns, though frequently the prime responsibility of purchasing departments, also impinges on the responsibilities of product design and production engineering. Equally, it affects and is affected by inventory control, stockholding and vehicle reception.

At the output end of the production cycle, marketing and distribution responsibilities have a similar relationship with production and design engineering. Warehousing and transport policies are also closely interrelated with one another and with the total management function at the input and output ends of the production cycle. The management problem of formulating and fulfilling those policies and functions and the problems of physical movement which come within the scope of the management problem are dependent for solutions upon a satisfactory relationship between all departments and areas of responsibility involved.

To make that relationship a harmonious one several management concepts have evolved, each inviting a broader span of control and a more strategic approach to the cost effective movement of materials.

Those concepts are often interpreted in different ways and may give way to confusion unless properly defined. One definition is illustrated diagrammatically in Figure 10:1. In it, "materials management" is shown (as it is understood by the majority of people who use it) to be concerned with the acquisition, storage and delivery to production of goods and materials. "Physical distribution management" is shown to be concerned with the warehousing, transport and distribution of finished products, while the term "business logistics", rarely used in the United Kingdom, is

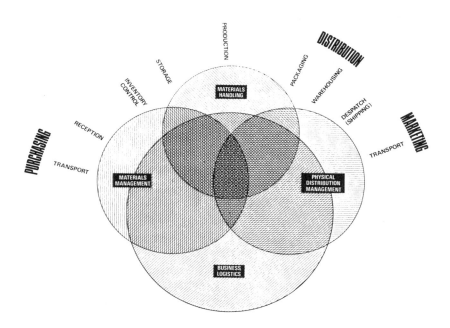

FIGURE 10:1   THE MOVEMENT OF GOODS: OVERLAP OF RESPONSIBILITIES
This is one idea of how the concepts of "materials management" "physical distribution management" and "business logistics" are related to "materials handling" which can be described as the systematic physical movement of goods and materials. The areas of overlap present management with its most serious materials handling problems

shown to describe a company's total approach to the movement of raw materials and finished products. The systematic physical movement of goods within those conceptual frameworks is defined as "materials handling."

The aim of systematic materials handling is to get materials to the right place, at the right time, in the right quantities in good condition at minimum cost. The achievement of that aim means that goods and materials should be presented for transport, storage and in-factory movement in a form which is as convenient as possible to handle, given the intended use of the materials.

The equipment selected for use at different stages of the handling/transport cycle should be chosen with the limitations – such as weight, size, shape and perishability – of the goods and materials which have to be handled, in mind. A third factor – environment – is also important in achieving a satisfactory handling system. The economical layout of a workshop or store, the presence of heat, cold or damp which could have an adverse effect on materials, questions of labour relations, safety, architecture and packaging all have a direct effect on and are affected by the way materials are handled.

The achievement of satisfactory materials handling systems means co-ordinating different activities often in different departments of a company and sometimes in different companies so as to optimise the cost of assembling, storing and transporting materials from their point of manufacture to their point of use.

The activities where most handling costs occur are:

1   Loading or unloading transport vehicles
2   The reception of goods and materials and their storage before processing and assembly
3   The sorting of raw-materials and components
4   The movement of materials to and between work stations
5   During inspection and packaging
6   In finished goods storage
7   In the sorting and subsequent storage, which occurs during distribution.

These activities are frequently costed as part of wider ranging activities such as transport or production. Because they are not identified as separate cost centres they often turn out to accumulate avoidable costs. When cost centres have been identified, improving a handling system depends upon analysing direct and indirect costs.

The most important direct costs are: investment costs in equipment, equipment operating costs, equipment maintenance costs, equipment depreciation costs, labour costs and the cost of space given up to movement, storage and sorting as opposed to production.

The most important indirect costs are: the cost of materials in store or between processes, the cost of operator and machine downtime, the cost of damage to goods or materials, the cost of output lost through poor plant layout or bad materials management.

Making a materials handling study

Choosing the most suitable systems for the reduction of direct and indirect handling costs requires a fresh critical approach to procedures which are probably founded on habit rather than reason. Such an approach nearly always requires the introduction of work-study techniques. Sometimes it is sufficient to go through the standard procedure of asking: What is being done? Where is it being done? When is it being done? Who is doing it? How is it being done? And of backing those questions up with the subsidiary questions: Why is it necessary? What else could be done? and What else should be done? The answers can do much to improve layout and eliminate unnecessary operations. But in more complicated situations it becomes necessary to record the facts as a prelude to analysing them. For this purpose, flow process charts and diagrams may be used, and relevant details, such as distances between operations, the time taken for each operation, the quantity or weight of materials moved, may be noted. Standard work-study symbols help to simplify the charting.

Figure 10:2 shows a flow process chart using work study symbols, while a pre-

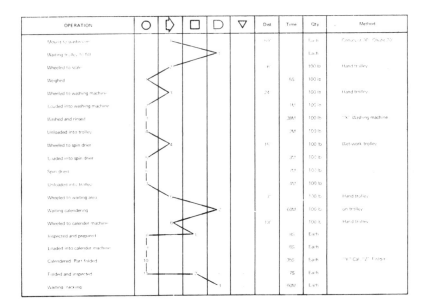

FIGURE 10:2   FLOW PROCESS CHART USING WORK STUDY SYMBOLS
This example was taken from the booklet Materials Handling 1 published by the Department of Trade and Industry

printed form suitable for analysing movements is illustrated in Figure 10:3.

The equipment

A broad functional distinction can be made between equipment used for continuous movement – such as conveyors – equipment used for discontinuous movement – such as cranes and industrial trucks – and equipment for potential movement – such as unit load equipment, pallets and containers. Within that framework a further distinction can be made between equipment for horizontal movement, equipment for vertical movement and equipment for a combination of vertical and horizontal movement. Another important distinction – that between the handling of bulk materials and discrete items – needs to be made when talking about materials handling in general terms, because often the problems encountered are very different.

Unit load equipment

The principle behind the unit load is the elementary one of making a more convenient and economic unit out of smaller units which it is less easy and less economic to handle, transport and store separately. Or alternatively in the case of bulk materials

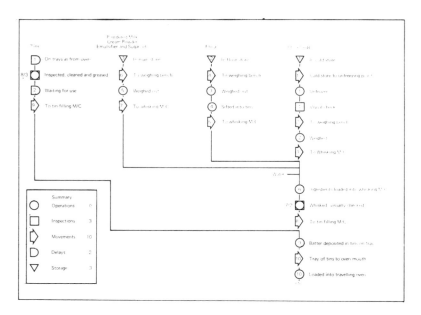

FIGURE 10:3   AN EXAMPLE OF A PREPRINTED FORM WHICH CAN BE USEL
TO ANALYSE MOVEMENT
The example, which shows a chart used in a laundry, is taken from Materials Handling
published by the DTI

like powders as opposed to discrete items like cartons, the principle may be to
provide suitable containers for the handling, transport and storage of economic
quantities of materials. To reduce handling to a minimum goods should, in principle
be kept in the same unit loads as long as possible.

The size and type of unit load depends upon a whole range of factors of which the
most important are: the goods or materials to be handled; the size, weight, strength
and shape of intermediate packs; the type of storage required; the type of transport
required; the type of handling equipment which may be available and the quantitie
of goods and materials to be handled.

The basic types of unit load equipment are:

Pallets. These may be made of wood, metal, plastic or other synthetic materials. The
may be flat decked or have corner posts or sides. The object of corner posts is to allov
stacking without damaging the contents. Pallets with sides are used for items that do
not stack easily. An increasingly popular development is the *wheeled-cage pallet* used
for the temporary storage and transport of groceries. The advantage of this type o
unit is that it can be moved easily by hand in premises where there may be no
mechanical handling equipment. *Pallet converters* may be used to turn flat wooden
pallets into the equivalent of post pallets. Specialised wheeled pallets are shown in
Figure 10:9

The use of *expendable pallets* is generally confined to long-distance transport operations where the cost of returning empty pallets would be prohibitive. Unfortunately, expendable pallets are by definition not very strong and in many long journeys they do not stand up satisfactorily to the numerous fork liftings to which they are subjected.

Pallet pools are one answer to the problem of returning empty pallets and reducing the high cost of pallets which are not returned. Most European countries have pallet pools – run, in nearly every case, by the railways. The pools work on an exchange basis and there are frontier agreements which create what is in fact a single European pallet pool. The pallet used has a plan area of 1200mm × 800mm and the standard design is generally known as the European railway pallet. There is no national pallet pool in the United Kingdom and little likelihood of one being established. Certain sections of the food industry – which uses more pallets than any other industry – have, however, shown interest in the idea of a *pallet recovery service*. Here a group of interested suppliers may form an agreement to collect and return one another's pallets from customers. Other recovery services are being run on a purely commercial basis by pallet manufacturers. It is conceivable that pallet recovery services could in time grow into pallet pools, limited to certain industries or types of distribution.

Stillages. The distinction between pallets and stillages is somewhat blurred by usage which varies from industry to industry and locality to locality. Generally speaking however it is safe to say that a "stillage" is designed rather for a specific function – perhaps keeping goods off the ground or moving them from point to point in a factory, while the more sophisticated pallet is designed for the short as well as the long-distance transport of goods and their economic storage. The main physical difference between pallet and stillage is the distance between the ground and the deck of the units. Because a pallet has to be stored and transported in the minimum space, designers go to great lengths to keep a pallet's height to the minimum while leaving room for the entry of forklift forks and the fingers of pallet trucks. If insufficient room is left, pallets and their load can suffer damage.

Freight containers. The large-scale introduction of freight containers during the last five years has considerably influenced materials handling in the factory and elsewhere. The use of container services by shippers has meant first that shipping should adjust to the problem of making full use of the space inside containers. That means using pallets (if pallets have to be used) or packs which fit the standard 8ft × 8ft profile and 10ft, 20ft, 30ft and 40ft module most economically. The standard European railway pallet (see above) has proved a most unsatisfactory unit for large-scale container transport while the popular UK 1000mm × 1200mm pallet is only satisfactory if stacked in a special "pin wheel" pattern. The ideal pallet size for container transport is 1100mm wide with lengths ranging from 1100 to 1300mm depending upon the length of the container module in which the pallets are to be stowed.

The second problem presented by freight containers is that of filling or "stuffing" them. Problems of floor loading and height limitation – about 80in for a forklift truck

– make the movement of pallets in the interior of a container more hazardous than may at first be apparent. It is also important that containers should be uniformly loaded. Unevenly loaded containers can become distorted during transport hindering their pick up by automatic crane spreaders and holding up the loading or unloading of a ship.

Intermediate bulk containers (IBCs). Some dry-freight containers can be used to handle powders and other bulk materials by inserting a detachable plastic liner. But a more specialised way of transporting and handling bulk-materials is to be found in IBCs. These have the merit of forming good storage units and provide a method of in-process handling. Units can be brought into a factory and fitted to tilting devices which can tip materials at a controlled rate into feed hoppers.

Other types of unit load equipment include: *tote box systems* which are frequently linked to modular racking and trolley units for bringing components to work benches. Discrete items such as cartons may be formed into unit loads by *strapping* them or *shrink wrapping* them. Cartons and other packs may sometimes be handled by clamps thus disposing entirely of the need for load boards. A *push-pull forklift attachment* is sometimes used to handle cartons or sacks supported by a sheet of cardboard or similar material. The use of this device eliminates the need for pallets and therefore saves space in storage and transport but, as with other free-stacking systems, can present stability problems.

Systems for continuous movement

The use of fixed-path continuous handling equipment requires an intensive, consistent, high-volume throughput to justify the space it takes up and the relative inflexibility of its use. The advantage of continuous handling systems is that once installed they perform the job for which they are intended efficiently and quickly and do not as a rule require the presence of skilled operators. They may, when throughput justifies it, be partially or completely automated.

Conveyors are used to handle bulk materials and discrete items. Bulk handling conveyors include *belt conveyors* in which the belt is troughed and rides on rollers, *pneumatic conveyors* in which materials are sucked or blown along tubes, enclosed conveyors sometimes described as *en masse* drawn along by the movement of a chain, *screw* or *auger conveyors* in which materials are propelled forward by the Archimedian screw principle, and *vibratory conveyors* in which materials are moved at different speeds by varying the frequency and speeds of vibration under the conveying surface. There are numerous variations of these methods which apply both to vertical and horizontal movement.

Discrete items may be conveyed on beds of *rollers,* or *wheels,* or on *flat belts* or *slats*. Roller and wheel conveyors may be powered or items may be pushed along them by hand or be allowed to gravitate if the conveyor is suitably angled.

Recent developments indicate a potential for *air film conveyors* in which compressed air is allowed to escape from holes or louvres in the upper surface of a plenum chamber. The film of air so created can carry light objects in the direction of the air flow or allow heavier objects to be moved on what amounts to a friction-free surface.

Chain-driven *overhead conveyors* transport items by suspending them from carriers which are moved by chain-linked trolleys running on an overhead rail or track. The numerous variations of this type of conveyor range from simple light-duty systems for transporting objects like garments in a dry cleaners to motor vehicle assembly systems. An important type of overhead chain conveyor is the *power and free system* which allows carriers to be separated from power sections for automatic transfer to gravity spurs and to be picked up automatically from free-running sections. Overhead conveyor systems are often automated or equipped with semi-automatic addressing systems.

An increasingly popular type of conveyor is the *underfloor dragline conveyor*. This consists of a chain moving in a channel in the floor. To the chain are attached carts or trolleys which may be removed for manual handling as required or directed automatically to spurs. This type of system is found particularly useful in warehouses where large numbers of different products have to be picked from racking distributed over a wide area. The carts are filled on their way round the store and addressed to different spurs where they accumulate for vehicle loading. Driverless tractor systems, in which tractors guided by a wire buried in the floor follow a prescribed course round a warehouse, are used in the same way.

Continuous movement systems like conveyors require intensive usage to justify the investment involved.

Discontinuous movement

The most common form of discontinuous movement is provided by industrial trucks in their various forms (see Chapter 9). Various models are shown in Figures 10:4–10:7

Forklifts, which in all their forms combine vertical with horizontal movement, are the most versatile and varied in form and function. They range in lifting capacity from 1 cwt or less to 50 tons. Smaller capacities may be pedestrian operated. At the lower end of the capacity scale there is a choice of power source between battery electricity, petrol, liquid gas (LPG) and diesel. Heavy-duty trucks are nearly always diesel powered. In the range up to 8000 lb, battery power is the most popular and, since there are far more trucks of these capacities in use, battery-powered units account for a very large proportion of forklifts.

Various attempts have been made to compare the running and purchasing costs of owning and using diesel and electric trunks. In the case of diesel trucks the purchasing price is less but the running costs are higher while the opposite is true of battery trucks.

FIGURE 10:4 STANDARD
COUNTER-BALANCED
FORKLIFT TRUCK WITH
DOUBLE TELESCOPIC
MAST
This machine is powered by
liquid petroleum gas

FIGURE 10:5 A REACH
TRUCK
These machines, which are
battery powered, differ from
counterbalanced forklifts by
having masts which reach forward within the wheel base of
the truck. Thus a truck in a
narrow aisle remains stationary
while a load is picked up or
placed in racking

FIGURE 10:6   A SIDE-
LOADER
Used primarily for long loads,
these operate in narrow aisles
and are useful as transporters
supporting their loads on the
carrying platform on either side
of the forks

FIGURE 10:7   AN ORDER
PICKING TRUCK WHICH
ALSO SERVES AS A SIDE-
LOADER
The mast rotates to allow stacking on either side of the storage
aisle and an order picker can be
elevated on separate platform.
There is a growing need for
this kind of machine which
was pioneered by Cleco Electric Industries

FIGURE 10:8   A STACKER CRANE

These machines usually run on rails set in the floor but may also be suspended from racking or from an over-head bridge like a travelling crane. They are used for the positioning and retrieval of pallets. Their advantage is that they can lift to greater heights than forklift trucks – 100 ft and more in very narrow aisles and can be automated

FIGURE 10:9   WHEELED PALLETS

Provide a link between warehouses and retail outlets. These Lenson pallets are used in conjunction with tail lifts on the backs of delivery vehicles. The tail lifts allow one man to unload pallets and wheel them into retail premises

Hoists and overhead cranes

Another form of combined vertical and horizontal movement is provided by hoists which can be suspended from overhead runways along which they may be pushed or power driven or be incorporated in the crabs of overhead travelling cranes to lift and transport in two directions over the area spanned by a factory bay.

Independent hoists may be hand or power operated. Powered hoists are used wherever the frequency of lifting makes manual operation too slow and too tiring. Selection of powered hoists used to be based almost entirely on load capacity, hook travel and lift speed. But problems of servicing and reliability and the need to provide precisely the right kind of unit for a particular kind of work has resulted in a set of guidelines laid down by the Fédération Européenne de la Manutention (FEM) in 1968. These are based upon the class of operation and the load spectrum. The first is based on the average number of hours per day in which a hoist may be expected to lift and lower – a calculation derived from hook travel distance, lift speed and the number of working cycles. The second identifies the number of maximum or near-maximum loads, of medium loads and of small loads which a hoist may be expected to handle. By looking at those factors a hoist may be selected as precisely as possible for the workload required of it.

The majority of hoists are electric powered but some are operated by compressed air motors. Loads may be suspended by chain or wire rope. Chains tend to be heavier or more bulky, but are less liable to damage than wire ropes.

Overhead travelling cranes have complete access to an area in a building, limited only by their long and cross travel. Their load range is generally $\frac{1}{2}$ ton to 150 ton but can be higher for special applications. British standards 466 and 2573 refer to classes of crane in terms of hours of service each year.

Class I – intermittent use only – in stores or light machine shops for maintenance and similar applications.

Class II – general use in factories, workshops and warehouses in more arduous working conditions.

Class III and IV – custom-built heavy-duty cranes for use in steelworks, foundries, grabbing or magnet applications.

Cranes may be top running, in which the end carriages run on top of parallel gantry rails, or underslung, in which the end carriage wheels ride on the lower flanges of roof-supported parallel L-section rails.

Other mechanical aids

The range of mechanical handling aids for factory use over and above those already mentioned is extensive. *Mobile cranes* with telescopic jibs which can easily reach through doorways have many yard and factory uses for occasional rather than intensive movement. *Stacker cranes* – in their simplest form like upside-down forklift trucks suspended from gantries, and in a more advanced form running on rails fixed to the floor between racking aisles – are used in stores and factories for transporting and positioning pallets and similar loads (see Figure 10:8). *Hydraulic dock levellers* and *tail lifts* designed to assist in the loading and unloading of vehicles are finding increasing use in dispatch and reception bays. The former adjust to allow forklift trucks and pallet trucks to pass from the edge of a loading dock onto the deck of a backed-up vehicle. A tail lift, which is particularly valuable when vehicles have to be unloaded quickly at premises where there are no handling aids, consists of a folding elevating platform, which transfers a man and a light truck between the ground and the deck of the vehicle to which the lift is fitted.

Materials handling and transport

It is difficult to tell where materials handling begins and ends. According to some definitions it is little more than an activity and according to others it is a concept similar to or even identical with materials management and physical distribution – a total concept concerned with the movement of goods and materials and with the management of the way in which the goods and materials are handled. For the purpose of this book the term must be taken to refer to physical movement over short distances rather than to the control of materials.

Long-distance transport is generally accepted as a management problem in its own right, but the handling of goods onto and off transport vehicles is a materials handling problem of fundamental importance to good transport management. The speed and efficiency with which goods and materials are loaded and unloaded affects transport economics because the longer vehicles (or ships or planes) spend out of active use the more the total transport cost is going to be.

With this link between external transport and transport inside factories and warehouses in mind, it is easy to see why management is concerned about providing efficient reception and despatch facilities. And why, for that matter, handling facilities at ports and terminals, particularly in the age of super container ships and jumbo jets, are so important if maximum returns are to be obtained on investment in transport.

No account of materials handling as a component of materials management should therefore omit to mention the existence of numerous devices to assist in the filling and emptying of lorries and freight containers. Or of the cranes, straddle carriers and giant sideloaders which are used to handle containers. Two aids to vehicle filling and emptying have been described above – the dock leveller and the tailboard lift. In addition to these, there are simple dock ramps bridging the gap between loading dock and vehicles elevating platforms, and rail-running mechanically elevating transporters known as Jolodas for moving pallets and other loads from the tail to the head of vehicles.

There are, in fact, few handling problems to which mechanical solutions cannot be found. What is often lacking is the materials management support which mechanical ingenuity requires to make sense out of its solutions. The best handling equipment is almost useless unless there is a sufficient number of loading bays to receive peak traffic without (as often happens) vehicles having to wait as long as four hours or even return to destination still loaded. In the same way, the right number of loading bays is of little help if there is insufficient room in the marshalling area behind, to sort and check what has been delivered.

Materials handling thus requires the support of an efficient system of communications between the departments in a company through which materials are moved. And more difficult and even more important, between companies supplying and purchasing materials to and from one another.

Chapter 11

Buying materials: internal relationships

The purchasing function consists of buying parts and materials and services from external organisations in return for a price. The average manufacturer spends more than half its income on purchases of this kind. The average retailing organisation spends at least three-quarters of its income on the purchase of merchandise. Price is important, and is considered in the next chapter; but it is much less important than what is provided for the price, and cannot in fact be evaluated except in relation to what is provided.

The basic purchasing objective is to ensure that what is required is in fact available when it is required. As part of the materials system, the purchasing function has to *manage suppliers* so that they perform to the required standards, including:

1   The specification, where this is partly or wholly drawn up by the supplier
2   Conformance with the specification, and quality control as it applies to bought-out parts and material
3   Agreement of volume required, delivery schedules and lead times
4   Conformance with agreed delivery schedule, on-time delivery
5   Agreement of price and terms of payment

A secondary purchasing objective is to ensure that the *cost* of making available what is required when it is required is reasonable in the light of both internal and external relationships. This chapter is particularly concerned with the internal factors; the next chapter considers the selection of suppliers and the external factors.

Internal constraints

Many internal decisions taken by colleagues in other departments constitute constraints on the external decisions taken by purchasing staff. When a designer specifies a casting as the method of production for some part used in one of the end products, obviously he limits the number of sources available to the buyer to foundries. When he specifies the material as aluminium, the number of potential suppliers is further reduced; only aluminium foundries remain on the list. Specifying a particular alloy of aluminium may further reduce the choice.

When the production controller decides to alter his scheduling to cope with changing requirements from marketing, machine breakdown, or whatever, the buyer (or someone else) has to rearrange material call-off. If this happens often with the same supplier, the buyer's task when negotiating a further contract may be made more difficult.

When a financial controller delays payment to solve an internal cash-flow difficulty, or refuses to release capital to take advantage of a supply market opportunity, again the buyer's performance is affected. Conversely, if the buyer makes an error in selection and the supplier delivers material behind schedule, or there is quality failure, the whole production programme may be affected. While his failure to anticipate market changes might result in inflated or depleted inventories affecting production, warehousing and finance.

Each member of the management team has problems to overcome and constraints within which he has to work. The corporate management problem is to optimise overall. What appears to be the best line of action for the buyer, the production manager, the finance manager or any of their colleagues, is not necessarily right for the company as a whole. Whenever such difficulties occur, the efficiency and effectiveness of the system as a whole is affected. And, as we have argued elsewhere in this text, compartmentalised thinking tends to exacerbate such difficulties. Problems occur *between* departments rather than *in* them.

Effective purchasing management is concerned with ensuring that it is involved with the other key functions in the business *at the right time.* And, as we shall see later, the right time is that when the key decisions are made in the business. It is our opinion that none of these decisions are more important than those related to the products which are to be included in the company's range.

Some problems as perceived by purchasing

During the course of consultancy assignments over the last two decades, we have frequently asked representatives of the various functions in the materials system to indicate problems caused them by other departments. At a recent workshop the purchasing function listed the following as their concerns:

1 Poor information ex marketing
2 Inaccurate/generally over-optimistic forecasting
3 Even when the overall forecast is reasonable, the breakdown by product is always poor
4 Production has no appreciation of supplier capability
5 Production keeps changing its schedules
6 Specifications are often incomplete

7 Some specifications are written in such a way as to force us to purchase from a single source
8 Overspecification resulting in unnecessary cost, long lead times and fewer potential sources
9 Finance do not pay their bills on time
10 We do not have time to prepare properly for negotiation
11 "They won't listen"

It was interesting in the discussion which followed, for the purchasing staff to hear the views of their colleagues from other functions. And since this list is fairly representative of those prepared by the purchasing function in other businesses, it is worth commenting on one or two of the items discussed.

The examples quoted to illustrate the poor quality of information received from marketing were many and varied. Marketing accepted some of the criticism as valid but pointed out that the liaison was a two-way process. Purchasing had not involved itself in product decisions, nor had it informed marketing of supply problems or opportunities which might have given the company an advantage in its marketplace. At least part of the forecasting problem stems from the same cause. Forecasts are based upon information, thus the quality of that information has a vital bearing on the outcome. While it is true that sales market forecasts are based largely upon information gleaned for end markets, the actual results can be influenced by supply market performance. For example, price increases, poor quality of components and irregular supply, can all have a negative effect on sales performance. In addition, in the longer term, new developments in the supply market can have a considerable impact on product design and thus market share. Consequently, forecasts of likely sales penetration should include consideration of relevant supply market data.

In general, it is reasonable to argue that companies will succeed in meeting their end market needs effectively when they make the right product decisions. And making the right product decisions ought to involve input from the purchasing function.

A key point is that virtually all major decisions made in a manufacturing concern are influenced by answers to the question "what products should we include in our range". Indeed the product strategy which is evolved must be the core of the entire planning effort of the company concerned. In the present age of fast developing technology and rapid changes in demand, the ability to maintain the right range of products requires the continuing attention of management. In our view, that need for continuing attention includes a positive role for the procurement function.

To decide on the composition of its product range, the company will use a variety of techniques in researching its markets. The results of these surveys will enable management to monitor its products in relation to the point they are at in their life cycle. The concept of the "product life cycle" is widely used and a brief description of the idea here will aid current discussion.

The product life cycle

The product life cycle concept is an attempt to describe distinct stages in the life of a product in terms of sales volume. Each of the stages identified include opportunities and problems for the company with respect to its strategy and profitability. If management can identify the "position" of the product concerned on the life curve, it should enable pertinent action to be taken, particularly with regard to marketing strategy.

Fig. 11:1 is an illustration of the stages which are typically included in product life cycle diagrams. During the first stage, the volume of sales rises slowly, then if it proves to be popular there follows a period of quite rapid growth. The longest stage, "maturity", is that in which product sales either grow more slowly or are stable, and, finally there is a stage of rapid sales decline.

The lower part of the diagram illustrates a typical cycle in profit terms. Clearly, during the introduction stage, and in what might be thought of as the pre-introduction stage, the company incurs costs often far in excess of revenue. These costs relate to research and development and initial marketing and promotion. However, as sales increase, so losses decline, until a stage is reached where profits appear. These profits grow and tend to reach their peak in the early stages of maturity, whereafter they fall slowly in the face of competition until the decline stage when they quickly convert into losses.

The typical profit cycle illustrated in Figure 11:1 suggests the need for management action in a number of ways. First, the company should strive to reduce the length of time taken to get the product into the stage of rapid growth. Second, it should do everything possible to elongate this stage in the product's life. And third, it should try to stretch the profitable part of the mature phase.

From the marketing viewpoint, attempts to increase sales invariably involve increased expenditure. However, this expenditure may have an adverse affect on the profit cycle. Thus, management is faced with the classical marketing problem of weighing promotional costs against increased sales so as to produce an acceptable profit. Yet sales prices towards the end of the maturity phase are often lower in real terms than at any previous stage in the product's life (e.g. black and white television sets and pocket calculators).

Growth in sales

Buzzell identified four possible causes for slow growth in sales. There were:

1 Delays in expansion of production capacity
2 Technical problems ("working out the bugs")
3 Delays in making the product available to customers, especially in obtaining adequate distribution through retail outlets
4 Customer reluctance to change established behaviour patterns

As will be seen from this list, supply may be directly involved in two areas and

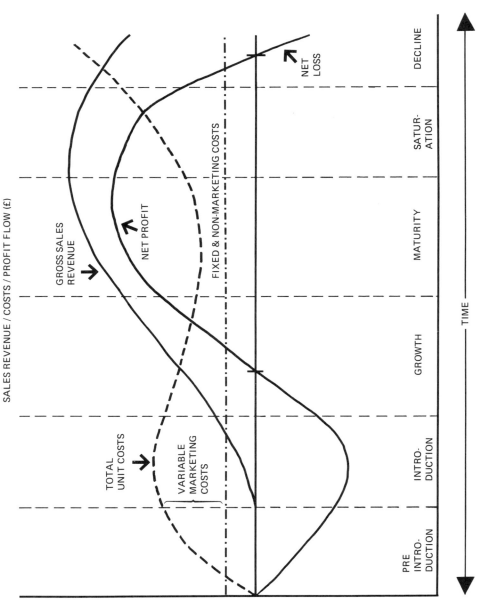

FIGURE 11:1 PRODUCT LIFE CYCLE INCLUDING COST AND PROFIT FLOW

indirectly in one other. For instance, the delays in expansion of production capacity could relate to machinery, construction contract or material/component supply delays. Technical problems could include material/component specification problems in transfer from pilot to bulk production. The third item could, of course, result from failure at any of the earlier stages, with the potential of supply aspects being contributory.

Then, just as these and other related aspects can contribute to delays, so can effective supply management markedly assist in minimising development time and ensuring that the product is available when it is wanted. Much of the pertinent action at this juncture should relate to effective procurement planning and management in the pre-production stage. Indeed examination of related supply difficulties will often show inadequacies in pre-production management. In many organisations a major reason for such difficulties is that the procurement function does not become involved early enough in the planning stage. In consequence decisions are taken which would not have been, had procurement been consulted. Among the resulting problems for the function are inadequate lead time for sourcing, monopoly sources, and inflated prices which pre-empt future as well as present negotiations. These problems may be exacerbated where there are several stages in the development of the item concerned, for example, tooling, pattern equipment and samples.

One approach to planning

In one organisation where this type of problem was common, we found that the purchasing department was spending the majority of its time on remedial action. Because of schedule problems buyers were trying to source quickly, trying to reduce supplier lead times and, inevitably, were finding themselves in a poor bargaining position. Apart from anything else, the philosophy became "get it at any price, we'll beat them down later". There were additional problems too, in that quality control suffered at various stages as systems were short circuited to ensure delivery. Inevitably with the emphasis on "fire fighting" there was little time to think and plan. As one buyer put it, "we were all progress chasers with 'delivery yesterday' as our watchword".

In this organisation the usual arguments were put forward as to why things could not be improved. For example, there was no time to plan because of the pace of activity and few purchasing staff. Even that was not entirely true, for the purchasing manager did make efforts to plan, which had some effect, but those plans seemed to be overtaken by circumstances. There was no doubt that the staff were stretched and that they worked hard and conscientiously, and had developed skills in "making things happen". Nonetheless, the 'if only' syndrome applied: "if only we had known about that requirement x weeks earlier we could have sourced more effectively: if only we had known that engineering intended to use that specification we could have told them that it had a monopolistic source, a long lead time or a high price: if only we had the time to seek out new potential sources etc. etc."

On close examination of the company structure we found that there was no liaison between the organisation's product development department and purchasing. If there was a need to obtain information from the supply market this was done by the people in product development. However, even that was limited, for the group worked on the basis of "acquired knowledge". That is, the members were familiar with the materials and components involved and made assumptions about availability based upon their experience. We had been called in originally because the company's sales department was losing sales because of inability to get the product to the market place at the planned time. Further, that there were problems with products during the introductory phase, so it was believed, mostly to do with manufacturing quality. Inevitably, the investigation through, engineering, production, and quality control suggested reasons for the difficulties which were appearing at the various stages of manufacture. Not surprisingly, there was a resultant effect stemming from supply problems at the various points in manufacture and, as is often the case, purchasing became the focus.

Among other things, our report recommended that purchasing should be represented at new product discussions at the conceptual stage of development. In due course a procedure was developed which was regarded by all parties as an unqualified success. The basic idea of the procedure as far as lead time is concerned was that, using pertinent information and working backwards from the expected launch date, purchasing would indicate when they required drawings, released etc. The design-/development programme was then structured around this.

In practice, purchasing found that the information they were able to provide at the conceptual stage influenced the thinking of the designers. In time, when the effects of better planning began to work through the system, the purchasing manager found that he was able to instigate a series of supply market reviews. He developed component or material dossiers in a variety of fields and tied these in with the economic forecast service which the company subscribed to.

As an experienced industrial buyer he already knew a great deal about the markets in which he worked. However, as he put it, "This system made me look at the markets in a different way. I found that I was monitoring developments on my own initiative rather than waiting for representatives to tell me about them". He went on to say that he believed that such advance information on the development of an important component had allowed his own company's designer to incorporate an important selling feature in a product at an earlier stage than competition. It seemed that, quite apart from the direct advantage to the organisation of the improvements in planning, there was a greater involvement in product development throughout the organisation. In effect, people were beginning to take a total business view instead of being compartmentalised!

Sources of product ideas

In the foregoing case, product development stemmed from the need:

1   To extend its life in the maturity stage

2   To replace an existing product which was in decline or

3   To add an item to the existing product line to fill a need

It is reasonable to postulate that most product development starts in this way. However, as is suggested by the comments of the purchasing manager in the case, the supply market can be the source of new ideas. There are at least two classifications of product development stemming from the supply market. The first results from innovation at some supply source, the second occurs when there is a failure of some kind in the supply market. For example, the latter could involve an extensive fire or strike at a sole supplier, or from the termination of the final seam in the case of a mined raw material. In such cases the buying company is forced to re-source, often at short notice. Once again, despite what might be thought of as adequate inventory levels, procurement is then carried on in disadvantageous circumstances.

In addition, in the case of certain raw materials, the properties which they bring to a product formula may be unique. Further, in terms of that formula there may be considerable interaction between the material and other ingredients. In consequence when it is necessary to replace a material, the balance of the mix may be upset on a number of accounts. In turn this necessitates the company's laboratory reformulating the recipe with potential effects on other purchase contracts. This may happen too, when the price of a particular material increases at a rate which makes it uneconomic to use it in the products concerned.

These and other factors suggest the need for a basic "what if?" question. Purchasing managers would be wise to ask the question of key materials – "what if supply failed for some reason or the material became uneconomic, what would we do?" In some cases the question may be thought to be purely academic. In others the development staff may not give great priority to contingency "what-if?" projects. Others might argue that the instances of serious failure are so few that the cost of insurance is greater than that of meeting an emergency when it occurs. Yet, searching the supply market for alternatives is in itself a way of developing new products and many product ideas do emerge from the supply market. As the famous US economist Schumpeter put it "The kind of competition that is decisive is that which comes from the new commodity, the new technology, the new source of supply . . . "

In general, these comments have been concerned with product improvement rather than new product development. However, the basic ideas expressed are relevant in both instances. Whether the product is new or an adaption of an existing product, its development begins with the generation of an idea. Sources of successful new ideas are extremely important to those concerned with the development of new products, for one problem is the proportion of ideas which are screened out to produce one good one. According to the well known Booz, Allen and Hamilton report, 58 new product ideas must be screened to find a good one. Their other statistic that 50 per cent of all new products fail after reaching the introduction stage, emphasises the importance of sound ideas.

Given a purchasing management which is marketing oriented, then the supply market can be the source of many viable ideas. These ideas may arise by chance or as a result of the promotional efforts of suppliers but it is possible, too, to generate such ideas as a result of effective source market search by purchasing. However, this presupposes that purchasing management is aware of the scope of company product policy. The point is that an organised search is likely to be far more productive in the long-run than some ad hoc method. As Kraushar puts it: "product development requires venturesome management and it requires an integrated management versed in several types of skills". Purchasing should be "tuned-in" too.

Clearly purchasing will not be searching the supply market solely for product development ideas. Few procurement departments have the resources to undertake such a task. The searching will be undertaken as an adjunct to supply market research, perhaps where the search is for an alternative supplier, or alternative material.

The screening process

Having generated the idea, the next stage in the development process is a screening of that idea as to its suitability to proceed to the development stage. Clearly procurement has an important part in this. The proposed product needs to be considered against what might be thought of as a "compatibility profile". For example, production would consider it from their viewpoint seeking to see if the product might be manufactured alongside existing items with current equipment, or what modifications need to be made to accommodate it. Marketing would be concerned, among other things, with whether the product could be promoted and sold through existing distribution channels, and, at what price. Procurement, in turn, needs to be concerned with the availability and price of material to meet the stated schedule.

At this point prototypes are manufactured and tested in a variety of ways. If the product is to be packaged then this needs to be developed in line with the promotional activity. Clearly procurement will be involved with the packaging but it is possible that they may be able to generate a cooperative promotion for the product with the supplier. For example, if the product is to contain a material or a component supplied by a well known company, then both marketing departments might wish to promote collaboratively. This is quite common with man-made fibres for example and there is no reason why the idea should not be adapted in other fields. Of course, the decision whether to go ahead with such an idea has to be made by marketing. However, procurement will be the liaison point and could well put up the idea to their colleagues for consideration.

Venture teams

While the ideas put forward in this Chapter may appear attractive to some readers, they may feel inhibited by the organisation in which they work. This may be because of the organisation structure or because of the personalities involved. Indeed, many studies have shown that the organisation can promote or stifle initiative. As was suggested earlier, the proponents of logistics management are motivated by their desire to reduce friction in the system by engendering a company-wide attitude among managers. In turn this is thought to promote the positive kind of attitudes which are being discussed here.

In concluding this section, it would be helpful to indicate an approach which has been used to stimulate and coordinate product development. The examples quoted tend to be from large companies simply because they are faced with the problem of generating entrepreneurial attitudes in what could easily become a bureaucratic environment. Then, because they are big and have tackled the problem, they tend to be written about. The point is that the concepts are as defensible in the small or medium sized organisation, where they tend to be even easier to promote.

Dow-Corning, Westinghouse and Monsanto are examples of companies which have entrusted new product development to venture teams. The idea here is that a group is brought together specifically from various operating departments and given the task and responsibility of bringing a specific product into being.

Some team members are assigned to work full-time, while others contribute on a part-time basis. An advantage of this system is that conventional departmental boundaries do not exist. The team work together towards the achievement of the stated objective, each contributing his specialist skills. The closeness of the team helps to ensure that communication problems are minimised and they work this way through the various stages of development. In consequence many of the potential problems faced in conventional organisations which stem from poor communications are avoided. Development is thus often both faster and smoother.

Once the product has reached the introduction stage the venture team disbands and the product is taken over by the marketing function. Apart from these advantages the venture team idea is thought to be an extremely useful training method by at least one of the companies mentioned. As one executive put it "The team members return to their jobs with a much wider conception of the role they play as members of our management team."

Clearly there is a role for procurement to play in this approach. Too often at the moment, the preliminary purchasing work is undertaken as an adjunct of some other function (e.g. R & D or production engineering). As a result, because of the background and training of these specialists, the commercial aspects of the development from the supply side receive little emphasis. In addition, the creative opportunities provided to the buyer by his work environment may be lost.

In this chapter a basic argument has been that there is a place for procurement in product development. From the company viewpoint, product development should be undertaken with a keen awareness of environmental opportunities but in such a way as to: reduce the risk of failure; get the product to the market in the shortest possible time; and maintain its profitable maturity as long as is possible. Procurement has a constructive part to play in all these phases. Nothing has been written here about the importance of cost effective purchasing through the life of the product, a well-known and accepted role for procurement.

Long-term buying agreements

The agreements to be discussed in this section have been given a variety of names including *blanket ordering and contract buying.* In the majority of cases they relate to the situation where a buyer places a contract for his requirements for a period (say six months or one year) with the proviso that the goods are delivered in batches against his subsequent instructions. A typical form used in conjunction with contract delivery is illustrated in Figure 11:2.

There are a number of advantages in making such an arrangement. One saving is in the amount of paperwork involved. For instance, if a buyer is using ten units per month, he might, in a year, place twelve orders each for ten units. With the blanket order method he places one order for the year and then calls off against the contract by telex, telephone or some other convenient method like the form illustrated. Since many companies have multiple order sets a considerable amount of paper can be generated each time an order is placed.

There is also a saving in buyer's time. He has to carry out one negotiation instead of a possible twelve. Most important perhaps is that once a contract is made, the calling off can be carried out by a clerk thus releasing the buyer for more important work. In the larger organisations this can be done by computer.

Another favourable factor in this is the continuity between buyer and seller which helps to obviate mistakes in specification (typing and communication errors) improves liaison (both companies are aware of each other's systems) and helps the supplier in his production scheduling.

In turn this can result in more competitive pricing which is an important factor in the negotiation of the contract. Since the buyer is effectively saving considerable time by using the method, he can devote part of this to ensuring that he is well prepared for the contract negotiation.

Lead time should also be shorter since, given a reasonable pattern of call off, the supplier will probably manufacture in anticipation of requirement. Certainly he will aim to optimise on the batches he produces from the production viewpoint. A more flexible schedule should also result.

In turn this should improve the inventory cost position of both parties. Where the supplier can be persuaded to hold some stocks against call-off it could even mean that the buying company can operate effectively on a hand-to-mouth basis.

Another factor is the important one that in many cases a stable price can be negotiated for the period of the contract. In times of rapidly increasing costs this can be an extremely valuable factor.

While these advantages apply there are also some hazards which the manager ought to note. These were listed by respondents to a *Purchasing Magazine* survey as follows:

1   Inability to take advantage of spot offers
2   Less supplier contact
3   Possibility that the market may fall
4   Chance that fire or strikes will disrupt the supplier's production

Delivery instruction

Division _____

Contact _____

Date _____

Authorised _____

If you cannot comply with this instruction or disagree
with any figure shown please notify us immediately.
If no such notification is received it will be recorded that
the quantities and conditions are acceptable to you

Please note conditions overleaf

Part number	Description	Order number	Details of last delivery	Total quantity received	Arrears from periods	A Delivery required			B Manufacture only authorised— not delivery			C Raw material only authorised— not manufacture			For internal use only
						Period	weeks ending		Period	weeks ending		Periods			

FIGURE 11:2 CONTRACT DELIVERY INSTRUCTIONS FORM

5   Inability to negotiate individual orders
6   Ineffectiveness due to design changes
7   Poor service due to supplier complacency
8   Buyers tendency to forget review and control aspects
9   The possibility of overbuying

Not all these points will apply in every situation. Some may be effectively countered by good management, but as with any other technique, long-term purchasing must only be used when it is clearly cost-effective. Given the right conditions it can be a most effective tool.

Scrap

Every production organisation produces scrap or waste which results from its manufacturing operations. Some companies are able to find uses for all but a small proportion of this, but few can completely eliminate waste of some kind.

Much scrap, especially engineering industry waste, can be sold. Consequently management has the problem of ensuring that they obtain the best value from this residue. Of course, it is better to prevent it in the first place, but even in the best-managed factories some scrap is inevitable and every company needs to decide a policy on its disposal.

Whether the scrap is disposed of by direct sale to another company or scrap merchant, sale to an associate or subsidiary, or re-use in another department it pays to segregate it at source. Generally speaking, sorted scrap is worth more than mixed scrap.

In many companies individual bins are kept for grades or types of metal and scrap is deposited straight into these. For example, there might be bins for high-grade alloy turnings, brass stampings and mild-steel off-cuts – each marked with a simple colour code to ensure that only that type of scrap is deposited into that container. In considering this it is useful to seek advice from the scrap merchant. Many merchants provide skips or containers for scrap arisings and are prepared to advise on the best use of this equipment and which types of scrap to keep separate. The scrap merchants prefer clean scrap which has been kept separate because it saves expensive sorting in the merchant's yard or employing the middleman who makes his living from sorting. Within a factory it need not cost any more to keep the material separate and there is a worthwhile return for a little planning.

Generally speaking the most satisfactory arrangement for disposing of scrap is to negotiate a period contract with a known merchant. Scrap merchanting is a highly competitive industry and high arisings of well-sorted scrap are particularly attractive to the larger companies. Most of these now have expensive shearing and baling equipment which needs a great deal of scrap to feed. In consequence, it pays to consider two or three companies before arriving at a decision. Apart from the price, other factors to be taken into account include binning equipment provided, additional services offered and frequency of collection.

In an industry where there are still many Steptoes dealing in cash, it is wise to have all transactions on a proper business basis with weighbridge tickets and collection notes tallying with monthly payment advices. Apart from the requirements of the auditors, management controls are easier with a tally system.

Even though there is a contract, large-scale disposers of scrap will need to watch the prices of scrap on the metal markets. Non-ferrous scrap in particular is subject to considerable fluctuation in price. Ferrous metal on the other hand has hardly changed in price during the last fifteen years.

We mentioned earlier the possibility of selling surplus direct to another company. This might well be advantageous in certain cases. However, care should be taken to ensure that hidden costs (such as handling, transportation and provision of bins) do not eliminate any advantage.

In this chapter we have paid greatest attention to the important relationships relating to product decisions. This should not be taken to suggest that other relationships are unimportant. Effective liaison with e.g. production and finance can be crucial to success. However, we have little doubt that developing the kinds of relationships which we have described with regard to product development will have the biggest positive impact on the company system.

Chapter 12

Buying materials: supply
sources

One type of supply source is *internal* in the sense that parts or materials are procured from another plant or division within the organisation. Often the main reason for setting up or acquiring such a facility is either to reduce the cost or to increase the availability of the parts or material concerned. Yet, as with many other capital expenditure decisions, the calculations on which the original decision were based do not always work out in practice, and some difficult questions arise in connection with transfer pricing (the determination of the prices at which parts or material are transferred from one part of the organisation to another).

"More executive time is taken up with transfer pricing problems in this organisation than with consideration of our competitors", a senior executive of a European based multinational told us. The Scandia case (p. 295) illustrates how complex and intractable such problems can be in vertically integrated multi-plant organisations. It is desirable to balance group resources in the most profitable way, satisfy the various stakeholders that this is being done, contend with the often powerful personalities of key managers and nurture their enthusiasm and motivation.

Often transfer pricing policy leaves much to be desired even in otherwise well managed organisations. Symptoms include continuing *ad hoc* negotiations at various levels, festering relationships, and a general belief that the system is unfair. Both internal buyer and internal seller often feel, with regard to the same transaction, that the system is penalising them. "People tend to employ accountants to look for loopholes in the group system", one manager told us. (See for instance in the Scandia case, Svenson's behaviour as regards the third party shareholder, or Curtis's in masking the actual contribution figure.)

Transfer pricing

Three basic approaches are adopted to the determination of transfer price. It can be based on:

1 Cost
2 Market price
3 Negotiation

Each approach has advantages in some circumstances; each has disadvantages. Market price is particularly attractive in a decentralised organisation where the profit centres all trade externally as well as internally. The market is arbiter in any dispute and there is little need for group headquarters to intervene. Profitability of each subsidiary can be measured realistically. But on the other hand sub-optimisation in respect of group resources may be encouraged. Profit centres may compete with each other at costs which are collectively avoidable. There may be strategic implications too. Assume, for instance, that the protection of a vital supply source was the reason for vertical integration, and that later the market price becomes uneconomic, perhaps because the supply industry now has surplus capacity. This could result, at the extreme, in the demise of that subsidiary company. The whole purpose of the vertical integration would then be destroyed. But, perhaps, the most telling disadvantage derives from the fact that price is only one indicator of cost. Unacceptable levels of quality failure and/or unreliable delivery or service can have a greater effect on the buyer's profit than price alone.

Clearly, the separation of the alternative approaches in this discussion into three generalised types is somewhat artificial. For example, cost-based prices will be affected by market movements, and there will be the need to negotiate acceptable agreements with all three types. Nonetheless, the categorisation can be extremely useful when considering the correct approach in a particular circumstance. If nothing else, by specifying the advantages and disadvantages of each type, management will be more aware of the need for sensible, workable policies.

Some strategic considerations

In our experience, too frequently, the strategic considerations which relate to transfer pricing are given inadequate attention. Yet, over time, they may have an important influence on the efficiency and effectiveness of a group as a whole.

The rationale for transfer pricing can generally be seen to derive from the policy commitment to manage vertically integrated organisations on a decentralised basis. This stems from the proposition that the conferral of autonomy upon sub-units will enhance the motivation of their management teams to a level unattainable in the centralised alternative. Clearly, the style of organisation will have considerable effect on the managerial approaches which are adopted, as well as the strategies which are suitable. If, as is typical, each subsidiary operates as a profit centre, the management of a particular company might argue that it is being penalised by group policies.

There is also the fundamental question as to whether the buying company can obtain its input goods from non-group suppliers. Where it is the case that they cannot, it is especially important to pay attention to transfer pricing, if internal inefficiency is not to be disguised.

If equity and a common sense of purpose are to be achieved in decentralised structures, then it becomes essential for any disputes to be resolved by a well accepted and respected arbitration procedure. The key to this lies in corporate cohesion – our next major focus of attention.

This second issue, which is pertinent whatever kind of strategic approach is under scrutiny, concerns the managerial ethos of the group and its constituent parts. Perhaps the most important question to ask here is whether there is mutual trust within the group. In many cases this stems from what could be termed "good team spirit": a mutual acceptance of the veracity of other people within the system, and recognition of their abilities and effectiveness.

Competent management has the capability to modify strategy as the passage of time reveals changing circumstances. This adaptation may be accomplished in a reactionary fashion, where the organisation frequently becomes resigned to and frustrated by the cost of tardiness. In contrast, a proactive management philosophy will anticipate change and regularly question the capacity of time honoured systems to cope with it.

The third issue for consideration relates to the availability and quality of financial and other management information. The market price approach, for example, pre-supposes that there are established competitive markets. Further, that the company can obtain the necessary data.

More fundamental is the consistency of the costing and budgeting methodology employed by the companies within the group. Cost behaviour and other factors will be influenced by the state of order books. Equally, the quality of information regarding long term as well as short-term capacity within a group can have a considerable effect on decisions governing the allocation of scarce resources.

Finally, there are many issues which do not fall into any of the foregoing categories; perhaps their common denominator is "risk". For example, how important is it to have a solus supplier of the material in question? If that supplier did not exist, would some outside dominant source acquire too powerful a position? For multinational groups of companies, are there profit repatriation, currency or duty factors to be considered? Are there political risks involved? Is the internal purchase decision affected by patent or commercial secrecy considerations? What are the longer-term forecasts as to the "shape" of the market? And, where the supplying company is in a region which attracts government subsidy, could that provide economic advantage to the group as a whole?

Supplier pricing

Prices are affected by many factors and should not be considered to result from a straightforward logical process. The right price is not always to be measured by last year's price, or the lowest price quoted; and "what the market will bear" is often a difficult rule to apply. Pricing decisions by external suppliers are based on informed opinion, cost information of varying accuracy, and strategies of varying degrees of sophistication and formality. They are affected by customer reaction and the state of the market: for instance industrial buyers in 1981 were paying prices at least as low as in 1980 for many goods, despite double figure inflation. Suppliers badly in need of business will try hard to find ways of offering lower prices.

Customers of course welcome lower prices, and of course they are not in business to wet-nurse suppliers. But while the prime concern of a business may be its own survival, a secondary concern may be the survival of key suppliers. Future supply market structures are the result partly of present supply decisions by major customers. Is a given supply organisation viable at the agreed prices?

Cash flow is another key consideration for any business, especially when money is tight. Terms of payment, and particularly the observance of agreed terms, need to be carefully considered. In the 1930s William Morris (Lord Nuffield) made a practice of paying in accordance with the contract agreement. One *quid pro quo* of this, though, was keen prices from his suppliers and improved quality and service. The security of the payment date helped suppliers manage their business more effectively while complying with Morris' requirement.

Already, from this short discussion, it will be clear that price is but one aspect of cost. Thus, when considering what price is "right" in a particular case, several questions come to mind:

1   Have the buyer and seller explored every avenue to take unnecessary cost out of their mutual "system"? There is evidence to suggest, for example, that this mutual approach can lower the manufacturing costs and selling prices of the supplier, while maintaining net profit levels. Quality and delivery failure are very much part of the potential field of search in this respect.
2   Is the buying company aware of the economics of the suppliers business? Most buying companies readily accept the desirability of such knowledge. Few, however, have the staff or skills to be adequately informed in this respect.
3   What would be the longer-term effects of tight/low pricing on particular suppliers/markets?
4   In which ways can the supplier absorb cost increases without "cutting corners" to the detriment of their performance and resulting increased real cost to the buying company.

Whatever decisions are taken need to be periodically reviewed. For example, increasing energy and transportation costs may be outside the control of the supplier. As such costs work their way through the system, the impact upon particular suppliers and supply markets needs to be watched carefully. In some cases the disappearance of viable UK sources could prove to be extremely unattractive in the long run.

None of this is to argue for a "soft line" on pricing. It is clear to us that some buying companies have paid more for supplies than they need; and that some have little data on suppliers cost and price structures. Deciding what a price ought to be necessitates professional management decisions stemming from careful analysis of sound data.

Though the extent and accuracy of that data will depend upon, for example, the importance of the material in question to the buying company, and the ability of that company to influence supplier pricing. Most buying companies have more power to influence supplier pricing decisions than they realise. Using that power properly and professionally can have a bigger impact of corporate viability than many other management activity.

It is extremely important that the buying company should seek to establish sound supplier pricing standards in the early stages of product development. Once a base price has been established, changes tend to be related to that norm. If it is inflated, then subsequent changes will be distorted by that base. It is important at this stage, too, to have in mind the "improvement curve" concept; as volume increases, cost per piece falls. Thus, if a supplier is making a special part to a customer's drawing, the price for the first batch should be reduced in real terms as the volume taken in a given period increases. Other important guidelines include the obvious, but frequently ignored, concept that the cost make up of a significant product should be scrutinized on an on-going basis over time. New materials, new processes and new ideas can result in considerable change in cost structures.

Selecting a supplier

When selecting a supplier the buyer is attempting to find a company or companies which will meet his needs. Those needs usually include reliability in quality and service terms, while the relevant pricing is competitive. It should be stressed that the effective buyer will not be searching for the cheapest buy. Rather he will be seeking to obtain the best value for his company. Clearly, any savings made on price will be quickly eroded if, for example, delivery times or quality standards are unreliable and production schedules are interrupted. Conversely, however, a specification which is too good for the purpose in hand, or stocks which are too high, can be just as damaging to company profitability. The buyer's task is to attempt to optimise his source decision, having in mind the commonly stated objective of his function: to buy the right quality product, in the right quantity, at the right time and the right price from the right source.

Clearly, not all source evaluation is critical. Poor choice of the source of paper clips will have a negligible effect on a company's success. However, certainly as far as production materials are concerned, poor source selection will, almost always, result in a detrimental trend in material costs. The time we spend in appraisal should consequently be related to the importance of the material or service required.

In evaluating a potential source of supply we have to take into consideration: technical ability; production capacity; financial stability; managerial ability in areas such as design, marketing, production and quality control; depth of service and industrial relations stability.

Presenting in a usable form all the information which has been collected about a supplier on these matters can be quite a problem. Numerical rating supplier-appraisal schemes are in use in some companies and are the subject of a good deal of discussion in purchasing circles. However, we do not consider that there is anything to be gained by adopting any of the numerical schemes which we have seen. They weight and quantify what are really subjective judgements. We believe that there is far more to be gained by developing our ability to judge suppliers than by putting inadequate judgements through mathematical hoops and assuming that by doing so they take on a scientific objectivity.

One aid to supplier appraisal uses two forms. The first form which is completed by the potential supplier includes the following data:

> Supplier name and address; address of other company plants; date company established; company structure (private or public limited company and so on); names of company officers; if part of a group, the name of the parent company and associated companies; company capital structure; major products; responsible executives in production, sales, finance etc.; present major customers; unions represented in the factory; number of employees in factory, office and management; annual sales revenue for the last four years; declared profit as a percentage; area of site and projected expansion plans; transport and equipment facilities; whether the company has met formal quality assurance requirements of other buying companies; design and development facilities; warehousing, tooling, printing, packaging and painting facilities; settlement terms and names and addresses of representatives who cover the territories in which the plants of the buying company are located.

Not every potential supplier takes kindly to the provision of all this data. A minority will not reveal things like their sales or profit record even after discussions, but even the fact that they are not prepared to provide such data may tell us something about the company. It may, for instance, mean that we ought to look even more closely at the operation.

The second form is completed by the buyer immediately following his visit to the supplier. With this form, the buyer ticks the box he considers to be relevant on a four-point scale – excellent, good, fair, poor – against:

1   External sales
2   Reception activity
3   Inside sales
4   Production area
    (a) Housekeeping
    (b) Relevant knowledge regarding buying company's needs
5   Production control
6   Storage area facilities
7   Handling equipment condition
8   Quality of
    (a) Work-in-progress
    (b) Finished work (this is meant to be an impression and does not replace proper quality checks)

9   Purchasing staff ability
10   Stock control staff ability
11   Transport and despatch staff ability
12   Working conditions – factory and office
13   Morale – factory and office

In addition, against "Attitude", he records "open" or "guarded" and "helpful" or "complacent", against the principal staff he meets in the various areas during his visit.

Supplementary data and certain other impressions may then be added as necessary: for example, number of days lost as a result of strikes during (a) the last twelve months and (b) the last three years.

Since the buyer has only to tick the revelant box in recording his impressions of these various areas, the form is easy to complete. The final panel on the form requires the buyer to state whether he believes that the supplier has the ability to meet the buying company's needs.

The general consensus of opinion among the buyers who have been using the form is that it is a useful way of recording in a systematic manner their general impressions; and that it is of considerable assistance in conjunction with the first form in arriving at their decision.

While the buyer forms an impression of quality matters during his visit, it is the task of the quality staff to assess suppliers in this direction. The final decision on whether to use the supplier is arrived at after due consideration of the commercial aspects via the two forms described in conjunction with the quality report.

In the end, of course, the proof of the pudding is in the eating, and in terms of improving selection performance much can be learned through subsequent reviews of supplier performance. It is a useful idea to file the three forms (the quality report plus the two commercial forms which we have discussed here) in the supplier's file. Periodic reviews can then be made with the original impressions in note form as a background to current performance history.

The importance of undertaking a thorough analysis of this kind in major purchaser decisions cannot be over-stressed. It is also important to leave the chosen supplier in no doubt as to the performance standards which are expected and to monitor that performance.

Vendor rating

The problem of appraising suppliers once they have been selected has attracted the attention of many writers in the purchasing field. Generally speaking the systems which have evolved from their discussions are structured around the idea of deducting "points" from suppliers who fail to deliver on time or who have items rejected because of quality failure or to whom a higher price is being paid. Usually, weights are given to quality, delivery, reliability and price, depending on how important each is seen to be by the buyer concerned. Although, in the more refined schemes each of these areas is sub-divided within these categories and additional factors are added.

To illustrate a simple case, "service" may be allocated a weighting of 25; "quality" 50 and "price" 25. The buyer then has to make an arithmetic assessment of supplier performance against the standards and weightings in accordance with a predetermined formula. A typical formula is:

Delivery   5 points deducted for each late delivery
Quality   The number of rejects taken as a percentage of the whole deducted
           from 100
Price   The lowest price quoted divided by the price paid to the supplier

Such a formula could result in a rating of 75.51 being calculated as follows:

Delivery $\qquad\qquad\qquad\qquad\qquad$ $25 \times (1.00 - 0.15) = 21.25$
Quality $\qquad\qquad\qquad\qquad\qquad$ $50 \times (1.00 - 0.39) = 30.51$
Price $\qquad\qquad\qquad\qquad\qquad$ $25 \times (95/100) \qquad = 23.75$
$$\overline{}$$
$$75.51$$

Some companies take action if the rating comes into a pre-determined bracket. For example, if the supplier falls below an 85 rating then he has to be brought into line. Others publish "league tables" in their reception lounges or send notice of ratings to suppliers with some indication of how they are performing against the norm. Computers are sometimes programmed to print out the rating in tabular form either for publication or in readiness for a negotiation session.

Such schemes were the vogue some years ago but do not appear to be much in favour today. The reasons for this disenchantment are numerous. Among them are:

1   If a manual system is used too much arithmetic is involved
2   The weightings fail to reflect current difficulties: for example, at certain times delivery may well assume the greatest importance, whereas it is not so weighted in the formula
3   Statistically it is argued that in adding the three things together we are trying to add apples, pears and oranges
4   Delivery difficulties are sometimes caused by short notice of changed schedules at the buyer's works: is it fair to deduct points from a supplier who has a normal delivery of 21 days who when asked to deliver in 14 days supplies them in 16?
5   The collection of data involving quality and delivery failure is expensive and complicated
6   Most buying departments comprise about three people and it is extremely doubtful if the necessary data could be collected effectively in these circumstances

The writers have found very few companies where such a scheme exists or where one is, where effective use is being made of it. Those who operate the system via a computer as a spin-off from the overall material control system argue that it costs very little to produce this extra information. They say that suppliers are impressed by it and that it is effective in bringing wayward suppliers into line. However, one wonders if this "bringing into line" would not be done anyway.

In the end we should ask ourselves of any system: How does it help me to be more effective in my job? Can that help be justified in terms of the time involved in producing the information and the expense incurred in collecting it? And, if we are utilising a form of quantitative supplier appraisal scheme, we should not fall into the trap of thinking that by expressing our subjective judgements in numbers we somehow make it all scientifically objective.

Is it not better to adopt a simple system of noting marked failures *and successes* or a simple sheet of paper which is retained in the supplier's file? This will then serve as a memory aid when reviewing contracts. Larger companies will have the resources to tailor a more sophisticated system to meet their specific needs. Our advice is to keep quality and delivery as separate factors.

Another aspect of appraisal concerns the adequacy of the suppliers with whom the company is currently dealing. Decisions taken many years ago may well have been correct at that time. However, since then things may have changed. For example additional qualified suppliers may be available, new processes may have been developed, new markets may have opened up and currency relationships may have changed. A most important point is that, in the key decision areas, both long and short-term effects are considered and subsequently renewed. With new technology and a "shrinking world", such reviews may well need to be carried out more frequently in the future.

One or more

If a buyer gives all his business to one supplier, does he get a better and more economic service than when he splits the order between two or more? Does he lose his competitive position by, in effect, creating a monopolistic source? If, on the other hand he uses more than one supplier is he dissipating his purchasing power, or is he protecting himself against shortage, fire and strike?

Decisions must be made after careful consideration of the relevant facts which currently apply. It may be to the short-term advantage of the buyer to give all his business for a particular item to supplier A, but there may be another supplier B obstructing A from occupying a monopolistic position. A might be prepared in the short term to sell at a loss in order to force B into a situation where he would be prepared to sell out, leaving A with the monopolist's advantage and the buyer with nowhere else to turn. In such circumstances it might be prudent for the buyer to support B even to his short-term disadvantage. In these days of takeover and merger, such incidents may well become more common, and buying strategies need to be carefully considered.

CHECKLIST – SINGLE OR MULTIPLE SOURCING

Some advantages of single sourcing

1 The supplier ought to be able to offer price advantages because of economies of scale
2 Personal relationships can be more easily established, thus, making communications more effective
3 Administrative work in the buyer's office is reduced
4 Closer relationships and a reasonable tenure can result in mutual cost reduction effort
5 Buyer-tied research can be undertaken
6 Tool and pattern or fixture costs are reduced and long-run tools may be used
7 Transportation costs can be lower and where pallets are used, common pools can be established
8 Quality control is made easier since there is only one location
9 Scheduling is made easier

Many of these arguments lose weight if the business involved represents a small proportion of the supplier's total sales.

Some advantages of multiple sourcing

1 With several sources there is insurance against failure at one plant as a result of fire, strikes, quality, delivery problems and so on
2 With more than one supplier a competitive situation can be developed: no one supplier can afford to become complacent
3 In cases of standard items, no tooling cost is involved and there are often no advantages for added volume
4 The buyer is protecting himself against a monopoly and may have the advantage of two sources of new ideas or new materials
5 There is no moral commitment to a supplier as when the total quantity would be a considerable proportion of the supplier's total sales
6 Giving orders to a number of suppliers increases flexibility in case of large additional call-off or decreased needs
7 Part business can be used as a base load in conjunction with which a smaller supplier may be developed
8 With two suppliers holding stock, the buying company can reduce inventory levels

International sourcing

Several companies in the motor car and tractor industries have established a pattern whereby they have a major source in the UK and one in Europe. One advantage (apart from any EEC or multiple plant considerations) is that, in many cases, a source already existed on the Continent, thus obviating the need to build up from scratch a competitive source in this country. There is the bonus point that two suppliers in this country could be both hit by strikes at the same time, which is less likely to happen when the second supplier is in a different country.

The trend to internationalise sourcing – to include all Europe at least in the search for qualified suppliers – is bound to be accelerated by the enlargement of the Common Market. It seems certain that, even in smaller companies, international contacts at buyer level will become the order of the day.

There are difficulties in dealing with sources overseas which are not encountered with domestic suppliers. Different legal systems complicate the contractual arrangements. Different languages complicate communications, although we are fortunate in that English (with an American accent) bids fair to become the *lingua franca* of the business world in the West. It is not the basic commercial documents, the quotation, catalogue, order or progress letter which present the difficulties; they can be translated. It is more the informal contacts between executives in the different firms, the telephone calls to get urgent information, which present problems. Even if a person is reasonably fluent in a foreign language, somehow it is extraordinarily difficult to use that language on the telephone.

Still, these are transitional problems; we have seen telephonists at the Luxembourg headquarters of an international corporation (whose official language was English) answering the telephone in four different languages with casual ease, while booking air flight reservations for an executive wanting to fly to New York via Paris. If the need develops, people will appear to meet it.

Transport arrangements are complicated by the fact that Britain is an island. Customs duties and tariffs must be investigated, payment arrangements made and possible alterations in rates of exchange considered. Even if we forget other aspects of purchase cost like quality, stockholding and delivery, the complications of pricing when buying from overseas can be considerable, for it is the delivered price in this country which is relevant when comparing alternatives. Freight charges, insurance, import duty and handling costs are among those which add to the delivered price.

If the reader intends to consider purchasing from a foreign supplier he should realise that communication problems can take many forms. Some companies have found that not the least of these relates to the question of quality and specification. It pays to ensure that the supplier is absolutely clear about the requirement – and this may involve far greater emphasis than in domestic buying, not because the supplier is not competent to produce, but because he may interpret the requirement in accordance with his normal accepted standards, which may differ from those of the buyer. It may well be necessary to closely monitor quality, particularly in the early stages of a relationship. Procedures and documentation can also be an area of difficulty unless the requirements are clearly outlined. As far as delivery is concerned, it often pays to look very closely at the route and mode of transport to be used. What is convenient for the supplier need not necessarily be the best or least costly for the buyer. With increasing containerisation and a developing expertise among carriers in this field, their advice may be worth taking. If the potential supplier is in an area to which British companies export material it could well be that very advantageous rates are obtained from the carrier particularly if his return loads are uneconomical.

As regards finding foreign suppliers, there are a number of useful continental directories; information can be obtained from the various commercial attachés in the embassies; a lot of data can be obtained from colleagues in other companies who may have experience in the area, and much can be gained from making contact with fellow buyers on the continent. But there is no substitute for going and looking, testing, advising and communicating. International purchasing is naturally more complicated than domestic buying.

Importing

Many companies are becoming more involved with overseas suppliers for the reasons given above. The large companies will probably employ a shipping specialist and the smaller companies can use a good shipping agent, while the banks and HM customs provide valuable assistance. Nonetheless, it is necessary for the buyer who is contemplating importing for the first time to be aware of the basic factors. In consequence we include here some basic data relating to this aspect of the purchasing task.

Once a supplier has been selected, terms and conditions of contract have to be agreed. The basic forms of price offered by the supplier may then take a number of forms. These include:

FOB (Free on Board). Here the transfer of title occurs when the goods are loaded aboard the vessel. The buyer has to accept all costs and risks from that point.

CIF (Cost, Insurance, Freight). Here the seller assumes all costs and risks until the goods arrive at the port of destination.

C & F (Cost and Freight). In this case the seller is responsible for all costs to the port of destination, but the buyer has to insure his risk.

FAS (free along side). The buyer is responsible for costs and risks on delivery of goods to the dock alongside the carrying vessel.

In addition "ex-works" and "delivery buyer's works" are two other common forms.

METHOD OF PAYMENT

The method of payment which will be agreed varies with the common practice in the industry concerned and the degree of mutual confidence between the buyer and seller. In some cases transactions are made against an open account as in the case of a domestic transaction. However, this is not usual, nor is the other extreme – cash with order. The most common method adopted is the letter of credit. This is issued by the buyer's bank and authorises the seller to draw against the document in accordance with the terms which have been agreed. These terms usually specify:

1 Total amount of credit
2 Currency in which it will be met
3 Date when the current credit expires

4   Documents which must accompany each drawing (such as bills of lading (see below), commercial invoice, insurance certificates and certificates of origin).

DOCUMENTS

The *bill of lading* is made out by (or for) the seller and is submitted to the agent of the shipowner for his signature. It serves as:

1   A formal receipt from the shipowners indicating that they are in possession of the material in good condition
2   A document of title to the goods (the consignee can take delivery by endorsemen and surrender)
3   A memorandum of the contract of carriage
4   It is also used for customs purposes.

The *commercial invoice* is similar to its domestic counterpart and is often the basis for customers clearance at the port of receipt.

The *certificate of origin* shows where the goods originated. This can be important in ensuring goods are to specification and is also used by customs to ensure that goods lie within certain groupings. It used also to be of importance where there was impor preclusion from certain states (for example between the USA and China). However the number of such constraints is diminishing.

CUSTOMS DUTY

Import duty is assessed either *ad valorem*; at a specific rate per unit of measure, or as a combination of both. In consequence it is extremely important to specify the correct classification. It is also important to submit the necessary documents in good time in order to obviate delays in clearance and possible additional storage charges

Goods which are destined for re-export are generally subject to special arrange ments and import duty may be avoided. In some cases they may be imported in bond and in others duty drawback may be arranged with the customs officers. Since this can be important where large quantities are involved because of the effect on cash flow, it is well worth examining the best routes which can be followed. HM Customs can be of considerable assistance here and our advice is to make early contact with them and obtain the benefit of their expertise.

Purchasing manuals and ethics

We have looked at some twenty departmental purchasing manuals in this connec tion. Pious platitudes appeared in some, but a detailed explicit guide to morals and manners in dealing with suppliers appeared only in one document. This was the one issued to all group purchasing staff and all main suppliers by Ethicon Ltd and other Johnson & Johnson group companies. In our experience this is so unusual that we reproduce an extended quotation from it by kind permission of the company.

Good sources of supply are an important company asset that no one individual's ill-considered action, no emergency of the moment, no opportunity of the moment, should be allowed to jeopardise.

Just as the interests of our customers are safeguarded by rigid company standards of quality, design, performance and value, so must the interests of our good sources be safeguarded by an equally rigid set of standards which will protect Johnson & Johnson's vital interest in retaining and developing good sources of supply.

The application of sound principles for source relations is a fundamental aspect of our business philosophy.

We are, therefore, outlining on the following pages *our concept of our responsibilities in good source relations* and what we believe to be the responsibilities of good sources to this company.

OUR RESPONSIBILITIES TO OUR SUPPLIERS

To be above all honest, open and square in all our dealings. To be guided always by an honest search for the answer to the question: What is the truly fair thing to do?

To fulfil without question all contractual obligations, not only to the letter of the contract, but also in the spirit of the contract.

To place, whenever possible, the facilities of our research, development and technical services at the disposal of our suppliers in order to help them with any problems they may encounter in supplying materials to our specifications and to aid them in developing better means for production and quality improvement.

To encourage exchange visiting by our suppliers' technical personnel to observe our respective plant operations, thereby promoting a better understanding of mutual problems and objectives.

To plan our procurement scheduling sufficiently in advance so that our suppliers will know our future requirements. Any major changes in those requirements shall be made with sufficient notice to assure ample time to make adjustments. Unforeseen emergencies shall be mutually interpreted and satisfactory action mutually decided.

To let our supplier know whether we consider our relationship short or long term. We are primarily interested in long-term relationships.

To provide our suppliers with carefully written, completely detailed specifications that will establish, without question, what we require.

To arrive at a complete written understanding with suppliers regarding inspection methods and procedures to be followed by the suppliers and our quality control department.

To arrive at a complete understanding of how unsatisfactory material will be handled. Before any returns are made, suppliers will be properly notified and approval obtained for any returns.

To maintain a consistent cost policy. We will not be opportunists of the moment and we will not be price shoppers as such. We believe that good suppliers will meet adequately all reasonable price competition and opportunist buying is usually shortsighted in the long haul.

To make certain that our sources of supply make a reasonable profit on our business. We have a substantial stake in their profitable growth, because out of their growth will come better quality, better services to Johnson & Johnson.

To maintain the dignity of our relationship, we prefer that social-business entertainment be paid by the Johnson & Johnson representative. We prefer, also, that the practice of commercial "gift giving" be completely discontinued.

To acknowledge that this is a human relationship and that honest mistakes may be made. In such instances acknowledgement of error will be made quickly and immediate corrective action taken.

To give prompt and courteous attention to all source representatives who come to call on us or who write to us.

To develop with our suppliers the knowledge and the conviction that our most important requirement is the end quality of the product or service being purchased.

To meet squarely any problem of unsatisfactory relationship. If substantial reason is found for a termination of relationship, after sufficient counselling, to provide all possible advance notice of termination to allow the source time to find other outlets for its production.

To maintain a source relationship committee consisting of the vice-president in charge of purchasing, quality control, and all buyers which will periodically review our source relationship with the continuing aim of improving present relationship, review any deficiencies and recommend corrective action.

OUR SUPPLIERS' RESPONSIBILITIES TO US

To supply materials or services to our specifications on a prompt delivery schedule.

To maintain inspection and/or quality control personnel and facilities adequate to assure consistent delivery of materials to specifications.

To realise that it is not sufficient to accept returns willingly or negotiate disposition of materials not delivered to specification. A supplier should view such instances objectively and work constructively with us to correct the conditions that brought about the delivery of unsatisfactory material or services.

To inform us, as far in advance as possible, of circumstances which may affect our cost or the source's service to us.

To maintain an efficiency of operation that assures competitive costs to us.

To maintain quality improvement of the materials delivered.

To grow with our business and to participate in our future growth planning so that facilities and material services are always sufficient to supply the steady and continued sales progress of our partnership.

To have the firm conviction that the most important elements in our successful partnership are the satisfactory servicing of the consumer with our mutual production and to maintain with us a constant vigilance to protect the best interests of the consuming public.

To look upon our association as a long-term working partnership.

Part Three

Management techniques and controls

Chapter 13

Negotiating

Materials systems in manufacturing organisations are made up of various sub-systems. In order for the overall system to be efficient and effective, it is necessary for the various sub-systems to collaborate. And since these sub-systems are managed by people who may be attempting to achieve conflicting objectives, there is an on-going need to reach agreement as to the best blend of aims for the system as a whole.

Whether these difficulties occur within the company itself, or with supplying organisations, among the approaches which will be used to obtain agreement is *negotiation*. That negotiation may be approached in a contractual sense with a third party, or to achieve performance or organisational agreement within the company. In either case, the successful manager will be an effective negotiator. In this chapter our intention is to examine some of the aspects of this important skill. In so doing, we will draw upon our experiences in helping many thousands of managers involved in the management of materials, to develop their skills in this area. Our focus will be on the *skills* of negotiation rather than the legal/contractual implications.

Some common errors

On the basis that it is useful from a self-development viewpoint to be aware of our weaknesses, we start with a discussion on some of the common problems which we have observed. It is interesting to note, many of the problems have applied to very experienced negotiators as much as to newcomers. Indeed, apart from the fact that the younger less experienced negotiator tends to want to "rush his fences", most errors have been demonstrated by a wide spectrum of age and experience.

Without doubt the most common error is a failure to prepare well enough for the negotiation. This error falls into several categories. First of all, the manager concerned does not allow sufficient time to prepare for the negotiation. Yet, as with most aspects of management, effective preparation is a key to success. The error is compounded, quite frequently, through not using the time available properly. Then a third aspect involves the manager being distracted during the time which he has set aside for preparation. There are always "reasons" which the manager can put forward as to why he did not prepare well enough. Time pressure, day-to-day problems to resolve, unexpected interruptions and the like, are common among them. However, the potential benefits of sound preparation for important negotiations are such that the effective manager will see most of these "reasons" as "excuses". Quite apart from the immediate implications of sound preparation in the negotiation itself, there ought to be considerable benefits as regards future operations stemming from good agreements.

That statement leads us into the area of negotiating which has proved the source of many other difficulties. That is, ensuring that what has been agreed in the negotiation actually happens. In the materials area, common post-negotiation failures include: late deliveries, incomplete deliveries and quality failure. One important aspect of this problem is the fact that people who actually undertake the negotiating are frequently not those who have to perform to the agreement. And in one respect, the jobs of the progress clerks and inwards goods quality managers of a buying company, exist because our experience suggests that agreements are not kept.

There are two main causes of post-negotiation problems. The first of these stems from the assumption on behalf of either or both parties that what they have agreed will be enacted by their colleagues. The second is that the interpretation of the agreement by either or both parties may differ. Clearly, both these problems may be obviated by effective negotiations. However, the frequency of failure in this area suggests that it warrants far greater attention from negotiators than that frequently given.

The third problem area is the initial period of the negotiation itself. The problems involved here stem from a variety of causes. Among them are: a lack of awareness on the part of some negotiators as to the importance of establishing the "atmosphere" within which discussions are to take place; a lack of awareness that the objectives and strategies which have been developed for the negotiation, are based upon a mixture of assumptions and facts (thus before proceeding too far with the negotiation, at least the key assumptions ought to be tested); and, less than adequate attention being paid to the clarification of the issues which are to be resolved.

Salesmen spend a great deal of time during their training in dealing with, as they term it, "the opening". Yet many negotiators pay inadequate attention to this aspect of their task. More general faults we have observed include:

1   A tendency to treat negotiation as a debate, scoring points off the other party in the process. Yet, if the objective is to seek agreement (as it is in the majority of negotiations), then such behaviour may be counterproductive. A key objective is to try to seek agreement which will leave both parties reasonably satisfied. Exploring differences where they exist in a constructive, positive manner will be much more likely to assist in the achievement of such an objective than "nit picking".

2   Over-estimating the other party's skills, information, strengths and intelligence. This is a common human failing, for as Shakespeare reminds us "Our doubts are traitors and make us lose the good we oft might win by fearing to attempt". In

many negotiating situations we can achieve higher goals than we believe to be possible.

3 Not controlling our emotions. This type of fault becomes most apparent when the parties to the negotiation have adopted entrenched positions. Apart from the overt problems of, for example, uncontrolled anger, the resulting atmosphere frequently obstructs creativity.

4 A tendency to start discussing the *means* before the *ends* have been clarified. At least part of this type of problem stems from the assumptions which we carry with us into the negotiation.

5 A lack of control of the flow of the negotiation, with the result that issues are re-introduced and new-found agreements undermined. Most problems in this area stem from poor preparation, whilst the bulk of the others result from poor management of the negotiation itself.

6 Not recognising that there are several parties to the negotiation. These are the companies or departments involved and the people who are conducting the negotiation. Adequate attention should be paid to the needs of the latter as well as the former.

7 Assuming that the other party (or yourself for that matter) has the authority to reach an agreement on behalf of his company. It is not unknown for negotiators to use this as a ploy. However, in most cases where problems have arisen, it has stemmed from a genuine misconception of the level of authority vested in the negotiator.

8 Poor definition of objectives. Either the goals of the negotiators are vague or they are couched in imprecise words like "maximise" or "minimise".

9 A lack of skill in using questions. Information is the "currency of negotiation" and questions are a key means of obtaining such data. Thus, it is important to use questions skilfully. Common problems here include: using the wrong type of question; asking multiple questions; and not ensuring that questions are answered.

10 Not listening effectively. It has been pointed out that when we go to school we learn to read and write but no-one teaches us effective listening. Yet this skill is one of the key aspects of any form of human communication. In simulated and real life negotiations poor listening is a common fault, about which few people are aware.

At this point it would benefit the reader if he were to consider which of these faults applies to him. Then to add to the list any others which he feels are pertinent in his case. From the point of view of self-development he could, then, start a personal checklist which might be used with advantage when preparing for important negotiations.

Preparing

Having identified poor preparation as the most common fault in negotiating, it would be helpful to give some guidance as to how to prepare effectively. The first rule is to allow adequate time. A simple idea is to use a 3:1 ratio as a guide. If you expect the negotiation to last six hours, then use eighteen to prepare. If that sounds ludicrous, simply consider the amount of time spent subsequent to previous negotiations in which you have been involved, putting things right. Generally speaking, effective preparation will pay for itself many times over.

A second rule is to ensure that the conditions are right for preparation (e.g. no interruptions, information at hand). A third is that the preparation should be managed effectively. This involves using the time available to the best advantage. Also, with team negotiations, ensuring that there is a common understanding of objectives and strategies.

In general we can list six key items of the preparation agenda:

1   Obtain relevant data
2   Define the working assumptions
3   Clarify the issues around which the negotiation is to take place
4   Define the objectives of the negotiation
5   Consider the alternative routes available to achieve those objectives
6   Develop the strategies/tactics which are to be used to achieve the objectives

With many negotiations the assembly of the data should be an on-going process, for it will involve information on long standing relationships. With a well-established supplier, for example, it is useful to develop a dossier on his business performance. This can save considerable time in the data collection stage.

Defining the assumptions which have been made involves asking fundamental questions, such as:

Does he really want the business?
Are his costs inflating at the same level as ours?
Would he be prepared to lose the contract if we said "no" to his request?

Obviously we will have an opinion on each of the questions, but until we test our assumptions we should recognise that they are no more than that.

Clarifying the issues involved in the negotiation is really an extension of the previous point. For example, we might believe that the negotiation is about a price increase whereas that is a secondary issue. In this case the real issue which concerns the other party could be the security of the contract, or a change in specification.

The definition of objectives appears to be such an obvious requirement as to not warrant comment. Yet it is not uncommon for negotiators to be unclear as to their goals. And this problem is exacerbated where team negotiations are involved.

In setting objectives it is useful to have a guideline definition against which they may be measured. Perhaps the most straightforward way, though, is to ask the following questions of the agreed objective. Incidentally, the practice of specifying the objective can, in itself, be an extremely useful discipline in preparing for a negotiation:

Can it be achieved?
Can we measure whether we have achieved it?
Is it motivating?
Is it clear? (particularly in team negotiations)
Does it take into consideration short *and* long-term implications?

It should be noted, too, that consideration ought to be given under this heading as to what we believe to be the objectives of the other party.

The strategies or tactics which we select as the final stage should evolve having considerations of such issues as: our ability to handle the method; its desirability in relation to the end we wish to achieve; and the effect on the other party of applying the chosen method. In addition, as with objectives, we should consider what strategies the other party might utilise.

Assessing strengths and weaknesses

As we have pointed out earlier, it is a common failing to understate the strengths of one's position and to over-emphasise the weaknesses. The converse of that, of course, is that sometimes we are surprised at the strengths of the other party. Nevertheless we are probably more often guilty of the former than we are of the latter.

Some useful guidelines which we might apply in helping us to make a more realistic assessment, include:

Your strengths
Your weaknesses
The other party's strengths
The other party's weaknesses

Initially, at least, you will find that in many cases it is most difficult to list the other party's weaknesses. Yet it is probable that *they* will have a similar problem with you. Generally speaking, we should assume, until we can prove otherwise, that we are in a stronger position than we currently believe. Following this advice, a participant in a recent negotiation workshop re-evaluated his perception of the relevant positions of strength and achieved an effective saving of 15 per cent over and above his previous aspiration.

Whilst emphasising the necessity to understand comparative strengths and weaknesses, it is important to point out that we are not advocating "beating" the other side. Our intention ought to be to obtain an effective agreement and this usually means that both parties will be motivated to perform. Some writers talk about this as a win-win situation, rather than a win-lose. The truth is, of course, that in most negotiations one party will do at least slightly better than the other. A key point in this, of course, is that a negotiation is not about sharing a piece of cake within the bounds of some neat formula. Generally speaking, it is more analogous to dividing a fried egg fairly between two parties.

Needs

Earlier in this chapter we pointed out that there were several sets of "needs" present in a negotiation. There are the needs of the companies/departments involved and those of the individuals. In this section we will focus upon the latter, for in our experience, little time is given to considering these needs either in preparation or in the negotiation itself. Since all business negotiations take place between human beings, human needs are present in every transaction. Sometimes those needs will have a greater effect than they will on other occasions. However, they are always present and *always* need to be considered.

Generally speaking we may use Maslow's list of Needs as a basis for our consideration. Those which are worthy of our attention here include:

Physiological needs
Safety needs
Ego needs
Self actualisation needs
Knowledge needs

The importance of each of these needs may vary from negotiation to negotiation, but they are all present to some degree. If we are able to perceive the dominant needs in the other party, clearly it will assist our position if our approach takes cognisance of them. An important point to note here is that our approach to satisfying the needs of the other party can be either helpful of unhelpful to the achievement of our objectives. An example will suffice to illustrate the point.

When a salesman is attempting to displace an existing supplier for production materials, he is faced, frequently, with a concern on the part of the buyer. That concern centres around the fact that change involves risk. The buyer's concern will be that the new supplier may fail. If the current supplier is performing well and is well regarded by production, then it is *safer* not to make a change. Consequently, assuming that there is economic advantage in making the change, the salesman has to satisfy the buyer's "safety" need if he is to make a sale. If the salesman concentrates his efforts on selling the virtues of his product to the exclusion of satisfying this need, then he is more likely to fail.

Perhaps the most important thing to recognise in analysing needs in a negotiation is that, as in other aspects of life, our own needs tend to be paramount in our minds. In consequence, as we approach a negotiation, we should do so in the knowledge that we should spend some time in trying to understand what will motivate the other party. Then, within the scope of meeting our negotiating objectives, we should set out to satisfy those needs. After all, the converse approach would probably result in making it more difficult for us to achieve our goals.

One important factor in satisfying needs in the negotiation situation concerns the place where discussions will take place. Too often, little thought is given to this facet of negotiation which, apart from anything else, can contribute markedly to the "atmosphere" of the negotiation.

If the negotiation is concerned with obtaining agreement, it makes sense to set out the room in a manner designed to assist that agreement. Comfortable chairs, good lighting and well thought out room arrangement can all assist. Why, for example, have the parties sitting on either side of a rectangular table? The implication of such an arrangement is that the parties are in conflict. Even where this is true, if agreement is sought, it makes little sense to emphasise that fact. Other factors which will assist, too, are coffee and tea being served at an appropriate time, a planned meal break and facilities for the other party/team to have another room to work in if they so wish. While some of these may be regarded as simple politeness, it is not difficult to adversely affect the atmosphere if they are handled badly.

Listening

As we pointed out earlier, a common failing of negotiators is that they do not listen effectively. Yet this important communication skill can be a vital factor in the success or failure in the negotiating situation.

Listening is probably the most under-rated skill in negotiating. Human beings typically "filter-out" communication during their everyday life. But in negotiation it is important that we *keep tuned in,* for many problems can arise from not hearing, or mishearing statements made by the other party.

Among the rules for listening which we should apply are those put forward by John Casson. He suggests that we should:

1 Stop talking
2 Stop the mental chat
3 Stop answering back
4 Let him finish and hear him out
5 Try to understand the speaker, not "beat" him
6 Not only listen but be seen to be listening
7 Keep down prejudices
8 Listen with patience
To this list we might add
9 Delay reactions
10 Try to distinguish between fact, inferences, assumptions and judgements.

Even casual observation of listening practices will illustrate many faults which stem from not taking one or more of these guidelines into consideration. But if a manager wishes to be an effective negotiator, then he should seek to develop his listening ability.

There is little doubt that fatigue affects listening ability. Consequently, it is important to ensure that the negotiator is as fresh as possible to commence the discussions. Further, that proper breaks are planned so as to ensure that in a long negotiation the constant pressure of listening and concentrating is alleviated periodically.

Another useful rule relating to this topic is not only to listen to what the other party is saying, but also to what he is *not* saying. The avoidance of issues can sometimes indicate a weakness in the partner's position.

Finally, it is worth emphasising that you should be *seen* to be listening. It is surprising how much difference obvious interest makes in encouraging people to talk. Those who have perceived bored indifference in their listeners will understand the converse effect.

Non-verbal signals

The idea that we can stimulate or discourage speakers by the way in which our bodies react leads us into our penultimate topic. It is a fact that we "speak" with our bodies as well as with words. In negotiations, for example, it has been shown that when there is an impasse, the parties tend to be either sitting upright or leaning away from each other. When there is agreement, or things are moving towards agreement, they tend to be leaning towards each other.

In the negotiation, the face may register, for example, surprise, concern, doubt or anger. And these are all expressions which life teaches us to recognise. However, the skilled negotiator will perceive these signals before they become obvious. He will be using his eyes and ears to gather information which will help him understand how the other party feels. We might describe this as being sensitive.

These signals are not only to do with the way in which the other person uses or places his body. They are also received and interpreted (knowingly or unknowingly) in respect of things such as:

1   The way in which a person dresses. For example, the same person dressed in a business suit, then in scruffy gardening clothes, will be perceived differently in each guise.
2   The type of voice. A high or low pitched voice may affect our perceptions, as will the accent of the speaker.
3   The other party's posture will suggest something about him to us. Rightly or wrongly we will have a different view of a person who slumps in a chair from one who sits upright.
4   The tone of voice used by the other party will also suggest to us something about his feelings. For example, when people are excited or angry, they usually speak in a higher-pitched voice.
5   Related factors are the rate, volume and rapidity of speech. Once again these change with emotions.
6   The direction and stability of the other party's gaze. Once again we draw inferences from this signal.
7   The gestures which the other person makes may also suggest something to us.

A vital factor to understand about all non-verbal signals is that until they are validated, our reading of them should be regarded as assumptions. Nonetheless, it is a useful rule when the body is "saying" something different from the words, to take note of the former first.

Team negotiations

The foregoing discussion has highlighted some of the facets which relate to the skills of negotiating. They apply whether the negotiation is to be undertaken by a pair of individuals, each acting for his own company, or by teams of negotiators. However, there are additional factors which ought to be taken into consideration when teams are involved.

The first thing to emphasise is that team negotiations are more complex than when individuals are involved. Apart from anything else it is necessary to ensure that the members of the negotiating team will work in conjunction with one another. Usually team negotiations involve a functional mix. For example, a team of three might include a buyer, a technical man and a lawyer. And there is a real danger that, unless the team is effectively coordinated, each will be concerned with his own specialism. It is not unknown for the tactics of one team to seek to "divide and conquer" in such a situation.

Consequently, it is important that the preparation includes agreement on the objectives of the negotiation and the manner in which they are to be achieved. It ought to be recognised, too, that team preparations will take longer than in the case of an individual. Thus adequate time should be allowed for the work.

Some guidelines which will be helpful in this preparation include:

1   The number of people in the team should be kept to the minimum. In many negotiations teams of two are adequate. While three may be necessary in some cases, the need for larger groups should be questioned. The principle here is that the more people there are, the more difficult it is to manage them.

2   A related point is that each member of the team should have a specified function. One should, always, be the leader of the team and one should act as secretary/note-taker. In technical/commercial negotiations the roles to be played by the individuals need to be defined and be clearly understood. One useful role which should be considered, where appropriate, is that of "observer". This can be extremely helpful in developing negotiation. However, when this approach is used, the observer needs to be well briefed as to his role.

3   The seating arrangement for the negotiation need to be part of the team's consideration. Many teams involved in negotiations tend to sit along one side of a rectangular table. This does not facilitate communication. Thus, it is our belief that the leader should aim to have his team sitting in an arc to assist visual contact. Team members should support each other at all times. In all team negotiations the role of the leader is vital to success. His tasks include:

Selecting the team
Organising the preparation
Managing the negotiation (e.g. timing, planned breaks)
Arranging for the agreement record to be prepared
Issuing the report which will result in action
Monitoring the implementation of the agreement to ensure satisfaction

In our experience there has been no hard-and-fast rule as to who should lead. Clearly, it ought to be the best man for the job. However we would venture an opinion that, everything else being equal, a commercial man will usually have an edge on a technical man.

Summary

Our observations of negotiations and negotiators over the last fifteen years suggests to us that a profile of an effective negotiator might read: He or she

Will plan well
Can deal with pressure (time, economic, psychological)
Will be an effective listener
Is skilled at asking questions
Understands people well
Observes well
Can handle confrontation
Will have sound business judgement
Will avoid excesses (alcohol, food and lack of sleep)
Will be a creative thinker
Will be committed to his/her cause once it is established
Will be skilled in dealing with risk
Will review and learn from major negotiations in order to continue to develop his art

Chapter 14

Quality assurance

by *R Wagstaff*

What is quality?

The word "quality" is commonly considered as implying high quality. A dictionary definition includes statements such as "degree of excellence; possessing high degree of excellence; concerned with maintenance of high quality (quality control)". Such implications can be misleading when applied to industrial situations. Excellence is expensive: the quality of bought-in items or manufactured products must therefore be controlled to ensure that they meet the user's requirements, and continue to do so for a given period of time, while avoiding excessive costs due to unnecessarily high quality.

The British Standards Institution defines quality more precisely as:

"The totality of features and characteristics of a product or service that bear on its ability to satisfy a given need".[1]

Reliability is an extension of quality, i.e. the ability of an item to perform a required function under stated conditions for a stated period of time. Reliability can be expressed as the probability that a product will operate satisfactorily for the stated period of time.

In the case of both quality and reliability the first need is to specify precisely the characteristics required, then to ensure that the materials and manufacturing processes used result in products which conform to the specification. Thus two distinct attributes of quality are evident:

1 Quality of design: the quality defined by the specification and a measure of the extent to which this meets the needs of the user
2 Quality of conformance (quality of manufacture): the extent to which a manufactured product conforms to the stated specifications

Quality assurance, i.e. all the activities concerned with the attainment of the required quality, thus encompasses all of the following:

1   A satisfactory design of product, thoroughly proven by testing to establish its reliability under service conditions
2   Specification of requirements, which must be understood by everyone concerned with manufacturing the product
3   Confirmation that outside suppliers and in-company manufacturing processes are capable of meeting the specified requirements
4   Motivation of all those concerned with manufacture of the product, inside and outside the company, to achieve the standards set by the specification
5   Verification that products conform to specification
6   Accurate and reliable means of inspecting or testing
7   Feedback of inspection results and user experience to prove that all the above stages are effective

The costs of quality

The objective of any quality control system must be to achieve the required level of quality at the lowest overall cost. The quality level desired should be chosen in the light of customer quality demands (and hence selling prices) and the costs associated with producing to various levels of quality (see Figure 14:1)

Only when the quality policy of a company has been defined can appropriate systems of quality assurance be adopted. Although difficult to quantify, it is evident that inadequate control of quality will lead to defective items which may be scrapped, reworked at additional cost, sold at lower prices as "seconds", or sold, (knowingly or unknowingly) as good items, which may lead to loss of customer goodwill. Other costs associated with inadequate *control* of quality are additional inspection, selective assembly, possibly the use of manual manufacturing methods instead of intended automated manufacture, disruption of manufacturing schedules due to required materials or components being rejected, and servicing of customer complaints. The lower the level of quality control in manufacturing, the greater is the likelihood of such additional costs, as shown in Figure 14:2.

On the other hand, quality control activities are themselves expensive. As manufacturing tolerances are tightened, production processes and equipment must be improved to allow greater precision to be achieved. Production rates are usually slower, and additional inspection using more sophisticated techniques may be necessary. The proportion of items rejected because they do not conform to specifications may also increase. In the case of bought-in materials and components, insistence on higher quality usually increases purchase costs and may reduce the number of potential suppliers able to meet requirements.

Figure 14:2 indicates the relationship between the costs of quality control and the costs of inadequate control. A company must select the level of quality control which allows it to achieve its quality objectives at the lowest total cost.

It is estimated that the total costs of quality in industry arising from prevention, appraisal (which includes inspection and testing services) and failure (which includes scrap, rework, replacement and repair under warranty, and handling customers'

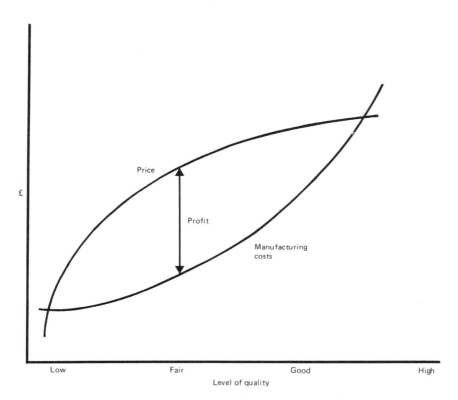

FIGURE 14:1   EFFECT OF DIFFERENT LEVELS OF QUALITY ON
MANUFACTURING COSTS AND SELLING PRICES

complaints) lie in the range of 4 per cent – 15 per cent of turnover, with an average of around 10 per cent. Based on the 1976 Census of Production figure of sales by UK manufacturers, quality costs in the UK could be of the order of £10,000 million per year.[2]

Specifications

A specification is a detailed description of the requirements to which products must conform. These requirements may include the chemical composition of the material to be used, its physical properties (strength, ductility, porosity, particle size, viscosity, electrical or thermal conductivity), dimensions of the product, its weight, colour, surface finish, etc. In each case it is necessary to specify the tolerance on each desired characteristic, i.e. the range of values over which a property may vary without causing the product to become unacceptable.

It is at this stage that the design, quality engineering, procurement and production staff can realise significant cost savings. Too wide tolerances can lead to problems in subsequent manufacture or use, as when a number of components must be assembled

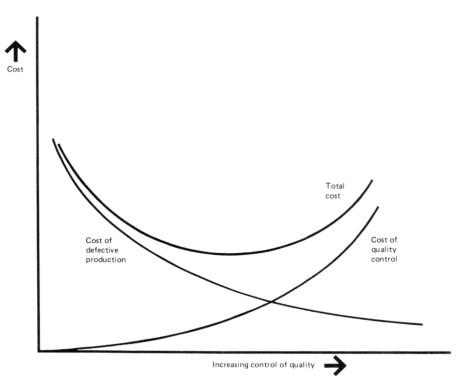

FIGURE 14:2   RELATIONSHIP BETWEEN COST OF QUALITY CONTROL AND
COST OF DEFECTIVE PRODUCTION

together. Typical examples of such problems include furniture manufacture where out-of-square components give poor joints and an unsatisfactory appearance; clothing manufacture where excessive cutting tolerances can lead to badly sewn seams which may pull apart in use, or to garments which vary too much from the stated size. In mechanical engineering inadequate clearance between moving parts can lead to seizure, but excessive clearances may prevent effective operation or allow loss of lubricants and hence premature failure.

On the other hand, excessively stringent tolerances lead to other increased costs. For most items previous experience will indicate the appropriate quality level to adopt but in the case of new designs and materials, testing of a product under actual or simulated service conditions may be necessary in order to establish suitable specifications.

Most of the desired properties of an item can be expressed in figures, e.g.

length 295 – 299 mm
weight 113.40g ± 2.83g

These are termed *variables* (Note that the method used to illustrate length involves specifying only the upper and lower limits. This format is preferred because it avoids the arithmetic needed to add and substract tolerances from a nominal figure, which could lead to mistakes.)

Attributes are properties which are not defined in figures, such as:

"all bar ends to be painted green"
"all edges to be free from burrs"
"all items to be stamped with part number"

In all such cases an item can only be classed as acceptable or unacceptable. Attributes are generally less satisfactory as standards because they can be more difficult to interpret. A statement that "timber is to be straight and free from cracks" does not define precisely acceptable limits. However, there are inevitably situations where certain desired properties cannot readily be reduced to figures, such as taste or smell in the food and toiletries industries. Colours are often checked by an experienced person comparing items with a previously agreed standard sample, or with two samples showing light and dark limits.

A standard commodity specification for tomato paste (see Figure 14:3), a widely used constituent of many foodstuffs, illustrates the use of both quantitative and qualitative requirements, and statements of the ways in which certain of these properties are to be measured.

When widely recognised standards exist for a product they should be adopted if at all possible. The starting point when establishing a specification for a product not previously bought or manufactured should be a review of current international, national or industry standards. The ISO Catalogue, British Standards Yearbook or appropriate industry associations should be consulted. A company standard should be developed only if no appropriate, more widely used standard exists.

Quality control of incoming raw materials and components

It is a basic principle of quality control that non-conforming items are identified as early as possible. Any work carried out on materials which are unacceptable is simply wasted money; it is not normally possible to recover from suppliers the costs of any work done on such materials.

Most companies operate some system of goods-inward inspection, although reliance on such a system alone is unwise. Incoming goods must be held in quarantine until all inspection has been carried out. Even for relatively simple chemical analysis this may take two or three days from receipt of the material to reporting of the results to production control and the user department. In the case of more specialised tests such as wear tests on textiles, creep or corrosion tests on metals, considerably longer quarantine periods may be necessary. This extends the real lead time for the material, and increases the buying company's stock levels. Holding material in separate quarantine or inspection areas may also involve double handling, but failure to do so allows the risk of material which has not yet passed inspection being used by mistake.

STANDARD COMMODITY SPECIFICATION	No. 0114

TITLE:
 	
    TOMATO PASTE (HOT BREAK)
 	
COMMODITY CODE: 0114
	Date Issued
	    1.4.81
	replaces —

DETAILS

1 GENERAL REQUIREMENTS

Tomato Paste shall be the product resulting from the concentration of the liquid obtained from clean, sound, well ripened tomatoes of red varieties. Free from skin, seed particles, black specks, foreign material, added salt or colouring and harmful contaminants.

2 ORGANOLEPTIC REQUIREMENTS

2.1 *Flavour and Aroma*
Free from scorched, bitter, green tomato flavours or other objectionable flavours or objectionable odours of any kind.

2.2 *Colour*
Gardner Colour difference meter targets at $12\frac{1}{2}\%$ total solids by refractometer: L 25 ± 1, a $25+$, b $+$ less than $\frac{1}{2}$a.

3 ANALYTICAL REQUIREMENTS (on sample(s) as designated by an approved random sampling method)

3.1 *Consistency*
Consistency below 10.0 cms measured by Bostwick consistometer at $12\frac{1}{2}\%$ total solids by refractometer 25°C for 10 secs.

3.2 *Copper (as Cu)*
Not more than 50 p.p.m. calculated on dry residue.

3.3 *Lead (as Pb)*
Not more than 5 p.p.m. on the concentrate.

4 MICROBIOLOGICAL REQUIREMENTS

4.1 *Mould Count*
Not exceeding 50% positive fields as determined by the Howard Mould Count Method.

4.2 *Insect fragments*
Free from insect eggs, hairs or fragments.

5 MANUFACTURING AND PACKAGING REQUIREMENTS

5.1 *Screen Size*
The tomato paste shall be processed using 0.60 m.m. finishing screens.

5.2 *Cans*
In accordance with can specification attached.

5.3 *Filled weights*
5.1 kg Gross for Net.

5.4 *Cases*
In accordance with case specification attached.

FIGURE 14:3   COMMODITY SPECIFICATION FOR TOMATO PASTE

Any material rejected after delivery increases transport costs unnecessarily. For these and other reasons many manufacturing companies are placing greater reliance on supplier quality assurance (q.v.). Inspection of incoming goods from approved suppliers can then be reduced to a minimum, which may be little more than a check on documentation and quantities, and possibly a visual check for damage in transit.

Incoming goods inspection will still be necessary for supplies which are bought from non-approved suppliers, at home or abroad, where the cost of a supplier quality assurance approval survey may not be justified. Where incoming goods inspection is necessary it must at least ensure the following:

1 Identification of inspected material to distinguish it from that awaiting inspection
2 The use of suitable sampling and test procedures
3 Control of inspection, measuring and test equipment
4 Segregation of non-conforming material
5 Maintenance of inspection records which can be related to other documentation (purchase orders, works orders/batch cards, customers' orders)

Control of quality in manufacturing

Every manufacturing process suffers from variability. The task of quality control in manufacturing is to ensure that the variations in the properties of a manufactured product are contained within the specified tolerances. The success, or otherwise, of this control determines the conformance quality of the items produced. The emphasis will vary depending on the type of production, but in most cases the following elements will be involved:

Specification of requirements: accurate, adequate and up-to-date
Control of incoming raw material, as outlined above
Control of tooling
Control of manufacturing processes
Calibration of instrumentation and measuring equipment
Inspection

JOBBING PRODUCTION

Production runs are short, work is usually only to customer's order, and often customer's specification. It is difficult to establish standard inspection programmes in such work, and common practice is for skilled operators to be responsible for setting equipment, making or assembling the product, and inspecting it, possibly with additional patrol inspection or technical support facilities. In such circumstances the quality assurance programme would emphasise:

Drawing and change control: work instructions to operators must refer to current drawings and manufacturing instructions. Obsolete versions must be withdrawn
Observance of manufacturing and inspection instructions
Maintenance of records of manufacturing and inspection data for each job

4   Checking that measuring and inspection equipment is calibrated. While this is essential in any type of manufacturing, it can more easily be overlooked if each operator retains instruments such as micrometers or gauges for his own use.

BATCH PRODUCTION

Three main forms of inspection are available:

1   Inspection of all items produced in a batch (i.e. 100% inspection)
2   Inspection of a sample of items from a completed batch
3   First-off inspection at the start of a batch, followed by periodic sampling during manufacture

Hundred per cent inspection is time consuming and is normally used only for small batches. Sample inspection after manufacture would be used where an entire batch is processed together but where it is unnecessary or impractical to inspect every item. e.g. heat treatment of metal items, firing of pottery.

Most batch production involves setting a machine, then processing a quantity of items individually before re-setting for a subsequent batch of different products. In such cases it is normal to carry out first-off inspection to verify that tooling, setting, operating methods and material are in accordance with specification. Where a machine is set by a skilled setter, but subsequently operated by another person, the first-off samples should be those produced by the production operator, to ensure that the operator is using the correct method. Typical problems which might arise are failure to coat a pattern or die with a mould release agent, or failure to apply lubricant correctly in presswork operations.

Once initial samples have been approved, further samples should be taken throughout production of the batch. The frequency of sampling should take account of production rate, the quality levels required, the variability of the production process, and the need for periodic re-setting. Control charting (q.v.) could be an appropriate aid for periodic inspection.

PROCESS PRODUCTION

In continuous process production the emphasis lies on process control, with inspection at intermediate and final stages to verify that controls are operating satisfactorily. Continuous in-process measuring of sizes, temperatures, etc. can be linked to process controls. A typical example would be the rolling of continuous steel strip or rod, where measurements of gauge and temperature at one stage can be used to adjust automatically the settings of rolls (roll gap, speed) at earlier stages (feed-back control) or subsequent stages (feed-forward control) to compensate for variations in the product.

Statistical quality control: control charts

All manufacturing processes suffer from variability, and all products will exhibit variations in their measured properties. Even two items with apparently identical dimensions will be found to differ if measured with sufficient accuracy. The use of statistical techniques to recognise and hence control such variability is an essential element of every quality assurance programme, two common applications being control charts and acceptance sampling. A thorough grounding in statistical theory is not generally necessary. Both techniques can be adopted by reference to standard procedures.

The theory underlying the use of the control chart originated by Dr W A Shewhart is that the variations in the quality of manufactured products can be divided into two categories, random variations and variations due to assignable causes. Random variations are those resulting from a large number of chance variations, each too small to isolate, but which together lead to the expected variability in final quality. If this expected pattern changes, it is inferred that some additional, or assignable, factor has caused this change.

The method relies on inspecting small samples (typically 4 or 5), measuring the property under investigation, and using the results obtained from this small sample to deduce the properties of the parent population from which the sample was drawn. The charts are constructed to give three signals which can be considered as a set of traffic lights:

> green = safe to proceed
> amber = warning, re-check process
> red = action, stop process

Let us consider the production of an engineering component having a specified diameter of 9.78 to 10.00mm. Suppose the manufacturing process is set to produce pieces with a diameter of 9.90mm, and that the inevitable random variations lead to the items having a standard deviation of 0.03mm as shown in Figure 14.4.

If a single item was inspected it might be found to have a diameter of 10.00mm (i.e. at the upper limit of tolerance) and one might therefore deduce that the process needed adjustment. There is, however, a chance of about 1 in 2000 of the process producing this size even when it is correctly set at 9.90mm.

Other problems which may arise when using single items as the basis for control are that the distribution of the parent population may neither be normal nor may it follow any standard distribution; it is difficult to detect changes in the process average from individual measurements unless the change is large; and there is no indication whether a change is in the mean or the standard deviation, or both.

If, on the other hand, a sample of 4 is taken, it is extremely unlikely that all four pieces will lie towards one extremity of the distribution as long as the process is operating normally.

The use of a small sample instead of individual results overcomes other problems.

1 It is immaterial whether the parent population is normally distributed or not, since the sampling distribution of the means will be sufficiently close to normal for all practical purposes
2 The number of sample means which fall more than a specified distance away from

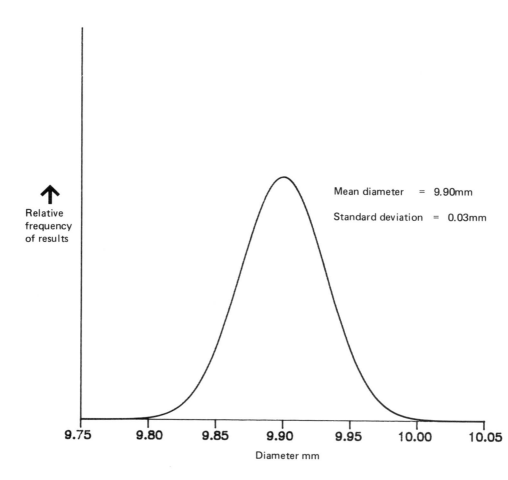

FIGURE 14:4   DISTRIBUTION OF DIAMETERS

the overall mean will indicate the degree of control in the process
3   The ability to detect changes in the process average is greatly increased
4   Samples allow detection of changes in process variability as well as process average

Suppose four such pieces have diameters of 10.00mm, 9.88mm, 9.95mm, 9.89mm, giving an average of 9.93mm (although the machine may still be correctly set at 9.90mm). There is no apparent need to adjust the process, but we must decide how far the average diameter of our sample can be allowed to vary before adjustment becomes necessary.

Knowledge of the properties of the normal distribution shows that the standard deviation of the sampling distribution of the mean σ_m is related to the standard deviation of the parent population σ as

$$\sigma_m = \sigma/\sqrt{n}$$

where n = sample size. With samples of 4, the distribution of the means will have a mean of 9.90mm with a standard deviation of 0.015mm as long as the process continues unchanged. Detection of changes from this pattern provides the basis for the control chart.

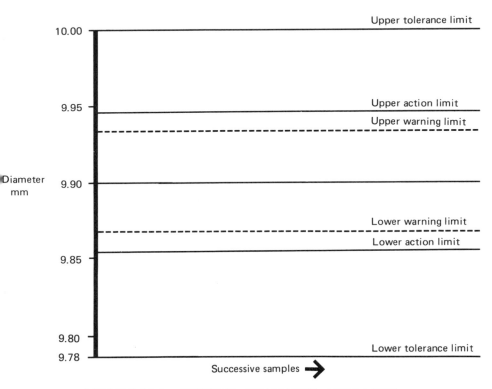

FIGURE 14:5   CONTROL CHART FOR AVERAGES

Figure 14.5 shows the principle of the control chart. The change of the mean diameter of a sample of 4 items falling above 9.945mm, (or below 9.855mm) is only about 1 in 1000. When it does happen, it is most likely that the process has changed, and that individual items may therefore be larger than 9.99mm (or smaller than 9.81mm). The process should therefore be stopped, the reason for the change investigated, and corrective action taken.

The chance of the sample mean lying above 9.93mm (or below 9.87mm) is about 1 in 40, i.e. it would be expected to occur once in every 40 samples. When it does happen, however, there are grounds for suspicion and the usual procedure is to take another sample immediately before deciding whether adjustment is necessary.

The sample means can be plotted on the chart using time or number produced on the horizontal axis, which will highlight any drift in the manufacturing process, as often occurs due to tool wear. As illustrated in this example, the control chart limits do not need to be set symmetrically within the tolerance. They may be moved towards one extremity (in this case towards a nominal diameter of 10mm), but this of course reduces the effective tolerance available to the producer.

This example also illustrates the importance of the relationship between process variability and the specified tolerance. If the production equipment is set to give a mean product diameter of 9.90mm, the variability quoted ($\sigma = 0.03$mm) would result in 5 items in 10 000 having a diameter greater than the upper tolerance of 10.00mm. If the mean diameter shifts to 9.95mm, as illustrated in Figure 14.6, we

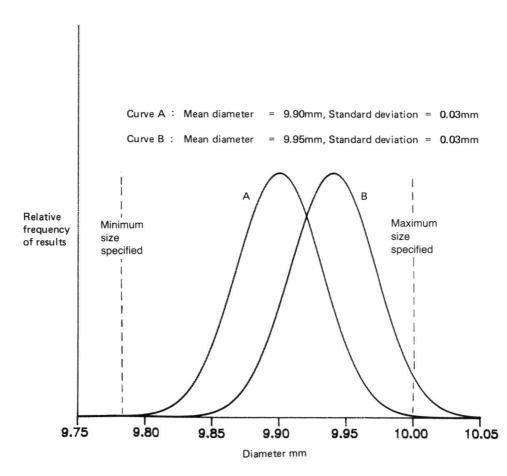

FIGURE 14:6   SHIFT IN THE DISTRIBUTION OF DIAMETERS

would expect 4.85 per cent of the output to exceed the upper tolerance, i.e. nearly 5 per cent of the items would be defective.

A production process with less variability is illustrated in Figure 14.7, where the standard deviation on diameter is 0.02mm. In this case when the process is set to give a mean diameter of 9.90mm we would not expect any items to be produced outside the tolerance limits; (if they are, we should immediately look for an assignable cause). Furthermore, even if the process drifts so that the average diameter increases to 9.95mm, we would still only expect about 6 items in 1000 to fall outside the upper specification limit.

This simple example illustrates the importance of determining process variability, and comparing it with the required product tolerances. From a buyer's point of view the converse should be considered: given the specification for an item, what normal degree of process variability must a supplier achieve if he is to be regarded as being capable of producing consistently acceptable output?

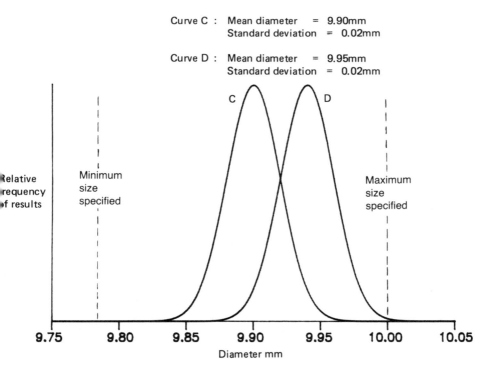

FIGURE 14:7   DISTRIBUTION OF DIAMETERS WITH LESS VARIABILITY

Detection of changes in variability

It is possible for the process mean to remain the same (i.e. 9.90mm) but for the variability to increase. The sample means would lie outside the warning and action limits more often, and action could be taken to adjust the process (both up and down) more frequently, but the process would still not be under control.

Another form of chart, the range chart, is necessary to control this aspect. To construct a range chart, the normal range between the largest and smallest measurement in each small sample (4 in the above case) is found for about 20 samples taken when the process is operating normally. Range limits are set by multiplying the average range from the initial 20 samples by a factor which depends on sample size. For the case illustrated, warning and action limits could be set as shown in Figure 14:8.

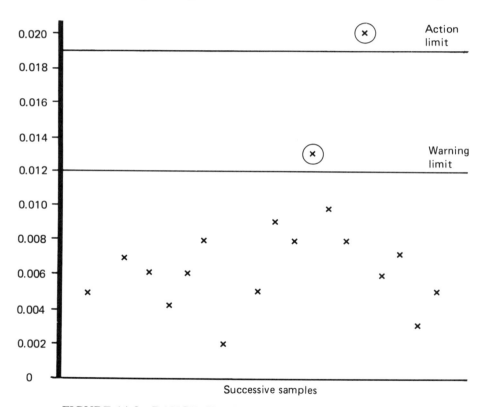

FIGURE 14:8   RANGE CHART FOR SAMPLES OF FOUR ITEMS

Control charts can be constructed for attributes, where the decision to accept or reject a batch depends on either the number of defective items in a sample, or on the total number of defects in an article. The basic principles of construction are similar to charts for quantitative data, but the method is less sensitive.

Acceptance sampling

Inspection is an expensive activity. Products where defects are not critical need not be subject to a hundred per per cent inspection. To allow a few defective items to get through is not a serious matter. In a box of 100 cheap ball-point pens it is not critical if two or three do not write properly, but the proportion which are defective should not be allowed to rise significantly.

In industries where the product is a vital one, where lives may depend upon its quality, or where the costs of failure would be abnormally high, every effort must be made to ensure that every item is satisfactory. There is no substitute for 100 per cent inspection; in fact 100 per cent inspection may be necessary at various stages of manufacture, and at final assembly.

Even 100 per cent inspection is not necessarily absolutely reliable. An interesting paper by Peter Cavanagh and Alec Rodger reports results of 100 per cent visual inspection of glass jars. Jars, from three different suppliers, were divided into three grades based on initial inspection results. Each jar was then inspected by each of four inspectors on 30 separate occasions, making 120 inspections for every jar. The research showed significant variations in the results of the inspections. The authors add:

> "You may be interested to learn, in passing, that not a single one of the 648 survived without at least one rejection. For a time it looked as if one jar would escape condemnation. After going through 60 of its 120 inspections its reputation was still intact, even if the jar itself was not unblemished. When the investigators got out this apparently perfect jar to have a good look at it, they found a surface flaw an inch long on its side. Reference to the log book in which marked particularities of jars had been noted confirmed that it had been there from the outset.[3]

Some experiments have indicated that if inspectors are faced with batches for 100 per cent inspection, then the inspection tends to be less reliable than if sample methods are used.

Other obvious applications of sample inspections are when inspection is costly or time consuming, or when destructive testing must be used.

If it is recognised that some proportion of a batch of products is likely to be below the specified quality, but a certain proportion of such defective items in a batch can be tolerated, it is possible to apply sampling plans which give reasonably reliable results at minimum cost.

All too frequently sampling inspection is used without adequate consideration of the appropriate sample size. Instructions such as "inspect ten per cent" are given, but testing one sample from a batch of ten tells one nothing about the other nine. Testing ten per cent of a batch of 50 000 would be quite unnecessary; a reasonable sample from which sufficiently reliable results could be obtained would be 500 items, i.e. one per cent of the batch.

Statistical sampling plans must be tailored to each particular inspection situation.

Once a sampling plan has been chosen, it gives an inspector a simple set of instructions for inspecting each batch of items. In essence the sampling inspection tables say:

> For a batch of size N take a random sample of size n.
> Inspect all items in the sample.
> If the number of defective items is less than or equal to the acceptance number c, accept the entire batch.
> If the number of defective items is more than c, reject the entire batch.

For any given set of conditions a small, *known* risk is taken of making a wrong decision on the evidence from the sample.

The sampling plan depends on four factors:

1 *The batch size* A batch is a definite quantity of items which have been produced under conditions which are presumed to be uniform. If one type of item has been produced on two alternate machines, it would be normal for the manufacturer to keep separate the output from each machine, and to draw a sample from each batch. In this way the output of each machine is checked, and should quality decline the cause may be attributed more easily. When using sampling inspection for incoming goods, each consignment from a supplier would normally be regarded as a separate batch. The assumption is made that items sent in one consignment are more likely to be alike than are items in different consignments.

2 *The acceptable quality level (AQL)* The AQL is the level of quality (i.e. the percentage of defects) which is only just acceptable as a process average. For example, if an AQL of 1.0% is set, we should be prepared to accept up to this percentage of defective items without question. The fact that an AQL is stated should not be construed as meaning that a manufacturer has the right knowingly to supply defective products. It is always better to have no defective items than any specified proportion.

3 *Inspection level* The inspection level defines the relationship between batch size and sample size. Normal inspection is used unless otherwise specified. This seeks to balance inspection effort and reliability. If greater reliability is required, e.g. if there is reason to suspect that the process average has deteriorated, tighter inspection may be called for and larger samples would then be taken. Conversely, if the inspection effort can be lessened, reduced inspection and hence smaller samples may be appropriate. Special sampling plans are available for situations where very small samples must be used, e.g. when inspection is extremely expensive or where destructive testing must be used, and where low reliability of sampling inspection can or must be tolerated.

4 *Whether single, double or multiple sampling is to be used* Single sampling plans, which are the simplest to operate, accept or condemn a batch on the evidence of a single sample taken from the batch. The inspection effort may be reduced without loss of reliability by adopting double or multiple sampling. A smaller initial sample is taken, followed by a second if, and only if, the result of the first is inconclusive. For example:

"Take a sample of 32 items. If there are no defectives accept the batch. If there are 2 or more defectives reject it. If there is one defective only, take a further sample of 32 items. If the second sample contains no defectives or only one defective, accept the batch. If it contains two or more, reject the batch".

Using this plan, the decision would in most cases, be made on the evidence from a sample of 32 items; only occasionally would two samples be taken. If single sampling were used under the same conditions a sample of 50 items would be taken from every batch.

The risks involved in acceptance sampling

While the use of acceptance sampling is straightforward, the selection of an appropriate sampling plan for any given situation requires an understanding of the risks which are being taken. Suppose that we are concerned with inspecting large batches of items, which can be classified as good or bad. A simple example might be checking electric light bulbs to ensure that they work. A manufacturer, major user or distributor of such items may wish to verify that quality control in production was effective and that there had not been excessive damage in transit. It would be unrealistic to insist that every bulb works; an acceptable quality level of 2.5 per cent might be agreed between supplier and purchaser. We would thus be prepared to accept batches with one or less defective bulbs in 40. A simple inspection plan might therefore seem to be to take a sample of $n=40$ and inspect them, i.e. test to see if they light. If one or no bulbs are defective, accept the batch; if two or more, reject the batch. The maximum number of defective items permitted in the sample is called the acceptance number c; in this $c = 1$.

However, it is of course not certain that a random sample of 40 bulbs out of a large batch would contain two or more defectives even if the batch itself contained significantly more than 2.5 per cent. The probability that any given number of defectives will occur in a sample from a large batch may be calculated from the binomial distribution. If a batch contained no defective items (and assuming that inspection itself is faultless) clearly our sample of 40 would be accepted correctly. We can say that the probability of no defectives (P_0) is 1.0000.

Another batch may in fact contain 5 per cent of defective bulbs, although we do not know this. The probability of taking a sample of 40 which contains no defectives may be calculated as $p_0 = 0.95^{40}$, i.e. 0.1285.

Similarly, the chance of a sample of 40 containing only one defective may be calculated as

$$p_1 = 40. (0.95)^{39} (0.05)^1, \text{ i.e. } 0.2706.$$

The chance of our sample containing either no defectives or one defective is therefore $0.1285 + 0.2706 = 0.3991$. We can see that the sampling plan proposed ($n=40$, $c=1$) will give a result which leads to the batch being accepted on about 40 per cent of the occasions even when the actual percentage of defective bulbs is 5 per cent, i.e. twice the acceptable quality level.

The calculation may be repeated for various values of the percentage defective in the batch as shown below:-

% defective in batch	Chance of sample of 40 containing 0 or 1 defectives
0	1.0000
0.5	0.9828
1.0	0.9393
1.5	0.8874
2.0	0.8095
2.5	0.7358
3.0	0.6615
5.0	0.3991
7.5	0.1877
10.0	0.0665
15.0	0.0121

Plotting these results gives what is known as the operating characteristic, or OC curve, of the specified sampling plan as shown in Figure 14:9. Note that the OC gives the probability of accepting a batch with any given percentage of defective items on the evidence of a sample of 40 and an acceptance number of 1 (or less) defectives.

Now the risks involved in operating this particular sampling plan can be appreciated. Although we have agreed that up to $2\frac{1}{2}$ per cent of defective bulbs is acceptable there are 4 chances in 10 that a batch containing 5 per cent of defective bulbs will be accepted, nearly 2 chances in 10 (p = 0.1877) of accepting a batch with $7\frac{1}{2}$ per cent of defectives, and even a slight chance (p = 0.0121) of accepting an exceptionally bad batch containing 15 per cent of defective bulbs.

On the other hand there are about 2 chances in 10 (p = 1-0.8095 = 0.1905) of rejecting a batch containing only 2 per cent of defective bulbs, i.e. a level of defectives which is less than the maximum we have agreed to accept. We may therefore decide that the risks of making an incorrect decision on the evidence from this sampling plan (n=40, c=1) are too great. Compare this scheme with two others n = 80, c = 2; and n = 200, c = 5 as shown in Figure 14:10.

Comparing these three OC curves we see that the larger the sample, the more discriminating is the sampling scheme, but even a large sample (n=200) involves risks of making incorrect decisions. A more discriminating scheme is not inherently a "better" one. It is more reliable, but involves inspecting larger samples and hence is more expensive. It is, therefore, more appropriate in some circumstance and less appropriate in others.

In deriving these illustrative OC curves it has been assumed that the probability of defective items being present in the sample remained unchanged throughout, i.e remained as the proportion defective in the batch. Where finite batches are involved there are, of course, only a limited number of defective items in the batch and the probability of drawing a defective item varies from trial to trial. For example, if one has a very large number of packs of cards, the chance of drawing an ace is 1 in 13.

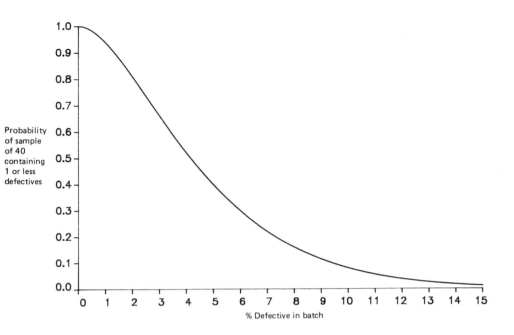

FIGURE 14:9   OPERATING CHARACTERISTIC (OC) CURVE FOR THE
SAMPLING PLAN $n = 40, c = 1$

Even if one has already drawn three cards at random, and all were aces, the probability of drawing another is still 1 in 13. However, if one draws three aces from a single pack of cards, the probability of drawing a fourth has changed considerably; there is only one ace left in the remaining 49 cards, and the probability if therefore 1 in 49.

The OC curves derived for sampling from finite batches therefore take account of this aspect, but the principles for selecting a sampling plan remain the same. Both producer (supplier) and consumer (purchaser) carry some risk. The producer's risk is the chance that the manufacturing section or supplier wrongly rejects a batch of material which contains less than the maximum acceptable percentage of defects. In most cases the producer would submit such a batch to 100 per cent inspection to sort good items from bad. At the end of this exercise he would find that the percentage of defects was in fact less than the maximum allowed, and he would thus have incurred unnecessary inspection costs. This risk is therefore termed the "producer's risk".

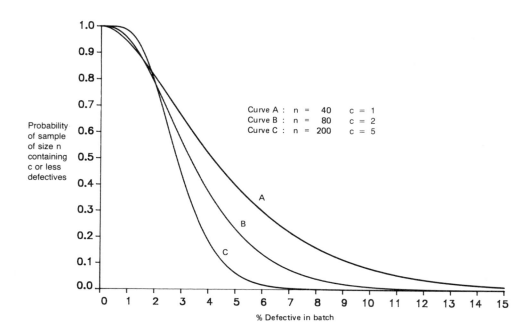

FIGURE 14:10   THREE OC CURVES FOR DIFFERENT PARAMETERS

On the other hand a user or purchaser carries a risk of wrongly accepting a batch which contains more than a maximum permitted percentage of defectives. This is termed the consumer's risk, and is often set as 10 per cent. This does not mean that 10 per cent of all batches accepted should have been rejected. It means that the plan gives the wrong answer on 10 per cent of the occasions when the percentage of defects exceeds the permitted maximum level. Suppose that over a period a supplier sends 100 batches of bulbs, 80 batches being good and 20 batches containing more than the permitted maximum percentage of defects. We would expect to accept wrongly 10 per cent of these 'bad' batches:

Sampling schemes may therefore be tailored to give a high level of protection to either the producer or the consumer. In the former case the maximum allowable percentage of defectives is called the acceptable quality level (AQL). In the latter case the maximum percentage of defects is referred to as the "lot tolerance percent defective" (LTPD); the consumer therefore seeks a high degree of protection against accepting batches containing more than this figure.

Once the degree of protection required is known, standard sampling plans may be drawn from standard tables such as those given in BS6001:1972. A guide to the use of these tables is also available (BS6000:1972). Where the particular property being checked can be measured, rather than simply classified as good or bad, and where the variability in that property follows the normal distribution, inspection can be based on the measured property in much the same way as for control charts. The sample sizes are usually much smaller than those for sampling plans based on attributes. For details see BS6002:1979.

Supplier quality assurance

Maintaining the necessary levels of quality of bought-in raw materials, components or finished products is a key part of any quality assurance programme, and the inspection of incoming supplies is frequently necessary. But inspection at this stage cannot change quality levels: it can only sort bad items from good. Increasingly, buying organisations are seeking to ensure that their suppliers operate adequate quality assurance systems, so that the buyer can rely on incoming goods being of acceptable quality. Among the many factors contributing to this shift of emphasis are the following.

1   In high volume manufacturing industry (e.g. assembly of cars, electrical appliances etc), rejections of incoming items could lead to costly stoppages in production.
2   With many complex products, the required level of quality can be assured only by adequate quality control throughout all stages of manufacture. It is not adequate, nor practicable, to rely only on inspection of incoming products to detect faults. The buyer has no option but to rely on the supplier operating a sound quality assurance system, and may therefore seek reassurance that the supplier's QA system is adequate. In many cases this reliance on the supplier extends to his design capabilities also.
3   The growth of legislation placing greater demands on manufacturers to ensure the quality of finished products means that they, in turn, are demanding better quality assurance from suppliers. Industries particularly subject to such legislation include aircraft and automotive engineering, nuclear power plant manufacturing, and food processing. The growth of product liability legislation is likely to give a further boost to the vetting of suppliers' quality systems.

Large organisations generally carry out their own assessment of major suppliers. Alternatively such assessment might be carried out by a third party: the Kitemark scheme operated by the British Standards Institution is a widely known example of such a scheme, giving purchasers an assurance that items so marked comply with a

British Standard. It involves not only the testing of the product, but also inspection of the manufacturer's works. More recently, BSI has established a system for the registration of firms of assessed capability,[4] which involves assessment of firms which are applying against specified quality system requirements including scrutiny of the firm's quality control manual and periodic site visits. Firms which meet the appropriate quality standards are then included in the register.

The initial widespread use of formal schemes to assess the quality capabilities of suppliers, (as opposed to inspection of finished products) was in the field of military procurement. The NATO Allied Quality Assurance Publications were adopted in slightly modified form as a series of Ministry of Defence standards, (05/21 to 05/29). The requirements laid down in these provided the basis for a series of guides (BS5179:1972) on the assessment of manufacturers' quality assurance systems. The recommendations given in BS5179 were subsequently incorporated in BS5750:1979 as requirements.

The appraisal of the manufacturer's QA system needs to reflect the type of work which he is to undertake. Many systems for vetting suppliers' quality capabilities classify work into three categories, reflecting the extent to which one relies on the manufacturer.

Quality systems

QUALITY SYSTEMS FOR FINAL INSPECTION AND TEST
At the simplest level it may be possible to assess the quality of a product by final inspection. If one is to rely on the supplier for such final inspection, it would obviously be wise to check that the supplier does, in fact, use appropriate inspection facilities, that instruments and test equipment are properly calibrated, that sampling inspection methods are sufficiently reliable, etc. One would also seek reassurance on other factors such as the ways in which the manufacturer checks incoming materials and segregates any rejected materials or items.

QUALITY SYSTEMS FOR MANUFACTURE
For many manufactured products, conformance with requirements can only be ensured by proper control throughout production, including inspection at a number of intermediate stages. Work of this nature inevitably requires that the manufacturer has a more extensive system of quality control if a customer is to rely upon it. In addition to those aspects involved in quality systems for final inspection and test, the manufacturer must use a reliable system of giving work instructions to production operatives, and therefore needs a reliable system to ensure corrective action if faults arise during manufacture.

QUALITY SYSTEMS FOR DESIGN AND MANUFACTURE
In both the above categories, the supplier is responsible for manufacture but is not responsible for design. Where a supplier is to be responsible not only for manufactur-

Requirements	Level of approval		
	Final inspection	Manufacture	Design and Manufacture
Appropriate quality system	√	√	√
Appropriate organisation and defined responsibilities	√	√	√
Periodic review of the quality system. Records of such reviews to be available to purchaser's representative		√	√
Q A planning system			√
Control of design activities, including design reviews			√
Documentation and change control to ensure up-to-date production and inspection procedures are followed		√	√
Work instructions to ensure adequate standards of workmanship		√	√
Manufacturing operations carried out under suitable conditions		√	√
In process inspection at appropriate stages		√	√
Inspection and testing of completed items		√	√
Control and calibration of inspection, measuring and test equipment	√	√	√
Use of specified sampling procedures	√	√	√
Adequate records of inspection, etc to substantiate conformance to specified requirements	√	√	√
Quality control of purchased materials, components and services	√	√	√
Control of purchaser-supplied material		√	√
Effective systems to distinguish between inspected and non-inspected materials and products	√	√	√
Identification, control and disposition of non-conforming material	√	√	√
Suitable packaging, handling, storage and delivery to maintain product quality	√	√	√
Appropriate staff training schemes	√	√	√

FIGURE 14:11   REQUIREMENTS TO BE SATISFIED BY SUPPLIERS FOR THREE LEVELS OF APPROVAL

ing a product, but also for its design, a buyer would seek further reassurances that design activities and any related product testing were also sufficiently rigorous.

These three levels of quality requirements provide a rational basis for assessing potential suppliers. The *minimum* criteria to be satisfied if a buying organisation is to rely on a supplier's quality system are suggested in Figure 14:11.

Quality audits

Any management system should be subject to periodic reviews to check its effectiveness. The quality audit is to the quality system what the accounting audit is to the financial system. The accounting audit seeks not only to verify the accuracy of a company's accounting and financial records, but also to review the effectiveness of the control system itself. Similarly, the quality audit seeks not only to check on the quality of a finished product and the performance of the inspectors, but also to review the adequacy of the entire quality assurance system. Most aspects of the quality audit are the same as the aspects investigated under a supplier quality assurance survey. Specific aspects would include:

1 Checking that measuring and testing equipment is correctly calibrated, that calibration has been carried out regularly and that records support this
2 Checking that operators and inspectors have, and follow, up-to-date drawings, work instructions and inspection methods, and that practice conforms to the quality control manual
3 Review of inspection records and analysis of rejections
4 Review of customer complaints
5 Rechecking work passed by inspectors. A typical example from the motor industry illustrates the extent of such re-checking. Complete vehicles are taken periodically from final assembly, together with the production inspectors' records. The vehicle is then completely dis-assembled by a quality audit team, who recheck the quality of items used (dimensions, surface finish, etc) and the quality of manufacture. The latter includes checking the torque applied to fasteners used in assembly, the quantities of lubricants and coolants used, the fit and alignment of sub-assemblies such as lights and steering, and numerous similar checks.

Quality policy and management

Figures 14:1 and 14:2 indicated the need to select the target levels of quality and quality control. Increasingly the activities of customers and other bodies, particularly governmental, are influencing the quality policies and practices of manufacturing companies. A manufacturing company which wishes to sell (directly or indirectly) to organisations which operate supplier quality assurance systems, will have to operate a quality assurance programme adequate for the desired class of approval.

Industries such as automotive, aerospace and electrical equipment manufacture, where finished products are subject to legislative control on standards of safety, already have extensive quality assurance schemes. Manufacturers in other industries can expect to have to follow suit, if this is not yet the case. Other, more general, legislation will also lead to manufacturers extending their QA systems to meet customer demands.

ORGANISING FOR QUALITY

Quality is everybody's business. The achievement of the desired level of quality requires effective contributions from every function. It should be appreciated that:

1 Responsibility for defining customers' quality requirements rests primarily with the marketing function
2 Responsibility for the design and specification of a product rests primarily with design and production engineering
3 Responsibility for producing goods to specification rests primarily with manufacturing

What, then, is the role of a quality assurance department? Rather than try to usurp the quality responsibilities of other functions, the quality department should advise and assist on all quality tasks, and coordinate and monitor them throughout the whole organisation. Activities which are likely to be the direct responsibility of an independent quality function are:

1 Developing the quality assurance programme and quality manual
2 Operation of the quality control programme
3 Exercising control of incoming and defective materials
4 Metrology and calibration of test equipment
5 Analysis of quality records, particularly defect/failure analysis
6 Measurement and reporting of quality cost
7 Ensuring that training in quality matters is effective throughout the company

It should perhaps be emphasised that the responsibility of the quality department for operation of the quality control system (2 above) must give adequate authority to quality control staff to reject defective items and, if necessary, to halt production. Many organisations assessing the quality assurance system of a supplier place particular emphasis on the organisational aspects:

Effective management for quality assurance should be clearly prescribed, and delegated personnel should be given both the responsibility and authority to identify and evaluate quality problems and to initiate, recommend or provide solutions.
A management representative, preferably independent of other functions, should be appointed with authority to resolve matters pertaining to quality.[5]

Quality circles

The belief that quality is everybody's business underlies the concept of quality circles which are helping to improve quality in a number of companies. Examples include Rolls Royce's Aero Division in Derby, where cost savings of over £500 000 were achieved in 2½ years. Machining problems on turbine blades leading to scrap rate of 4 per cent were investigated. As a result of improvements identified by the operatives concerned, rejections were cut to 0.5 per cent, saving £26 000 per year. Defective welds on turbine blades were reduced from 24 per cent to 1.8 per cent. Investigations showed the need to amend welding techniques, and led to annual savings of about £77 000.[6]

Quality circles originated in Japan and are now used on a wide scale, over 10 million workers being circle members. About 250 companies in the United States have adopted the concept, and at least 40 companies in Britain, including BL, Ford, Marks and Spencer (and a number of its suppliers), Mullard and Wedgewood.

The concept is simple, although the practice requires a change from traditional management attitudes. A small group of operatives selects and investigates quality problems in its own area of work under the guidance of a suitably trained leader. In order to work effectively, the group members should be provided with appropriate training in carrying out systematic investigations, problem solving and the presentation of their proposals.

The quality circle is entirely voluntary, selects its own problems for investigation, and puts forward its own proposals. The involvement and commitment generated by this process encourages those directly involved, who are likely to know most about the causes of quality problems, to contribute their experience, knowledge and skill to the solution of these problems.

References

1   British Standards Institution BS 4778: 1971. Glossary of General Terms used in Quality Assurance.
2   Department of Prices and Consumer Protection. A National Strategy for Quality: a Consultative Document, 1978.
3   Cavanagh P and Rodger A "Some Hidden Determinants of Inspectors' Judgements", *British Journal of Occupational Psychology,* July, 1964 p. 156.
4   British Standards Institution System for the Registration of Firms of Assessed Capability B.S.I. 1977
5   British Standards Institution BS 5179:Part 3: 1974 p. 5
6   Hutchins D "How quality goes round in circles," *Management Today*, January 1981 p. 27.

Chapter 15

Quantitative techniques

Efforts to improve industrial productivity and performance have been aided by two different, indeed diametrically opposed, scientific approaches.

On the one hand the social scientists have studied the interactions of people working in groups of various sizes, the effect of communications, conflicts, coalitions, management styles, and so on. The results of this research together with opinions based on the experience of successful managers have led to useful guidance on better ways to organise and deal with people, as well as to some novel techniques such as value analysis and management by objectives, discussed in Chapter 18.

On the other hand there has been a massive invasion of quantitative techniques, spearheaded by the operations research specialists and the computer people, and made possible by the increasing numeracy of managers. (The numerate man is one who handles quantitative information with the same confidence and range of reference as the literate man handles verbal information.) Particularly in the areas of stock control and production control, where the objectives, constraints and resources can be defined precisely (at least on paper), new quantitative techniques have been appearing. Critical path analysis, Gantt charts, linear programming are some of the best known of these. And of course computers and electronic data processing are being used more and more in materials activities.

Gantt charts

A simple form of planning and control chart which is widely used in manufacturing industry is the *Gantt chart,* named after Henry L Gantt, an American engineer. Basically it consists of a rectangular grid or graph. The vertical lines divide the chart area into time units such as working weeks, and the horizontal lines divide it either by work tasks or by work centres. Thus, for instance, in a weaving mill, the looms (the work centres) could be allocated successive horizontal lines, and work booked against each loom could be shown by bars in the week spaces (see Figure 15:1). In this form the Gantt chart is a visual aid in shop loading and production control. Use of different colours for bars and sections of bars, and the incorporation of various

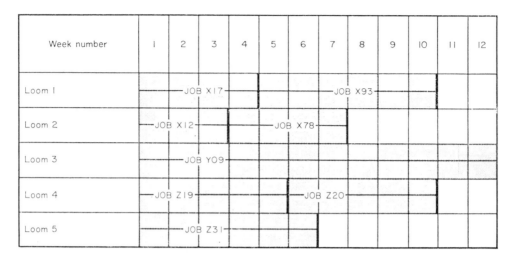

Week number	1	2	3	4	5	6	7	8	9	10	11	12
Loom 1		JOB X17					JOB X93					
Loom 2	JOB X12				JOB X78							
Loom 3		JOB Y09										
Loom 4	JOB Z19				JOB Z20							
Loom 5		JOB Z31										

FIGURE 15:1   GANTT CHART
Simple production control and shop loading application

gadgets in commercially available planning boards based on the Gantt chart, enable more information to be presented more clearly.

Figure 15:2 illustrates the use of a chart of this type to assist in planning and controlling the flow of materials for the production of a fighter aircraft. Called the "Aderyn," this particular model is being manufactured by the Welsh Aircraft Company limited against a British Government contract for counter-insurgency work in the foothills of Snowdon. With 20 aircraft at various stages of production, material flow is important both for manufacturing and finance.

In Figure 15:2, the term "GFE" stands for "government free issue"; that is, such items as radio equipment bought in bulk to a standard specification for all fighter aircraft and supplied to the aircraft manufacturers free of charge on embodiment load. The term "staging" means the marshalling of issue kits of equipment by stores staff. The prefix "a" before a capital letter means that subassembly work will be required.

The chart shows start and finish times for manufacture and assembly of the various parts of the aircraft, together with lead times for purchased parts and materials. It has proved very helpful in communicating, to Purchasing the constraints of Production, and to Production the time required to obtain materials. Cash flow, so critical in long time-span manufacturing, can readily be monitored by adding a cash scale at the bottom of the chart below "production weeks."

Critical path analysis

A more sophisticated way to present such information, which is widely used for certain production planning and purchasing applications, is officially known as

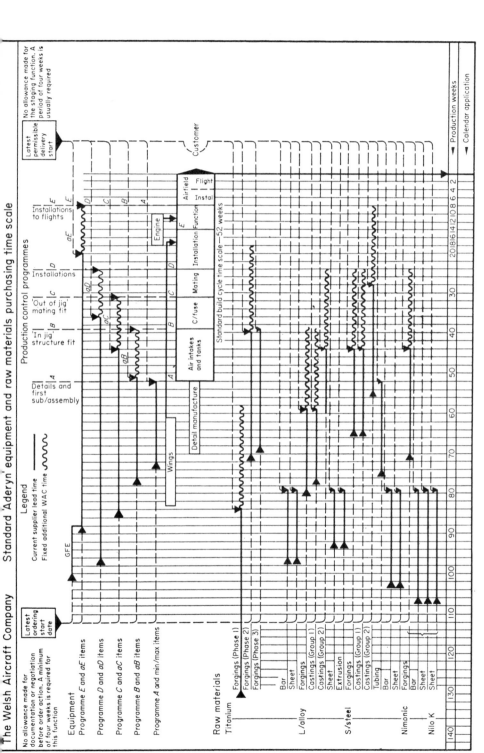

FIGURE 15:2 GANTT CHART

Purchase and production planning against time scale using a Gantt chart

Project network analysis, with PERT and critical path as popular alternatives. British Standard 433:1968 defines these terms as follows:

Project network analysis: a group of techniques for presenting information to assist in the planning and control of projects. The information, usually represented by a network, includes the sequence and logical inter-relationship of all project activities. The group includes techniques for dealing with time, with resources and with costs.

Critical path analysis: the project network analysis technique for determining the minimum project duration.

In calling this method more sophisticated we do not mean to imply that it has superseded bar charts and Gantt charts, which in their various forms still have uses for which they are very suitable. But the Gantt chart is basically a collection of time-scaled activities above a common time base, which cannot easily show the relationship between the various activities apart from the calendar relationship. The networks or arrow diagrams used in critical path analysis on the contrary show very clearly which activities *must* be completed before others can start, and which can be carried on at the same time.

Time requirements are shown in figures rather than geometrically by the lengths of the lines, but simple arithmetic enables total time required to complete a project consisting of a number of related tasks to be calculated. The critical tasks can also be identified and the amount of spare time or slack available for the tasks which are not critical can readily be worked out. All this can be most helpful in the planning and control of complex projects. Perhaps critical path networks are most useful when the main difficulty is that a lot of interacting jobs or tasks have to be considered jointly, while Gantt charts are most helpful when a number of non-interacting jobs have to be considered against the same time scale.

The word *project* is used in this connection to mean any group of related jobs, tasks or activities which have a definite common start and a definite common termination. "Projects" on which network analysis might help to get better planning, tighter control and more economic use of resources include:

1   Any large contract of a kind which does not often come up: new factory construction, major capital equipment procurement, or civil engineering contract, or where a lot of subcontracting is involved
2   A major reorganisation: switching to a materials management structure, setting up a new department, moving to a new location, installing a computer, or planning a merger
3   Anything novel and complicated such as launching a new product

COMPUTERS AND PERT

Network analysis does not require mathematical expertise or the use of a computer, except for a few advanced applications such as optimising the use of resources as well as minimising the project cost and duration when resources are limited, or predicting the probable duration as well as the probability of achieving it when no one is very sure how long some of the research and development is going to take. It is an exercise in logic rather than in reckoning. Admittedly one has to be able to add and subtract in order to work out earliest and latest dates for the various tasks, and it is convenient to have this arithmetic done by machine when a few hundred tasks are involved, especially as the standard computer programs make a number of checks for errors and print out the required figures at high speed in standard format. It is convenient, but it is not at all necessary.

THE FUNDAMENTAL INNOVATION

The fundamental innovation in network analysis is a simple way to represent interrelationships. In most projects which comprise a group of related activities there will be some which can be carried on at the same time if enough people and other resources are available, and there will be others which have to be done in sequence because one has to be completed before another can be started. This is illustrated by the network diagram in Figure 15:3.

These methods of planning the undertaking of a complex project and recording them in a network model or diagram can also be used to plan and control the interrelated activities in carrying the project to completion. PERT (=Program Evaluation and Review Technique) and CPM (=Critical Path Method), originally somewhat different in approach, have developed on similar lines and there is now no fundamental difference between them. The names are used almost interchangeably, although a three-time estimate for each activity (longest likely time, shortest feasible time, and expected duration), remains peculiar to PERT.

Glossary of network analysis terminology

Definitions in quotation marks are taken from British Standard BS 4335: 1968

Activity: "an operation or process consuming time and possible other resources." Represented usually by an arrow.

inspect   description of activity
1   duration of activity

and referred to by the numbers of its head and tail events. Thus activity 10–17 is represented by an arrow starting in event 10 and sticking into event 17. No activity starting in event 17 can start until activity 10–17 is complete.

Network: "a diagram representing the activities and events of a project, their sequence and interrelationship.

Event: "a state in the progress of a project after the completion of all preceding activities but before the start of any succeeding activity." Usually represented by a circle, numbered consecutively and showing also earliest and latest dates.

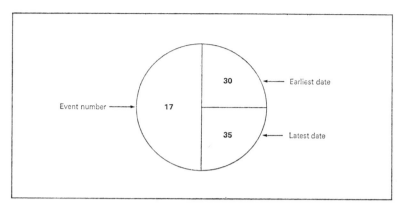

Duration: "the estimated or actual time required to complete an activity." May be in months on a long project, weeks or days. Shifts, or hours are occasionally convenient.

Earliest date: "the earliest date or point in time an event can occur." This depends, of course, on when the project starts and how long previous activities take to complete. Events can be timed in the abstract, starting with time 0 for the date of the first event, and this can be converted to calendar dates when the actual start date is known.

Latest date of event: "the latest date or point in time an event can occur" – if, that is, the whole project is to be completed in time. This depends on project completion date and how long subsequent activities should take to complete.

Critical path: "a path from a start event to an end event the total duration of which is not less than the duration of any other path between the same two events." This is the chain of activities which determines how long the whole project is going to take. There may be other paths, or chains of activities, which take less time to complete and so are not critical; there may be more than one critical path, but there will always be at least one.

Slack: "latest date of event minus earliest date of event. (The term slack is used only in referring to an event.)" Events with no slack are "tight" in the sense that they must be finished as soon as they can be finished; they are critical events.

Resource smoothing: "the scheduling of activities within the limits of their total floats, such that fluctuations in resource requirements are minimised."

Resource-limited scheduling: "the scheduling of activities such that predetermined resource levels are never exceeded and the project duration is minimised."

Resource aggregation: "the summation of the requirements of each resource, for each time period, calculated according to a common decision rule."

Critical activities: "an activity (or dummy) on the critical path." An activity is critical if it starts in a critical event, ends in a critical event, and if its duration is not less than the difference in time between the dates of the two events.

Dummy: "a logical link, a constraint which represents no specific operation." Usually represented by a dotted arrow: – – – –►

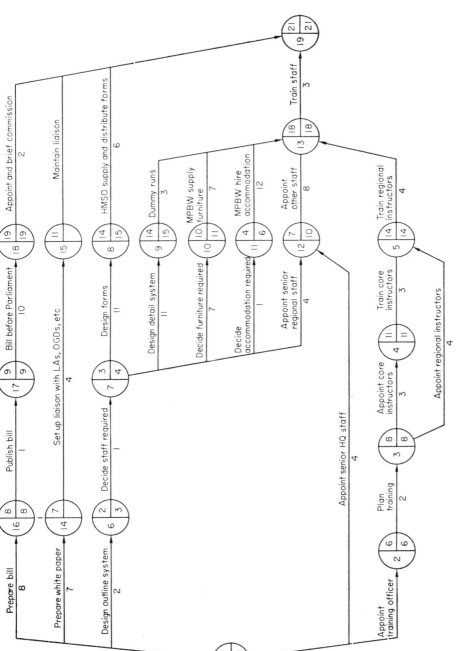

FIGURE 15.3   SIMPLIFIED VERSION OF ACTUAL NETWORK USED TO SET UP
NEW GOVERNMENT DEPARTMENT

Float: "a time available for an activity or path in addition to its duration."

Total float: "latest start date of activity minus earliest start date of activity."

Latest start date of activity: "the date or point in time after which an activity cannot be started" – that is, without delaying the whole project. This depends on activity duration and on latest date of following event.

Earliest start date of activity: "the date or point in time before which an activity cannot be started." This is the same as the earliest date of the event in which the activity starts.

Earliest finish date of activity: "the date or point in time before which an activity cannot be finished." (Earliest start date plus duration.)

Latest finish date of activity: "the date or point in time after which an activity cannot be finished" without causing a hold-up. Same as latest date of event in which activity finishes.

Interface: "an event which occurs identically in two or more networks or sub-networks."

Project network analysis – how to do it

Step one: define the project: list the *activities* or jobs which have to be done and which together constitute the project, determine where the project begins and where it ends.

Step two: ask for each job: what other jobs must be completed before this job can be started? What other jobs cannot start until this job is complete? A rough *network* or arrow diagram should be sketched to show these relationships.

Step three: redraw the diagram correctly, for maximum legibility and clarity. Insert *events* and number them.

Step four: find out how long each activity ought to take to complete. Realistic figures are wanted: not padded for safety or cut short to impress. Write each *duration* on the network under the corresponding arrow.

Step five: time the network. Write in each event its *earliest date* and *latest date*. Mark the *critical path*.

Step six: replan if required:

1   To speed things up when total project completion time turns out to be too long
2   To allocate, or level demand for, particular classes of skilled manpower, scarce machines, or other resources (*resource smoothing, resource-limited scheduling*)

All these steps are part of the *planning* process. When work actually gets under way, the network is used to *control progress*.

Step seven: project manager should keep close personal control of progress of the *critical activities*. Persons responsible for non-critical jobs should advise the project manager if delay occurs. The network shows how delays, planning errors and unforeseen snags will affect the project, and aids in deciding what action to take. Updating is done at regular intervals; for example, fortnightly.

Linear programming

One example of an OR technique which is already in process of being absorbed into general management thinking is linear programming, which has some specific applications in purchasing and in production planning and control.

Linear Programming (LP) consists of a related group of algorithms which can be applied to certain problems involving the allocation of limited resources to specified activities, so as to achieve results which optimise some objective.

The characteristic formulation of a suitable problem includes a statement of what resources are available and what results are desired. These are expressed mathematically in the form of *restraints* which express the limitations on available resources as *inequations* and an *objective function* (or "pay-off function") which it is our objective to "optimise." The latter is usually an expression for cost (to be minimised), or profit (to be maximised), or quantity.

The first step is to transform both objective function and restraints into a system of *linear* equations, converting inequations to equations by adding what are called *slack variables*. If this step cannot be taken, LP cannot be applied. The standard form of this LP system is as follows:

Maximise (or minimise) the linear expression
$$Z = a_1x_1 + \ldots + a_nx_n$$

Subject to the conditions
$$c_{11}x_1 + \ldots c_{1n}x_n = b_1$$
$$c_{21}x_1 + \ldots + c_{2n}x_n = b_2$$
$$\ldots$$
$$c_{m1}x_1 + \ldots + c_{mn}x_n = b_n$$
$$(x_1, x_2, \ldots, x_n \geqslant 0)$$

Once the problem has been expressed in this linear system form, LP provides systematic methods (algorithms) for trudging gradually but inevitably towards an optimum solution (converging iteration) and for recognising it when it is reached. More than somewhat tedious to do by hand, these iterations are well suited for machine processing; it is no coincidence that the term "linear programming" is reminiscent of "computer programming," or that increasing use of LP has coincided with increasing use of computers. The very fast error-free computations made possible by electronic computers enable LP to be used to solve problems involving masses of interacting variables which otherwise have been quite intractable and would have been dealt with by hunch or tradition.

The most general and powerful method is the *simplex* (so-called because of the geometrical interpretation of the n-dimensional case). Having transformed the objective function and the set of restraints into the standard system of linear equations, the next step is to find a first feasible solution. Often this can be done simply by setting all decision variables equal to zero. Next, the coefficients are tabulated. Several standard forms of tableau are used for this coefficient matrix; one version of the "contracted tableau" shows the objective function in the first row, the restraints in the remaining rows, the constants in the first column and the decision variables in the other columns. (An example of the better known "extended tableau" is given later.)

Next we test for optimality; if all entries in the top row except the one in the first column are zero or negative, we have reached the optimum solution. If not, we find the largest entry in the top row, go down its column and divide each entry in the column into the corresponding entry in the first column, and locate the entry for which this ratio has the smallest absolute value. This figure is called the *pivot*, and we now form a new table. The old pivot *column* heading becomes the new *row* heading and vice versa. Entries in the new table are computed as follows:

1 Replace pivot by its reciprocal
2 Divide all other entries in pivot column by pivot
3 Divide all other entries in pivot row by pivot and change sign
4 Replace each remaining term T_{st} by a new term $\dfrac{(T_{st} - T_{rt}T_{sh})}{T_{rh}}$ where T_{rh} denotes pivot

We test the new table for optimality in the same way, and proceed in this fashion until all entries in the top row except that in the first column are zero or negative, when the optimum values for variables will appear on the left of the left-hand column, with the value of the objective function appearing in the top row and shadow prices for resources above it.

Every solvable LP problem can be solved by simplex methods, but the simplex requires from M to $2M$ iterations to solve a problem with M constraints, and each iteration requires a number of divisions and multiplications. It would therefore be a waste of computer time and a standing reproach to our ingenuity if we failed to recognise that appreciably simpler solution algorithms work equally well for large classes of special cases.

If results and resources can both be expressed in terms of the same unit – truckloads, tanker-shiploads, tons – the transportation methods, especially the Hungarian method, may be applicable. A typical problem: How many tankers will transport how much oil from which sources to which refinery?

An even simpler class of LP problems known as *assignment* problems occur when each result employs one and only one exclusive resource. Again, special solution algorithms are available.

A number of successful LP solutions to blend problems have been reported. Examples are: a diet chosen from all the numerous foods which can be bought, to meet restrictions on cost and maximise a nutritional objective; optimum mixes of ingredients at varying prices to produce animal feed cakes at lowest cost, having regard to today's market prices for ingredients, and complying with standard nutritional specifications; a minimum calory diet for slimmers which satisfies the constraint of keeping body and soul together; paint recipes.

Scheduling a variety of production items among alternative production methods is another application – for example, laying out a blend programme for a petroleum refinery, with joint use of catalytic cracking, distillation equipment and so on; or scheduling heating oil production.

Allocating outputs of several sources to alternative destinations is another LP problem; mines to mills, mines to power stations, plants to warehouses, salesmen to territories. A purchasing application has been to optimise coal purchases by bulk users such as electricity generating stations and gasworks.

Problems in make-or-buy or subcontracting, which involve choosing from a long list of items which to buy out and which to make in, sometimes yield to the LP approach. A related – in principle an identical – problem is seasonal production planning.

Associated with every LP problem is a related problem called the dual; to every problem in maximising profits, for instance, corresponds one in minimising costs involving the same data suitably transformed and having the same answer. Sometimes this fact can be used to reduce the labour of calculation; sometimes it casts light on fresh aspects of the problem. Another useful feature is that new optimum programmes can be built on old optimum programmes by transforming them in the light of new restrictions; for example, by evaluating best allocations of a production complex *with,* and *without,* a proposed capital addition, we can in effect evaluate the worth of the capital addition.

Limitations on the use of LP are both theoretical and practical. Theoretical limitations have been described as "the postulates of linearity, divisibility, additiveness and finiteness" – that is, LP can solve only those problems expressible in terms of *linear* equations, whereas in practice restraints may be non-linear, or linear over a narrowly limited region – and so on.

Practical limitations include:

1 *Recognising* a practical problem as an LP problem is often very difficult
2 *Framing* the problem in LP terms – that is, setting up a statement of the problem in a form which is tractable to LP methods – is sometimes harder still
3 Assigning *numerical values* to the coefficients often requires much investigation and negotiation
4 The *computational labour* can be immense. One account of an LP approach to an Indian textile mill reveals an initial task of allocating 400 products to 100 kinds of loom; the final set of equations was 160×20, and this was solved without electronic assistance despite its daunting dimensions. But an LP program can easily outrun the capacity of an electronic computer.

Typical examples of the least cost mix problem occur in the animal food-stuff industry, where the following situation is common.

A manufacturer makes several products that are different mixtures of a common basic set of ingredients (for example, wheat, fishmeal, groundnut cake and dried milk). These ingredients are analysed in terms of the amounts of essential constituents which they contain. The constituents are of two types; actual nutrient substances (such as oil, protein and riboflavin) and non-substantial measures (such as the number of calories contained in a unit of an ingredient). The amounts of these constituents contained in a product determine its value as a food-stuff and also distinguish it from other products. Each product is defined by constraints specifying upper or lower bounds (or both) for some of the constituents and for some of the ingredients contained in it.

There is a very large number of possible or feasible mixtures that would satisfy the constraints for each product, and the factor which decided the best mixture from the point of view of the manufacturer is that of cost. Some ingredients are cheaper than others, and the manufacturer's problem is to determine the cheapest (or optimum) mix at any given time, which satisfies the given constraints for each product.

Solving the problem. To solve the problem, the following information must be known:

1 The amount of each constituent contained in a unit (pound, kilo, or ton) of each ingredient. This information is assembled in a table called the analysis matrix
2 The cost of each ingredient per unit weight (such as £ per ton). The list of the costs for all ingredients in the analysis matrix is called the cost row
3 The set of constraints that define each product. A constraint specifying a lower boundary is referred to as a minimum constraint. A constraint specifying an upper boundary is referred to as a maximum constraint. The term min-max constraint is a common name for both types
4 The set of exclusions to be implemented in the computation of each mixture. An exclusion is a constraint that specifies the upper boundary for an ingredient to be zero, thus completely excluding the ingredient from the mixture. In general, the analysis matrix will be constructed to include every ingredient that is ever available to the manufacturer. The function of an exclusion set is to limit the ingredients included in the computation to those that are currently available.

With this information it is possible to derive an optimum solution (assuming that a solution exists) treating the problem as a conventional linear programming problem.

In practice, it is usually found that optimum mixtures have to be computed for several sets of cost rows, since ingredient prices vary under changing market conditions and depending upon the source. For the same reasons and for reasons of varying availability, different sets of exclusions must be included in the computation. The special least cost mix program enables the user to compute optimum mixtures for any combination from a number of products, cost rows and exclusion sets, while requiring a minimum of data preparation. The programme prints out the results of the computation in a form that is particularly suited to the requirements of the animal food-stuff manufacturer. The programme outputs several lists for each product/exclusion/cost row. Essentially they are as follows:

1 A list of the amount of each ingredient per ton (or other unit) of the optimum mixture, together with its actual cost and range costs within which the solution would show the same ingredients to be in the optimum mixture

2   A list of the ingredients which are not included in the optimum mixture, each with its actual cost and the (lower) cost below which it would be economical to include it
3   A list of the amount of each constituent included in the optimum mixture
4   A list of the constituents or ingredients which are at their upper or lower boundaries as given by the min-max constraints. For each of these, the programme prints out the savings which would be obtained or the extra costs which would be incurred if the constraints were to be respectively relaxed or tightened and the limits within which these changes could be effected without altering the structure of the solution
5   The cost of the optimum mixture

Case study – production programming

The Ajax Company manufacturers three main products, *X, Y, Z*. Because of a backlog of orders, all quantities manufactured can be sold. The production planning department is required to produce a production programme for the following week. Each product requires processing at each of three production sections. The manufacturing time per product (minutes) at each section is given in the following table.

PROCESS	PRODUCT		
	X	*Y*	*Z*
Milling	*10*	*20*	*8*
Turning	*10*	*8*	*25*
Drilling	*15*	*5*	*6*

With overtime the company works a standard 50-hour week. The numbers of machines in each section are:

Milling section   12 machines
Turning department   15 machines
Drilling departmnet   11 machines

The company has a routine planned maintenance system and it is known that 2 milling machines, one lathe and one drilling machine, will be out of service for the week, and another lathe for about 2/3 of the week.
The selling prices of the products are:

PRODUCT	PRICE PER UNIT
X	£24
Y	£30
Z	£26

Manufacturing costs vary with quantities, but as fixed costs are small, can be considered constant at £20, £24 and £21 per unit of X, Y and Z respectively.

What quantities of products X, Y and Z should be manufactured to maximise the profit for the production programme?

SOLUTION
The profit margin for each product can be calculated by subtracting the manufacturing cost from the selling price.

$$\text{Profit per unit for product X} = 24 - 20 = £4$$
$$\text{Profit per unit for product Y} = 30 - 24 = £6$$
$$\text{Profit per unit for product Z} = 26 - 21 = £5$$

If infinite production capacity were available, infinite quantities could be manufactured and an infinite profit made. However, capacity constraints have been quoted for each section.

Milling machines available = $12 - 2 = 10$.
Milling capacity = $10 \times 50 \times 60 = 30\ 000$ minutes

Turning machines available = $15 - 1^2/_3 = 13^1/_3$
Turning capacity = $13^1/_3 \times 50 \times 60 = 40\ 000$ minutes

Drilling machines available = $11 - 1 = 10$.
Drilling capacity = $10 \times 50 \times 60 = 30\ 000$ minutes

A detailed study of the problem reveals that there is an infinite number of possible schedules, one of which will be better than all the others.

An intuitive answer would be to make as many of product Y as possible (as this has the largest profit margin) and use up any surplus capacity on X and Z. This approach quickly reveals that a balanced mix of products is likely to give better results.

Let us now examine the problems mathematically:

Let Q_x = number of product X to be produced
Q_y = number of product Y to be produced
Q_z = number of product Z to be produced

Then, considering the milling section, we can see that $10Q_x + 20Q_y + 8Q_z$ cannot exceed the available capacity of 30 000 minutes, that is

$$10Q_x + 20Q_y + 8Q_z \leqslant 30\ 000 \qquad (15.1)$$

Similarly for the turning and drilling sections we can deduce that

$$10Q_x + 8Q_y + 25Q_z \leqslant 40\ 000 \qquad (15.2)$$
$$\text{and } 15Q_x + 5Q_y + 6Q_z \leqslant 30\ 000 \qquad (15.3)$$

To indicate the negative quantities cannot be produced, we include the following constraints

$$Q_x \leqslant 0 \qquad (15.4)$$

$$Q_y \leqslant 0 \qquad (15.5)$$
$$Q_z \leqslant 0 \qquad (15.6)$$

Any set of values of Q_x, Q_y and Q_z that satifies these equations would be a feasible solution to the problem. However, we require to find the schedule that will give maximum profit and so our objective can be stated as

Maximise profit $= 4Q_x + 6Q_y + 5Q_z$ $\qquad (15.7)$

This can now be recognised as a standard linear programming formulation. Maximise (15.7) subject to the manufacturing constraints imposed in (15.1) to (15.6).

The solution shows that the optimum production programme is to manufacture 1523 of X, 392 of Y and 865 of Z giving a maximum expected profit of £12 769.

Part Four

People in
materials
management

Chapter 16

Staffing the materials departments

Materials managers do not just manage materials; they manage also the people who deal with materials. The best system would collapse without the people who make it work. The manager's job is to put their talents and energies to work so as to get the best out of them.

This calls for understanding of what the jobs in question involve, how they fit together, what sort of people are the right ones to do those jobs, so that suitable people can be selected, motivated and developed to perform the tasks of today and to rise to the challenge of bigger or more complex jobs tomorrow. No manager, irrespective of the size of his organisation can shrug off his responsibility for these matters, although in large organisations managers can call on personnel specialists for help in selecting, training and developing their people.

Job specifications

Precise, carefully drawn specifications for components and materials are widely used in purchasing and production. When it comes to specifying what is needed in the way of people to fill jobs, vagueness is the norm even though the future of the business is in the hands of the people it employs. Few people have the magic ability to size up men and situations in a flash; not enough to meet the need. Systematic approaches to complex tasks provide a working substitute for these scarce gifts and job specifications can help here.

At the same time the specification should not become a straitjacket: on the one hand we want to define the job, on the other hand to some extent we want the individual to be able to mould it. It is in the end a matter of striking a balance.

A job specification is defined in Ministry of Labour's *Glossary of Training Terms* (HMSO, 1967) as:

a product of job analysis – a detailed statement of the physical and mental activities involved in the job and, when relevant, of social and physical environ-mental matters. The specification is usually expressed in terms of behaviour – that is, what the worker does, what knowledge he uses in doing it, the judgements he makes and the factors he takes into account when making them.

This is more specific than a *job description,* defined as: "a broad statement of the purpose, scope, duties and responsibilities of a particular job." It is not a broad statement but a detailed statement, as in the following examples of job specifications for purchase cost estimators and buyers in a large engineering firm.

JOB SPECIFICATION: PURCHASE COST ESTIMATOR

Description of duties. Prepares estimates of costs involved in the external manufacture of a designated range of more complex proposed and revised assemblies and components, to inform company management of purchase cost indications of new or revised product designs, and to provide company purchasing personnel with price objectives. Discusses estimates with suppliers, as necessary, assisting purchasing personnel to negotiate the most favourable prices. Reports on cost variations between alternative designs and relevant parts of competitors' vehicles and carries out special studies as required. Maintains surveys of technical publications and obtains information on costs of parts, materials and latest production methods, by visiting company and suppliers' plants. Performs related duties as required.

Experience required. Equivalent to seven years' experience of manufacturing operations and estimating activities, including two years' experience of work study and three years' experience of estimating.

Education required. Equivalent to HNC in mechanical engineering.

JOB SPECIFICATION: BUYER

Description of duties. Secures and analyses quotations, and negotiates prices and terms with suppliers for the purchase of a designated range of more complex fixed assets, parts tooling, materials or services known to present a variety of special and/or technical problems in their procurement. Reviews requirements with production planning, product engineering, product planning, quality control and other relevant company and supplier activities, and may recommend changes to specifications. Interviews and confers with current and prospective suppliers to determine manufacturing capacities and capabilities and to negotiate prices, delivery terms and the like. Arranges for the testing of new products and assists, as required, in expediting the procurement of parts and/or materials in short supply. Coordinates matters related to standards of quality, changes to product design specifications, changes in prices, suggestions for cost reductions and the like, with company personnel and suppliers. Places renewal orders in accordance with specified quantities and prices. Investigates new sources of supply, by visiting suppliers, obtaining details of facilities and the like, and recommends new suppliers to senior purchasing personnel. May assist, in conjunction with specialist services, in solving production, design, quality and delivery problems. Arranges for any re-working of materials at suppliers' expense. May be required to train less experienced buyers. May perform various related administrative duties. May instruct personnel assigned to assist. Performs related duties as required.

Experience required. Equivalent to five years' experience as an Assistant buyer.

Education required. Equivalent to HNC.

Job analysis and the preparation of detailed job descriptions have obvious advantages and are particularly useful in large complex organisations, but they have a variety of applications in organisations of all sizes. These include the following:

1 As a guide to recruiting staff, externally or internally
2 Assessing short-term training needs – comparison of the skills, knowledge or attitude of the job holder with the job specification can highlight areas which need development
3 Assessing long-term training needs. Job specifications can be useful in planning development programmes for those earmarked for advancement, for instance in considering job rotation through purchasing, production control, stock control and so on
4 Developing specific objectives or assignments for the job holder

They can also form a basis for performance appraisal, job evaluation and salary rating, and can assist indirectly in appraisal of potential.

Job analysis

Job analysis in the process of examining a job in order to identify its component parts and the circumstances in which it is performed. First, all revelant information should be collected about the job – by no means a simple task, and often time-consuming. Interviews with the staff concerned and comparison of their view of their jobs with the views of others often throws up discrepancies – grey areas where overlap occurs or misunderstandings of requirements. This can clarify the job holders' understanding of their tasks, with resultant improvement in performance.

Reports and records relating to the job in question should also be examined. The man who is doing a job often does not mention some basic part of the job simply because it is so familiar to him. The analysis should establish:

1 Why the job exists
2 What has to be achieved
3 How the objectives are to be achieved
4 Its relationship with other jobs in the materials system
5 The value of the job in terms of salary

WRITING THE SPECIFICATION

Brevity is important in writing the specification. Subheadings help in organising the data and in presenting it in a way which facilitates comparison of one job with another, for instance for salary review purposes. Three subheadings often used for managerial and professional jobs are:

Purpose
Major accountabilities
Scope

Under "purpose," a clear short statement of the key objectives should be made. The idea is to indicate the part of the material department's stated objectives to be accomplished by this job.

These are amplified and given in greater detail in the next section, "major accountabilities." The emphasis should be on results expected, in measurable terms where possible.

Further, the description should state what authority and discretion there is in the job as far as designing and changing the structure of the organisation and its staffing is concerned, when the post is managerial. When the job is not managerial, the authority and discretion in the job should be clearly defined as it affects the job role.

Other aspects which should be included are: accountabilities for training, selecting, promoting and dismissing people. It should also clearly state to whom (in job title terms) the job holder will be responsible.

The "scope" section shows how the job fits into the materials organisation in terms of who reports to whom; most frequent and important internal contacts; and, where applicable, external contacts; membership of work groups (such as a value analysis team) and various company consultative committees (like the works council); where it has a management aspect it also briefly specifies the scope of subordinate jobs. In many cases, it also indicates the type and depth of knowledge required to perform the task, including technical or professional know-how, managerial skills and ability to work with people.

Finally, the specification should indicate the nature and importance of matters which should be referred to a superior for a decision. It should indicate the frequency of formal reporting between boss and subordinate, and also clearly specify the most significant decisions which may be made without reference to a superior.

Many more subheadings may be useful if the job specification goes into considerable detail; fourteen are used in the next example.

EXAMPLE OF A JOB DESCRIPTION

Job Title: Supply officer
Title of immediate supervisor: Senior supply officer
Summary of the job. Works under the general supervision of the senior supply officer. Assigns and guides the work of four to eight schedule and progress assistants in the progressing and scheduling of orders, after the initial bulk supply meets company performance standards. Resolves material supply difficulties liable to cause

shortages by ensuring suppliers overcome related problems; making decisions on schedule revisions or obtaining authorisation to prevent or overcome shortages. Provides material supply information to senior supply officer and at request of other departments so that company manufacturing programme can be finalised, introduction dates of engineering alterations established, and the reasons for production arrears detailed for management. Informs senior supply officer of unsatisfactory suppliers so that buyers can be informed and remedial action instigated to resolve the problem.

Detailed description of duties:
A. Principal or regular duties.

1   Assigns and guides the work of four to eight schedule and progress assistants engaged on the preparation and issue of delivery schedules and routine progressing duties. This in accordance with established departmental procedure, after initial bulk supply meets company performance standards, has to ensure that materials are scheduled for delivery and stocked with the minimum of delay in accordance with a predetermined inventory level following computer stock control information.

2   Interviews suppliers' representatives and contacts suppliers by telephone, correspondence and personal visits, in cases of persistent arrears and/or regarding items that continually appear on shortages by supplier. Has to ensure appropriate progress action is instigated to clear them.

3   Resolves all short- and medium-term supply problems, and refers to senior supply officer only the most serious and long-term problems. Does this by detailing the implications and making recommendations in order to ensure the earliest and most economical resolution of the problem.

4   Liaises with production control and inspection departments in order to provide materials supply information and to ensure planned inventory control of material stocks is maintained in the interests of cost control.

5   Investigates personally, internal and external promises that do not meet the required delivery date and the implication of any increases to programme that indicate potential capacity problems so that he can answer for the delivery and surplus situation of all components under his control.

6   Collects specialist advice from a variety of sources on rejected materials supplied to the company, in order to decide whether they should be reclaimed on company premises, or returned to the supplier for redelivery, or for replacements. Informs senior supply officer of action, giving reasons so that action can be recorded and details assembled for assessment of supplier's quality performance.

7   Advises senior supply officer of anticipated limitations on supplier's total capacity, tooling, quality, and delivery promises, so that buyers can be informed for reference when renewing and/or re-sourcing supplies.

8   Informs senior supply officer of unsatisfactory suppliers so that buyers can be informed and remedial action instigated to resolve the problem or order placed with a new supplier.

B. Periodic or occasional duties.

Coordinates input to computer of material availability information (other than new parts) in conjunction with production control and programme planning.

Specific reports, analyses, information data. As required: Prepared reports and material progress summaries on supplier performance in terms of quality, delivery and capacity for senior supply officer.

Education and experience. Requires GCE "O" level in three subjects including English Language and Mathematics membership of the Institute of Purchase and Supply is desirable. Requires three years' commercial experience in an associated field. Needs a six-month induction period in order to become familiar with depart-mental procedures.

Initiative. Exercises initiative in ensuring that schedule and progress assistants prog-ress and schedule material to meet production requirements and avoid shortages; in progressing material shortages in the quickest and most effective way; in attending to and resolving problems causing material shortages by assisting the supplier with his own procurement and quality problems using the available specialist services; in notifying senior supply officer immediately of any critical problems liable to jeopar-dise production and in identifying suppliers whose material does not meet required quality standards.

Internal and external contacts
Internal spends up to 10 per cent of working day in personal, telephone and corres-pondence contact up to area manager level providing and obtaining material supply information, progressing components on shortage and resolving related problems.

External Spends up to 10 per cent of working day in personal, telephone, telex and correspondence contact up to manager level and with smaller suppliers up to director level providing and obtaining material supply information, progressing components on shortage, resolving related problems and assessing suppliers' production capacity.

Responsibility for accuracy – effect of errors. Checks detail of progress schedules prepared by schedule and progress assistants for accuracy, raises any queries with them so that information dispatched to suppliers is correct. Any incorrect details could result in an unduly high and uneconomic level of stocks or halt the flow of production with resultant financial loss to the company.

Confidential data. Has access to details of company's forecast capacity requirements and current component prices, divulgence of which would seriously harm company/ supplier relations and adversely affect the company's competitive position.

Working conditions and physical effort. Normal. Visits suppliers as necessary.

Responsibility for work of others. Spends up to 30 per cent of working day assigning and guiding the work of four to eight schedule and progress assistants.

Responsibility for supervision. Advises on the suitability of the schedule and progress assistants.

Dexterity. Normal company standard.

Additional specifications and comments. Incumbent must be tactful and diplomatic when representing the company in dealing with various levels of suppliers' contacts in order to maintain a good working relationship and to obtain the most effective cooperation from suppliers.

Incumbent must have a basic knowledge of engineering drawings, material specification and manufacturing processes.

Incumbent must be in a possession of a current driving licence in order to drive company's vehicles.

The person specification

Job specifications developed for recruiting purposes are often extended by developing personnel or man specifications – that is, an extension of the job specification in terms of the kind of man thought to be suitable for doing the job.

Standard strategies for personnel assessment or employment interviews include the Munro Fraser *Five Point Grading* – physical make-up qualifications and experience, brains and abilities, motivation, adjustment – and the NIIP *Seven Point Plan* – physique, intelligence, aptitude, attainments, interests, disposition, circumstances. The same headings can be used in translating the job specification into the man specification.

The seven point plan is widely used in personnel selection. Health, age, bearing, speech, appearance could be specified under the first point – physical make-up. "Disposition" refers to self-reliance; motivation; impact on other people and so on. "Circumstances" refers to social background and experience, domestic situation and so on. It is important to distinguish between what is thought to be essential, and what is merely desirable.

Essential qualities are those without which it would not be possible to perform the task to the required standard.

Desirable qualities are those which, while not essential, might be advantageous in certain circumstances. Thus preference would be given to the candidate who possessed them, provided he also had the essential qualities.

There is also a third category which is concerned with negative aspects. This category relates to attributes which would automatically exclude a candidate who might otherwise meet the specification.

Care should be taken not to over-specify when listing the *essential* qualities and the *negative* qualities, or it may prove impossible to find a man to fit the specification. Under *desirable* qualities, it is often helpful to list in order of preference alternative characteristics or backgrounds of experience which might be acceptable if the ideal candidate is not forthcoming. The specification must be realistic and achievable in terms of the market supply of people and what is offered in the way of salary and prospects.

Vague terms like "good education," "average ability," and "acceptable appearance" have the drawback that different people interpret them in very different ways. Education can be precisely specified in terms of qualifications obtained – "O" levels, "A" levels, degrees; although it is admittedly harder to specify precisely what education really is required to do a given job properly.

The point of all this is to reduce the risk of putting a candidate into a job he cannot perform adequately, and, hopefully, to find the man most suited for the job. If we begin with a clear idea of what the job involves and of what sort of person is most likely to perform it effectively we should be more likely to succeed in this.

A final point: jobs, like people, change. Specifications should be reviewed periodically.

Staff inventories

Staff can be considered as an inventory of talent. The inventory controller who is concerned with goods is working on forecasts of future demand. In the same way, we should consider our human resources in terms of future developments: pending retirements, promotions, and the possibility of some individuals leaving to better themselves, as well as of the forward plans of the company. The stock controller working with physical goods needs to know what he has available now as well as what future requirements will be and, in the same way, accurate and comprehensive information about each person available is needed in order to match the talent of staff to future requirements. Records showing education, qualifications, specialised technical skills, appointments within the firm and career experience before joining the firm, training received, a summary of appraisals, and personal particulars – age, mobility and so on – can be useful in smaller firms as well as large organisations. In conjunction with up-to-date job specifications and current training plans, the record system can provide a basis for materials managers to ensure that:

1 Sufficient suitably trained people are available for current and future needs
2 Individuals are helped to improve their performance, by encouraging self-development and training
3 Opportunities exist for promotion and advancement

Particularly in large organisations it is important to review the staff we have, before we look outside for people; indiscriminate outside recruiting will damage morale and ambition internally.

Recruiting externally

If, after considering the talent available in the company, it is decided to start the expensive process of outside recruitment, the next step is to consult the personnel specialist. Specialist employment agencies and display advertisements add to the cost, but it can be money well spent.

A good advertisement will attract people who have the necessary capabilities to do the job, while deterring those who are unsuitable from applying.

Advertise in papers and journals which are read by the type of man you wish to employ. You can get help on this by writing to ask publishers for a breakdown of their readership. They will be keen to assist in this way. From these breakdowns you will be able to pinpoint which is most likely to include the type of man you are after.

Do not be tempted to cram too much information in the advertisement. The advertisements which catch the eye use blank spaces well. Good staff are being chased by every company and if you want to attract the right man:

1   Have a good headline which clearly identifies the audience at which it is beamed – use the job title or the man title
2   Make the company sound interesting as well as the job
3   Indicate the reason for the appointment ("As a result of further expansion and promotions within the department")
4   State age range, educational qualifications, experience, as indicated by the job/man specifications
5   Indicate the salary range. If there is some pressing reason not to do this, consider such phrases as: "It is unlikely that those currently earning less than £X will be successful"
6   Mention any incidental benefits of the job. Tax considerations make such fringe benefits important for better paid positions
7   Give the closing date for applications

Standard practice nowadays is to use printed application forms. These standard forms facilitate comparison of applicants. Time spent on the applications stage is time saved at the selection stage. The task in the end is to match the job and the individual, not just to appoint the best qualified applicant. In this procedure, completed applications constitute the raw material for the appointment decision. On the basis of this a short list is drawn up of candidates to be interviewed. Candidates can then be selected on whatever basis is considered appropriate. Tests of aptitude, intelligence and/or personality are sometimes used. The usual basis is the selection interview, with initial screening carried out by the personnel specialist and the final decision resting with the person in charge of the materials or supply department. It is he who is best able to judge the needs of the situation.

Selection interviews

As for the selection interview, privacy and pleasant surroundings should be provided. Sufficient time should be allowed and interruptions avoided. The important thing is to get the applicant talking in a relaxed atmosphere. Do not ask questions which can be answered by a straight "Yes" or "No"; most people find it helps to prepare a list of open-ended questions in advance. Plan the structure of the interview so that it flows along logically instead of hopping from point to point at random. One purchasing director uses a typed list of 61 questions in interviewing prospective buyers. Some are specific questions about his immediate past experience (What products have you bought? What was your total spend? What limits were placed on your spending?) Others seek to explore his knowledge or attitudes (What has been your greatest achievement? Explain the meaning of *ABC* analysis. Explain the effect of stockholding on liquid capital resources. Do you consider yourself a tough negotiator?) Such details as: Is your wife willing to move? Any schooling problems? are not omitted.

Every opportunity must be taken to ensure that the applicant is given adequate information about the job and the firm; don't forget to let the candidate ask his questions, he is interviewing you and your company just as you are interviewing him. Careful planning will help the applicants to do justice to themselves; a useful aid is the National Institute of Industrial Psychology Paper number 3, *Interviewing for Selection*.

One purpose of the selection interview is to follow up clues gleaned from the application form. It is not necessarily the most important part of the selection process.

Having thus carefully defined the needs of the job and interviewed likely candidates, the final choice can be made. A definite offer should be made to the successful candidate. Any special requirements, such as need to travel, should be stated explicity; this can save a lot of trouble later on. Unsuccessful candidates should be treated with courtesy, and a personal letter from the head of supplies can help greatly in promoting the image of the organisation.

Chapter 17

Training and developing materials staff

Systematic approaches to training, education and development of staff should:

1   Enable the business to be run more efficiently and make more profitable use of its investment in staff, plant machinery, stock and premises
2   Enable individual members of staff to develop their abilities to the full, thus achieving their private goals while contributing to company objectives
3   Ensure that competent and knowledgeable staff will be available to meet future needs

Successful training and development policies will enable the company to attract and retain able people. A simple test of success is how easy or difficult the company finds it to fill vacancies with suitable people. The eventual result of unsuccessful policies could be takeover or bankruptcy. In these times of economic growth and technological change under competitive conditions, when more and more of the population are exposed to higher education and when management is getting more complex, even the family business, which has not traditionally been noted for its staff development programmes (except in the case of staff who belonged to the family), is making drastic changes and many examples could be cited.

This is true of the business as a whole but a further point must be made about the materials activities in particular, which in the past have often been under-privileged as regards the quality of staff and training. This point is that the materials department *must* recruit staff of the same quality as other major departments if they are to be able to make the contribution increasingly called for in today's conditions. Such staff *must* be given opportunities to develop and advance because, if they feel neglected or blocked, they will leave for more promising areas of business.

Education, training and development

Education is generally considered to be concerned with the acquisition of the knowledge, understanding and moral values required in all walks of life rather than the knowledge and skill required for some particular area of work. "The purpose of education is to provide the conditions for young persons and adults to develop an understanding of the traditions and ideas influencing the society in which they live, of their own and other cultures and of the laws of nature, and to acquire linguistic and other skills which are basic to communication." *Training* on the other hand is generally considered to be much narrower and more job-specific; the systematic development of the attitude, knowledge and skill required by an individual to perform adequately a particular task or job.

This account of "education" may be a little starry-eyed; some selection of topics for study occurs at quite an early stage, and it is quite usual to select at least some of the skill and knowledge areas which are relevant to job areas if not to specific jobs. To distinguish between the training content and the education content in the course of studies followed by a lawyer to qualification would not be easy in the light of the definitions given, and this is true not only for lawyers but for most of those described by Peter Drucker as knowledge workers. Old line managers often think of education as what is done at schools and universities, and training as what is done on the job or by the firm, but this also oversimplifies what happens to knowledge workers, who now include most people at executive and managerial levels.

The growing proportion of large firms and the sophistication of the industrial environment is increasing the number of people who are part of management at some level: at least 10 per cent of the workforce in Britain. One British-Dutch firm found that over 10 000 people were employed by them in management positions. A large materials department will include several managerial people as well as the materials manager himself. All those who direct and control the work of others as a large part of their jobs, as well as some people who do not manage people in this sense but because of the importance of their work enjoy a rank or status as high as those who do, are part of management. Job enrichment and similar approaches make every employee to some extent a manager, with some responsibility for planning and controlling at least his own work and hopefully some involvement in company objectives. *Management development* is the systematic process of developing effective managers at all levels to meet the requirements of the organisation. This involves the analysis of present and future management requirements, the assessment of actual and potential skills of managers, and devising means to match available staff to expected requirements.

"The key to good management training," according to a report by the Central Training Council (*An Approach to the Training and Development of Managers*, HMSO 1967), "lies in the care and personal interest taken by managers in training those placed under them. They must be prepared to spend time and effort on this, giving their subordinates the opportunity to acquire new knowledge and letting them have increased personal responsibilities. It is for each company to ensure that its managers are fully aware of the importance of their personal role in training and that their success in it will have a bearing on their own career prospects."

Role of the training officer

The old view of training and development in the firm was confined to job training for certain recruits – apprenticeships, sitting by Nelly – with the possible addition in advanced firms of a small elite corps of management trainees who did a milk round of working in most departments and acting as assistant to one or more top executives. This might have been appropriate in static conditions, but much more comprehensive training and development schemes have now become widespread in Britain, and the small group of management trainees has been replaced by a much larger graduate entry. The training officer has now become a familiar figure. His role is to assist management to discover and define training needs and to advise on how these needs can best be met; often he is also responsible for actually conducting or organising courses of training. Consultation with a competent training officer should stimulate and help the manager with diagnosis of training needs and prescription of methods but the manager cannot delegate his responsibility for training his people to the training officer.

Since many materials jobs are office work, the following extract from a Central Training Council report (*Training for Office Supervision* by the CTC Commercial and Training Committee, HMSO 1968) may be instructive.

Essential steps in developing training for office supervision

1   To define the role and responsibilities of the supervisor and to set down what he has to know and do in terms of office supervision. This involves job analysis leading to a job specification.

2   In the light of the job specification, the responsible manager should identify points of strength and weakness in the supervisor's performance and decide in what directions further training and education is needed. This involves appraisal of supervisors' performance and the preparation of a training specification.

3   The company must then decide how the various training needs can be met. This involves determination of training methods and a planned programme.

4   Finally it is essential to evaluate the training given, to see whether the supervisor's performance has reached the required standard. This involves evaluation of training – which may lead to subsequent modification of action taken in stages 2 and 3 above.

TRAINING APPRAISAL FORM FOR OFFICE SUPERVISORS
(Figure 17:1)
Questions 1 to 15 relate to the work of the supervisor as defined in the job specification over the previous twelve months and are designed to ascertain what training may be needed. If the answer to a question is "no," the appraiser must detail the evidence for saying "no" and the reasons, which may have to be discussed with the supervisor. The detail of the answer will show whether training is required; for

example, if the answer to question 1 reveals that work is not always produced on time, the reason may be:

1   The supervisor has insufficient staff
2   There is consistent delay in receiving information from another department
3   The supervisor does not organise the work properly
4   One of the staff is slow and unreliable

The last two may indicate a need for training; the first two reasons indicate a defect in organisation.

New employees

"The first critical point in a person's development within the firm is at the point of entry, and it is precisely at this point that many firms fail," writes one training expert. Outright rebellion, sterile conformism or creative individualism are the three standard reactions (according to Edgar Schein) of educated recruits who find their values in conflict with those of the organisation. It goes without saying which of the three we should try to cultivate. "The new recruit gets his guidelines from a variety of sources: from the official literature of the organisation, from examples set by senior people, instructions given directly by his superior, the example of colleagues who have been around longer, the rewards and punishments attracted by his own efforts, the response to his ideas, the amount of challenge in the assignments he is given."

Young recruits straight from school or more particularly college, are often well catered for now that training officers have come on the scene and spent some time on the problem. Some firms provide industrial training stints for external sandwich course students which put to shame the efforts of other firms to cater for their own new employees. Usually candidates, after a short induction course, are assigned to a series of departments, spending a week at least in each to get some idea of the work they do and the problems they face. Either a diary is kept, or short reports have to be written on each department outlining its operations, its current problems and the trainee's ideas for overcoming those problems. Some of these ideas are silly, as anyone would expect including the trainee; some of them are very good and worth adopting.

Project assignments which require the trainee to visit and work with people in several departments have included: location of a warehouse, utilisation of materials handling equipment in a finished goods store, economic forecasts of material trends, *ABC* analysis of raw stocks. Such assignments can be useful even with mature newcomers, one of whom told us: "I learned more about this outfit in two weeks than I did about my last firm in three years." A well-planned project assignment enables the newcomer to meet a wide variety of people in a working relationship, encounter difficulties and problems in interdepartmental communication, and learn a lot about the organisation. They should be realistic assignments which will be acted on where possible; although this obviously presents problems.

Name of supervisor

Age

Position held and date appointed

Brief outline of responsibilities

Number of staff

Details of staff (names, ages, duties)

1 Is the work of the office consistently produced on time?
YES/NO
COMMENTS

2 Is the work of the office consistently accurate and reliable?
YES/NO
COMMENTS

3 Is the output of work from the office satisfactory?
YES/NO
COMMENTS

4 Is the quality of the work from the office satisfactory?
YES/NO
COMMENTS

5 Does the supervisor have a defined programme for training his staff?
YES/NO
COMMENTS

6 Are all his staff fully trained or under training?
YES/NO
COMMENTS

7 Has the supervisor suggested ways in which the output of his office could be improved or the work simplified?
YES/NO
COMMENTS

8 Has he coped satisfactorily with new tasks and changes in routine?
YES/NO
COMMENTS

9 Has he given any evidence of cost-consciousness?
YES/NO
COMMENTS

10 Is he knowledgeable about the uses of office machinery?
YES/NO
COMMENTS

11 Does he use office machinery to the full?
YES/NO
COMMENTS

12 Is his written work satisfactory?
YES/NO
COMMENTS

13 Does he express himself clearly and adequately?
YES/NO
COMMENTS

14 Does he show a good appreciation of the firm's objectives, policies and products?
YES/NO
COMMENTS

15 Does he cooperate satisfactorily with other sections and departments?
YES/NO
COMMENTS

16 Is his control of staff satisfactory in all respects; for example, recruitment, appraisal, discipline?
YES/NO
COMMENTS

SUMMARY

What further training or development would make him a more effective supervisor?

SIGNED_____   DATE_____

POSITION_____

COUNTERSIGNED_____   DATE_____

FIGURE 17:1   SUPERVISOR TRAINING APPRAISAL FORM

External courses

A large number of external courses are available. Few of them are cheap. Some are excellent, but many others are of marginal value. Before sending a man on such a course it is advisable to study the course objectives, to study the man, and to attempt to match the two after discussion with the individual concerned. A close look should also be taken at the qualifications of the staff who run the course; not necessarily their academic qualifications but their qualifications to run a course of the kind offered. We do not buy expensive goods without careful investigation, and we are entitled to do the same when buying services.

Having decided to send a man on a course, tell him straight away, preferably several weeks in advance if more than one day's absence is involved. Sell him, as well as tell him, what the course is about, what we might get out of it, who is running it, who has experience with them. Discuss with him how his absence should be covered – or you may be the sufferer from a natural tendency to delegate upwards when away on a course. Encourage him to think of particular ways in which the course could help his needs. Explain about expenses.

After the course, call for a short report. Do not ask for criticism because this reinforces a natural tendency to resist instruction; ask instead for some positive lesson. A method used in Reed Paper Group was as follows: first the man was given a chance to catch up on things with his colleagues and assistants. Second, his boss saw him for a discussion of overall impressions of the course and problems which had come up in his absence. Third, within seven days the man had to submit a single sheet of paper to his boss covering:

1   One lesson he had learnt personally – for example, listening more, planning his time better
2   One lesson that could be applied in running his section, and how it could be put over to the staff
3   One lesson that could be applied to the unit as a whole – for example, induction courses – and how it could be planned

Naturally a report of this type would not always be appropriate. But it is important that attendance at courses should not be seen as a holiday, a rest cure or a punishment. It is particularly important with longer courses that delegates do not get back to the business brimming over with new ideas and good intentions only to be slapped firmly back in the slot. One training officer put it like this: "Management of a large organisation can move only as fast as change is accepted in related functions. If knowledge, skills and techniques of jobs are analysed and training provided in them, does this lead to frustration when intelligent people cannot make full use of what they have learned? How can time be made to develop knowledge and skills to do the real job, when all the pressures on time come from the more mundane and routine work, the system's detailed procedures, doing the work of other functions in order to keep the job going?"

In-company courses

Much of what has been said earlier in this chapter applies to in-company courses, which have the special advantage that they can be specifically designed for needs which have been found to exist in the department and company concerned. Case studies, projects and exercises can be developed from incidents and problems in the company, and confidential company information can be employed. They can also help to pull together a department with staff operating at several different establishments, or a newly reorganised department.

When training officers ask themselves where expenditure on training will bring the most return, the big spender departments are of particular importance. In companies where the cost of materials is a major portion of total annual expenditure, we should consider whether a relatively small expenditure on training materials staff in relation to what is spent on training sales staff might not make a worthwhile contribution to company profits.

The problem of having a number of senior people away from the office at the same time can be overcome by starting on Thursday evening and working through till Sunday lunchtime. Only one working day is lost, yet in a properly structured participative programme as much can be achieved as in many a Monday-to-Friday course. The drawback is that this does make inroads on the participant's own free time. In practice this has never been a problem as far as we are concerned. We advise that the course should be run in a comfortable hotel or conference centre, as some compensation. This is also an important factor in creating the right atmosphere. Often this is the first time such a programme has been run for materials people, who have noted that other departments have run conferences and courses in hotels. The feeling many have told us about, that they are at last being "recognised" by the company, seems to be a strong motivation.

We also try to arrange for someone from top management to be present for the opening dinner. This reinforces the previous point, and when the top manager can be persuaded to stay for the opening session, or even to make an opening address, he will himself be reminded of the potential contribution to results which the materials activities can make.

New attitudes matter a lot more than new techniques. This is why participative methods such as case studies and exercises are more effective on such courses (where they can be related closely to current problems in the company) than pedagogic methods such as lectures, useful as lectures are for certain purposes.

In many companies the attitudes to and among staff in the supplies field have been traditionally different from those which are demanded by the current economic environment. They could well be even further from the approach which will be required in the future. Management training can make a big contribution towards bridging this gap. If the initial training results in managers and their staff changing their perception of the need for job performance improvement, this will in itself result in improvement. If the training then helps to develop the skills and knowledge content in the areas where the need has been perceived, job performance will obviously be directly enhanced.

Five ways to set up in-company courses of this kind are:

1   Company staff devise, construct and organise the whole thing
2   Engage outside speakers or session leaders for certain parts of the programme and company staff do the rest
3   Employ a consultant to prepare exercises or case studies which the company integrates into its own course
4   Engage a training consultant specialising in the materials areas to help organise the course, develop materials for it and run certain sessions
5   Agree the training needs with him, lay down objectives and require him to organise all speakers and session leaders and develop course material as necessary.

The choice depends partly on the time and resources available.

If it is decided to utilise a specialist training consultant, the kind of service which he ought to provide may be summarised as follows:

Stage 1 Agree with responsible company executives the training needs, the objectives of the programme which is to be developed; and the constraints within which the programme has to function.

Stage 2 Liaison and discussion with functional staff in the company (background information); the development of cases and exercises from company experience as and if necessary; agreement on the staff to be used on the course. Structuring the programme.

Stage 3 Running the course; the integration of the work of the various session leaders and the channeling of the contribution from course members towards the achievement of the set objectives.

Stage 4 "Feedback" liaison with the responsible executives and the development of further training programmes if and as necessary.

The important thing with an in-company programme is that it should be tailored to the needs of the company and the staff who are attending. "Standard packages" dressed up to look like a special course should be avoided in favour of effective training and development programmes carefully designed to meet the needs of the individual company.

Chapter 18

Motivating materials people

Since the 1930s and the publication of the Hawthorne investigations, management science has become obsessed with the need to motivate people and has stressed the matter of individual commitment to organisational goals. The general message promoted, in particular by behavioural scientists, is consistent and is often labelled "human relations theory". The manager's job is usually described as to get results through the efforts of other people. The people are better educated than they used to be, and less inclined to do things because the manager tells them to; they need to be given a reason, or "motivated" as the jargon goes, rather than just given an order. Some managers are obsessed with the results they have to achieve; others tend to concentrate on the people they are in charge of. These are two quite different directions in which to look. We can represent this on a sketch map such as Figure 18:1, where concern for people is shown along the vertical axis and concern for results is shown along the horizontal axis.

This is a convenient way of showing the differing management styles which are adopted, either because of the personality traits of the individual manager concerned, or because of the needs of the situation, or because of company policy and tradition. At the bottom right corner we have the slavedriver type of manager who has minimum interest in his people and concentrates on output. The opposite type of manager is represented at the top left corner: look after the chaps and the results will look after themselves in his doctrine. He believes in patting backs and spreading a little happiness as he goes, and there are circumstances in which he can be effective. Which is more than we can say for the manager at map reference 1,1; his concern is minimal both for the people and for the results. No one would advocate this approach as one likely to succeed, yet managers can be found in this position – the yes-men, the effete relatives of the ruling family, some who had plenty of fire in their prime but are now peacefully waiting retirement.

Surveys have shown that most managers spend a lot of their time in the middle position, compromising between human relations and getting the output. Robert R Blake and Jane S Mouton developed this visual aid into the symbol of and basis of a whole package deal for reorienting managements. The ideal position is of course at

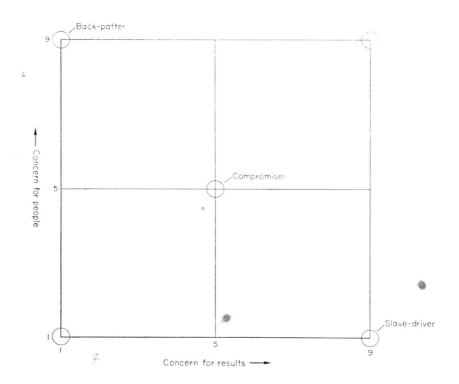

FIGURE 18:1   MANAGERIAL GRID
Showing different management styles

the top right corner: the 9,9 manager who maximises results through maximum involvement of his people.

Theory *X* and Theory *Y*

Writing in the same vein, Douglas McGregor (*The Human Side of Enterprise,* McGraw-Hill, 1960) sees much managerial behaviour as the result of a set of assumptions about people which he calls Theory *X*. The assumptions are that:

1   The average man dislikes work and wants to avoid it
2   He has to be forced, directed, and controlled to work
3   He prefers to be directed and has little ambition
4   The main thing he wants is security.

According to McGregor, Theory *X* was incorrect in its view of the average man. Management could get better results by basing its strategy on a different set of assumptions which he called Theory *Y*. According to Theory *Y*:

1 The expenditure of effort in work is natural
2 External control and threat are not good ways to produce results
3 The average man prefers to have some responsibility under proper conditions
4 Self-direction and self-control can be used in managing employees who will then exercise the imagination and initiative which external direction and control tends to repress.

To make this kind of brief summary of a mass of research and discussion one must simplify, and it is hard to avoid over-simplification. In advocating participative styles of management McGregor did not mean to unseat the manager from his inevitable hot seat. He specifically said that the manager still and always has to make hard decisions, to take responsibility for picking one course of action among many uncertain alternatives, to make mistakes and take the consequences. Good human relations are important but can never cut out all discord and disappointment.

Maslow and Herzberg

The best known of the school of humanist psychologists is Abraham Maslow, who in 1943 developed a model for understanding human motivation which was not particularly related to work experience, but which has proved very influential in subsequent management thought. He proposed that the needs we all have could be arranged in an ascending hierarchy with five main levels. Man does not live by bread alone, right, but if there's no bread it's hard to concentrate on abtract thought. The basic level of need is the physiological need for food, warmth and so on. Once needs are satisfied on any level, the next level up becomes the motivator. Above physiological needs Maslow places safety/security needs; then love/affection needs; then esteem – the need for the good opinion of other people and a decent self-esteem. The fifth and top level in this hierarchy of needs is the need to become the sort of person one is capable of being: mature self-actualisation.

The disappearance of needs as they are satisfied and the emergence of new higher level needs as the dominating motivator is not a conscious process; it is hard for most people to remember how pleased they were when they got their present jobs.

The Herzberg version of this, the "motivation-hygiene" theory, is based on research into what people feel about their jobs. The factors which really motivated people and made them satisfied with their jobs were not the same as those which caused dissatisfaction, so that the opposite of "job satisfaction" was not dissatisfaction but "no job satisfaction," and the opposite of dissatisfaction was "no job dissatisfaction." Factors which made for job satisfaction, Herzberg labelled "motivators" and factors which made for no job dissatisfaction he called hygiene factors. Attention to the hygiene factors will prevent job dissatisfaction but will not be enough to make people happy at their work or motivate them to produce.

Hygiene factors included security, status, pay, work conditions, supervision, and generally relationships with colleagues at all levels and company policy and administration. Motivation factors included growth, advancement, responsibility, recognition, the work itself and achievement.

Actually applying this in order to get more and better work out of people is full of snags. Expanding a meaningless job by adding more activities and challenges which do not lead to the individual's growth leaves it meaningless. Subtracting the hard part of the job – as work-study men frequently suggest – makes the job not only easier but more boring and meaningless, leaving the individual even less motivated. In fact the object of the exercise is itself counter-productive: you have to treat people decently, argues Herzberg, not in order to get more and better work out of them but because they are people. Otherwise it doesn't work.

A useful survey of human relations research and its application to motivation in the workplace is *The manager's guide to the behavioural sciences* by Margaret Brown, published by the Industrial Society.

Approaches to motivation

Some recent researchers into human motivation have tended to emphasise individual differences. The general approach followed by the human relations school is criticised as too general and simplistic, since people differ in their needs and aspirations, which also vary at different stages in life. D C McClelland (*The Achieving Society, 1961*) suggested for example that a useful way to classify individuals is in terms of their varying needs for achievement, affiliation, and power, while V H Vroom (*Work and Motivation, 1964*), and L W Porter and E E Lawler (*Managerial Attitudes and Performance*) based their analysis of motivation on the individual's assessment of the requirements of the job and his perception of the value of the rewards. Put simply, if someone works hard to achieve and then is disappointed by the reward, his future effort and performance is likely to be adversely affected. An important point is that what counts is not the objective value of the reward, or management's perception of the situation; it is the way in which the individual personally perceives the situation that is the significant factor.

The main difference between the two approaches is that the first relies on measures which extend and stretch the individual and make his working life more rewarding, while the second suggests that it is the job of the section head or manager to know and understand the individuals in his section, and to have a clearly communicated policy on reward for effort. For the practising manager both approaches have something to offer. A more detailed account may be found in *Behavioural Sciences for Managers* by R L Boot, A G Cowling and M J K Stanworth (Edward Arnold, 1977).

The social-science, behavioural school has had a considerable influence on one technique which began as little more than a standard work-study checklist: value analysis.

Value analysis and value engineering

Value engineering (VE) and value analysis (VA) are systematic methods using established techniques which identify the function of a product, component or service, set a value on it, and seek ways to provide the function while giving better value.

Better value is given either by improving the functional aspect without increasing the cost, or by reducing the cost without impairing the function. Plenty of case histories are available which record very large savings achieved by a variety of organisations, and the evidence is that VA has often paid its way by cutting costs, only occasionally by improving quality. But value analysts insist that VA must not be regarded as a cost-reduction exercise. Cost-cutting is associated in most people's minds with quality degradation – a natural but counter-productive association as far as VA is concerned. VA maintains or even improves the quality specification, we read in all texts on the subject. The emphasis is not on cost – paying the least for what you get – but on value: getting the most for what you pay.

There have been a number of unsuccessful VA programmes. There have also been many programmes which began well but ran out of steam in a year or so. Reasons for failure include:

1 Overselling. Some VA missionaries put it across as a new gospel, the answer to all business problems. It is not as good as that.
2 Insufficient top management involvement. Unless the top manager is convinced that VA can, and should, pay off and is willing to involve himself so far as is appropriate in the VA programme, it is likely to fizzle out, because it depends on interdepartmental teamwork.
3 Wrong emphasis. Cheapening the product, ruling out any quality improvement ideas, exclusive emphasis on cost reduction, does not arouse the enthusiasm which can be generated by a value improvement plan.
4 Boredom. When the novelty wears off, the VA team starts to look round for something more interesting, the team members drop out one by one until only the chairman is left.

There have also been many highly successful programmes; some early British ones are described in the British Productivity Council booklet *Sixteen Case Studies in Value Analysis.* According to the London consultants, Value Control Limited, "Results from a number of industries we have worked with in the United Kingdom and in Europe show a composite annual return of £8 for every £1 invested in value analysis. Any business can use value analysis, and with adequate training and guidance should expect a return of between 3:1 and 20:1 according to the industry and its products." Indirect savings in the form of better understanding both of one's own job and of the jobs of specialist colleagues, and better relations between departments, are also claimed to bring substantial benefits, though difficult to quantify.

"Value analysis," according to one authority in the field, "is the study of the relationship of design, function and cost of any material, product or service, with the object of reducing its cost through modification of design or material specification, manufacture by more efficient process, change in source of supply (internal or external), elimination, or incorporation into another item." A better way to do the job without reducing the quality of the job done is a simple statement of the aim.

All successful VA programs have been properly organised. The type of organisation which will be effective cannot be prescribed *in vacuo;* it varies from one business to another. Heinritz and Farrell argue (*Purchasing: Principles and Applications,* Prentice-Hall, 1965) that:

> Value analysis is not in the main stream of the buying job. It takes time, special attention and special talents. It is essentially a staff service to the buyer. . . . A full-scale value analysis program is most effective when provision is made in the departmental organisation plan for a staff analyst or analytical section, and when organisation channels are set up for communication and action with the departments that make the final quality decisions.

Successful VA programmes have also been put over properly – *sold,* as marketing men would say. Preplanning: what objections will he have and how shall I counter them? – a standard part of sales planning – should never be neglected.

Common sense with a fancy name, some call Value Analysis. But this is to ignore the merits of the team approach, the layman's guide to becoming creative, and the systematic method which are built into the value analysis job plan.

The questions value analysts ask when they put a part on the analyst's couch seem eminently commonsensical: What is this? What is its function? What does it cost? What is it worth? What else could perform the function? What would that cost? Would it perform better? Can we simplify it? Is there a standard part we can use instead? Do we need it at all? Sometimes the simple questions pay off. A lightning conductor manufacturer found that for years he had been fixing his nameplate on top of the product, where only the birds could see it. An engineering firm found it was paying £2 a piece for special 0.600 inch diameter bolts and nuts when standard 0.625 inch were available to closer tolerances at £0.025 each and would do just as well.

Do-it-yourself value analysis

Buyers – and design engineers – as part of their normal job routine aim at value for money, and the questioning approach characteristic of value analysis can help in this.

But stage one in the value analysis job plan is *organisation.* Essential elements are: to get top management backing, and then to enlist several departments, plus the talents and know-how of outside suppliers, in a systematic and creative *team approach.* The VA team approach not only pays for itself many times over in direct cost savings, but also contributes to the personal development of materials and other personnel. The team is drawn from existing departments and its members continue to spend most of their time in these departments at their usual work. They meet regularly to study selected projects, using their various abilities and their collective knowledge in a systematic plan.

The chairman or coordinator is the only full-time member. He should be someone who has been trained in value analysis. Training need not be a lengthy or costly process if the right man is selected – ideally a cost-conscious engineer with estimating and production experience, perhaps some work study too, and with a firm, pleasant, inventive, persistent disposition. A one-week training workshop will suffice. As many other people as possible should get some VA indoctrination: preferably in the form of a one-day seminar on company premises. This helps blast away such road-blocks as: it won't work; we tried that out in 1922; let some other firm try it first; you haven't worked here long enough to know what suits our requirements; that's what we've done for years by another name; that's not how we do things here; and so on *ad nauseam*.

It is natural to see attempts by value analysts to revise decisions which are my prerogative or share specialised knowledge I have made my own, as threats to my security and status, and criticisms of my performance. Design engineers have been heard to call analysts backseat drivers and armchair admirals, for instance. They tend to adopt a different attitude when value engineers are attached to them to perform the same kind of job at the initial design stage, and thus assist them rather than judge them and do their work over again. Quite apart from these psychological considerations, it is probable that greater cost reductions can be made at the initial design stage, when no cost commitments have been made apart from time and paper, than at later stages of production when there is usually something to be written off, some commitment to buy out of. But even designs which have been thoroughly value engineered on the drawing board can be worth value analysing two years later. Yesterday's decisions can often be improved in the light of todays' options.

Short training sessions for everyone who is involved in or affected by value analysis recommendations helps to increase the number of usable suggestions. They also greatly assist the process of implementation. Increasing the number of believers produces a better climate for acceptance. Get people enthusiastic about value analysis; give them full credit for their contributions, and the battle is half won.

The job plan

Having set up the organisation, spend some time on careful choice of the first object for analysis. It is psychologically important to make worthwhile savings on the first project. Steer clear of products which may be discontinued. Concentrate on high-volume, high-cost items, with perhaps a glance at lower volume items with a high profit margin.

Then use the standard job plan with its successive phases:

Define function: why do we want this thing? What is it for? Use a two-word definition, one verb and one noun; for example, for a toaster, "toast bread".

Information phase: collect all relevant facts – cost, drawings and specifications, production methods, markets, suppliers: anything which might help.

Speculation phase: having acquired understanding and information, the next phase is devoted to dreaming up alternative ways to accomplish the function. Consult suppliers and other specialists. Let the value analysis team have a *brainstorming* session; in this, as many suggestions as possible must be made, although the object is to cut the cost of performing the function (rather than the cost of making the thing in its present form), do not look at cost at this stage. It is considered important also in brainstorming not to breathe a word of criticism of even the most crackpot idea; not a hint, not even a quizzical facial expression is allowed to inhibit creativity. You've got to accentuate the positive, eliminate the negative; so that team members spark off ideas from each other. This exercise is enthusiasm and patience should be kept up until at least half a dozen ideas – preferably many more – have been jotted down. Only one really good idea is actually wanted, but the best way to get it is thought to be by means of this clear separation between the freewheeling creative stage, and the analytical evaluation stage, which is the next phase in the job plan.

Evaluation phase: even the necessarily critical evaluation process must not start with peals of merry laughter about, say Joe's fat-headed idea of making the power cables out of sodium. (Everbody knows what happens to sodium when it comes into contact with water? Yes, but can't it by kept dry?) Start with the plus points of each proposal; then list the drawbacks and think of ways to overcome them; then, lastly, look at cost. Evaluation may involve weeks of development work and visits to suppliers.

Presentation phase: having found the best value-for-money option it remains to present a definite proposal. Management may be solidly behind the value analysis programme, but will still want facts and figures to support specific proposals, with a clear statement of advantages. Keep the presentation to one page only. Supporting detail can be in an appendix.

Implementation phase: proposals approved for action need to be implemented by normal company staff. But someone on the value analysis team should be named to follow up every proposal until it is in operation; and also to see that credit is given where due.

What is "value"?

Value analysis sees "value" as a relationship between what you want, the function, and what it costs you to get it. It clarifies thinking to spell out something of the different kinds of value we place on things. An obvious one is *exchange value* – the cash worth of something in its present form, its market price. Behind this is *use value*, the cash worth to the user of what the thing does, its primary performance function.

As soon as you try to define function in the standard two-word format, you see that most things have more than one function. A motor-car's primary function is: "transport people." But expensive cars have obvious secondary functions such as: "reduce journey-time," "reduce travel-fatigue," "confer prestige," "symbolise status." The first two of these secondary functions increase the use value of the car, but the last two contribute to what value analysts call "esteem value" – the cash worth of those features which increase desirability without improving performance of basic function. Value analysis is mainly concerned with use value, but cannot afford to ignore secondary functions, including non-functional sales features; otherwise we might find ourselves value analysing a mink coat into a plastic mac.

In smaller organisations, instead of a full-time value analyst as team chairman all team members will be part-time, meeting perhaps once a fortnight for one afternoon. The cost of time, plus a week's course for one team member and one-day seminars for others, should be covered by savings achieved in the first six months.

The main problem in the small business is that pressure of work may gradually push value analysis into the background. It is a part-time activity, although a highly profitable one; less profitable activities which have to be done by a certain date, such as signing cheques or replying to letters, tend to take precedence. To overcome this problem:

1   Some member of top management must take personal responsibility for the VA programme. He will set up the organisation, provide sufficient authority, and review results. He will insist that team members spend a certain proportion of their time on VA.
2   Make sure that everyone involved in or affected by VA understands what it is, and what it tries to do; take considerable trouble to make these people helpers, not competitors.
3   Never present VA proposals in a way which implies criticism of people in the firm. Not "this wasn't done properly before," but "everything can be improved – even our own previous best efforts" is the line to take.
4   Don't hog the credit. VA teams should lean over backwards to give full credit to anybody who made any contribution to their work. This is, of course, one way to induce people to make bigger contributions to the VA programme, especially when cash awards or personal compliments from the boss reinforce the message. It also helps to reduce resistance to VA.
5   Use the supplier. Once a buyer gets interested in VA and becomes involved, he will involve his suppliers, whose expert knowledge enables them to play a big part. A standard form such as Figure 18:2 is sometimes used, as a supplement to (not a substitute for) special approaches.

Published illustrations of VA are often taken from the engineering industry. But we have come across profitable applications of the technique in chemicals, plastics, steel making, material handling, packaging and shipping, office equipment and supplies, maintenance and repair materials. External courses and management training have even been made the subject of value analysis.

Management by objectives

Highly fashionable at present, management by objectives (MBO) has been described variously as a "dynamic system of management which seeks to integrate the company's need to clarify and achieve its profit and growth goals, with the individual manager's need to contribute to the corporate objectives and develop himself." It has also been called "a do-it-yourself hangman's kit." The Treasury *Glossary of Management Terms* describes MBO as

Purchase cost value survey		✳ If the answer is 'NO', please obtain further information

Description of the item	Part/drawing number	Buyer reference

We are continually analysing our products for value and request YOUR help in this task through providing answers to the following questions which relate to the above part. Our aim is to eliminate unnecessary costs without adversely affecting the functional value of the part. You can help us through your specialist knowledge and this will be to our mutual benefit in ensuring continuity and volume of future business. Thank you

QUESTIONS	Tick as appropriate		SUGGESTIONS OR COMMENTS
	YES	NO	
1 Are you absolutely clear as to the function of the item in our equipment?		✳	
2 Remembering our basic precept, could costs be reduced in your view by relaxing requirements as to (a) Tolerances, (b) finishes, (c) testing _____ By how much?	a b c		
3 Could costs be reduced through changes in; (a) Material as specified, (b) ordering quantities, (c) manufacturing processes used —By how much?	a b c		
4 Can you suggest any other changes which would (a) Reduce weight (b) simplify the part (c) reduce overall costs? By how much?	a b c		
5 Does it appear to you that any of our specifications or quality control requirements are too stringent			
6 What is the greatest item of your cost in producing the item which we might possibly alleviate?			
7 Do you have a standard part which could be substituted for this one?			
8 Any other suggestions?			

Supplying company	Executive concerned	Your reference	If in doubt regarding any of these questions please consult our:
			Mr
	Title	Date	Telephone Extension

FIGURE 18:2   VALUE ANALYSIS FORM FOR CONTACTING SUPPLIERS

a technique under which targets are fixed as a basis for achieving greater effectiveness throughout the whole of an organisation or part of an organisation. The system involves the fixing of agreed and realistic targets for an organisation or part of it in precise quantitative terms; for example, to increase the output of work by x per cent, to reduce the time taken over a process by y per cent, or reduce the error rate by z per cent. The factors which impede the attainment of these objectives are then identified and courses of action, including training, are agreed in order to remove them. The results are periodically appraised and new targets set. It is important that individual targets are not only clear and realistic in themselves, but should also contribute effectively to the aims of the organisation. The approach is based on the view that targets agreed by a manager and his subordinates are in themselves an incentive and that they form a yardstick, against which performance can be measured.

As it is usually presented in this country, MBO is said to satisfy the five needs of the individual manager:

1 Tell me what you expect from me
2 Give me an opportunity to perform
3 Let me know how well I am doing
4 Give me guidance when I need it
5 Pay and promote me according to my contribution

The first requirement involves a very considerable effort in specifying what is expected of managers. Key tasks and standards of performance have to be worked out for each individual involved. Any manager has 101 different things to do, but quite a small proportion of these are the ones which have the big effect on his job performance. The 80/20 law applies here too: the key tasks, which have to be defined clearly, the ones which enable the manager to get the results required from him if they are done well, are few in number. The rest of what the manager does is not by any means unimportant, but it need not be spelt out in detail; it can be left to the good sense and experience of the individual concerned.

Often a "management guide" is prepared which sets forth for the manager his key tasks and his standards of performance, and shows what control data are required to measure performance against standard.

The next step is to draw up a "job improvement plan." The manager discusses his management guide with his boss, and one or two key tasks may be selected for improvement. At any rate, the aim at this stage is to agree, for each individual involved, one or more *specific objectives* – short, clear descriptions of definite results to be achieved in a set period of time. The specific objectives should:

1 Be accepted by the individual concerned – perhaps even suggested by him
2 Grow out of his normal job responsibilities but also be over and above them
3 Aim to solve current problems, improve performance in some key areas, and develop the individual concerned

This gives the manager his "opportunity to perform." In Bob Hodge's words:

> it creates the kind of environment in which every member of the department is concerned not only with getting the job done, but with actively seeking out opportunities for improvement and innovation. Properly managed, this can certainly increase the profitability of your company and significantly improve the effectiveness of your department. Most importantly, it will improve individual performance and lead to much greater job satisfaction for yourself and your staff. (*Modern Purchasing,* December 1969, page 32.)

Some specific objectives in the materials area:

> In conjunction with the company legal adviser, review our standard conditions of purchase and recommend any changes necessary to make them more appropriate for today's trading conditions, by 30 June. (This might be suitable for a legally qualified member of staff, or for a younger man who is studying commercial law to gain his diploma.)
>
> Develop at least two new suppliers for your major item purchased, by 10 September. (For a buyer who has dealt with the same source for ten years?) Carry out a comprehensive make-or-buy study for item X, consulting engineering, production control and industrial engineering, and make a final recommendation supported by detailed cost data by 1 December.
>
> Coordinate activity between supplier Y and the quality control department, and develop a programme of work to reduce the rejection level for component Z from 20 per cent to 5 per cent by 15 January.

One of the most important products of management by objectives is the discussion by each manager, both up and down the line, which clearly establishes expectations for performance and a willingness to undertake the objectives assigned. It is at this point that a capable leader not only participates in the establishment of objectives, but also communicates an understanding of why the particular objectives are important, and how they fit into the other activities and objectives of the organisation.

Progress reporting and performance evaluation

"Let me know how well I am doing" and "Give me guidance when I need it" were the next two needs. Regular progress reports should lead to the same kind of discussion as when the objectives were being set, when there is a case for modifying the original objective. Informal discussions between the individual and his boss should occur quite often, and perhaps once a quarter a more formal review takes place. This tends to be the crunch point, and the successful MBO programme depends as much on how these interviews are handled as it does on how the specific objectives are set.

Finally, "pay and promote me according to my contribution." Pay increases and promotion opportunities are related to success in achieving key tasks and the specific objectives in the job improvement plan.

Despite the fact that the term MBO and much of its methodology originated in the USA with the management authority Peter Drucker (*The Practice of Management*, Heinemann, 1955), the practice of MBO has not yet caught on in the USA as it has in Britain. But an article in *Harvard Business Review* ('Performance Appraisal: Managers Beware by P H Thompson and G W Dalton) singles out this particular aspect as one of its great advantages. Writers have advocated an MBO appraisal system for many reasons. Douglas MacGregor for instance favoured it as a way to help a manager stop "playing God" – that is, judging the personal worth of his fellow men. Alva F Kindell and James Getza were concerned about "quackery" – noting that conventional performance appraisal required managers to diagnose personality traits. For them, concentration on target-focused appraisals ensured a healthy emphasis on the task. Mayer, Kay and French were able to show that criticism had a negative effect on the achievement of goals, and that performance improved most when specific goals had been established. Our research prompts us to suggest several other advantages:

1 It is future-oriented . . .
2 It is an open, non-zero-sum system . . .
3 It is flexible

As Hodges pointed out, "the setting of good objectives is difficult, and using them to evaluate performance and assist in the development of people is also difficult." And yet, "in the area of performance evaluation lies one of the great advantages of managing by results-oriented objectives. By considering the accomplishment of results, it is possible for an individual to evaluate himself as accurately as he may be evaluated by his superior in the organisation." Subjective judgements about introversion, creativity, "lack of initiative" "too intellectual," can be thrown out. The manager can recommend people for pay increases, bonus awards, or promotion, on the basis of *results*; and he can justify his recommendations on the same basis, both to his superior, and to the subordinates in question.

Service centre or profit centre?

The organisational problem of whether to regard MM departments as service centres or as profit centres is really a motivational problem. Should the heavy costs incurred in supplying parts and materials be regarded as expenses incurred in providing a service, or as outlay made to earn a profit? Both views are in principle tenable. Both affect the attitudes of those concerned. Which works best in the motivation and appraisal of materials people?

Most of the people employed by a manufacturing organisation work in production, and this has been seen as the line management area, the field in which management proper was in operation. Everything else was seen to some extent as a service, staff or advisory area. Sales provided a service in selling the product, transport in taking it away, design in specifying it, purchasing and stock control in providing parts and materials to make it, production planning and control in working out what to make and when. Such an attitude may not be unreasonable in seller's-market conditions. It is dangerously inadequate in conditions where the very existence of an organisation depends on its ability to make and market profitably products which customers will prefer to buy. Money management, product management, materials management, loom up alongside people management as danger areas or contribution areas.

The service area view of MM is powerfully expressed by Donald E Farr in *Handbook of Business Administration* (edited by H B Maynard, McGraw-Hill, 1967): "Operationally it becomes a service function parallel in importance to manufacturing, marketing, engineering and finance, basically established to assist them in their operations."

According to Farr it is because "too many unrelated people have independent control over some phase of material cost with no central control exercised" below top level, that total material costs tend to be excessive. Farr's view of materials management is shown in Figure 18:3. There are four major operational areas: engineering

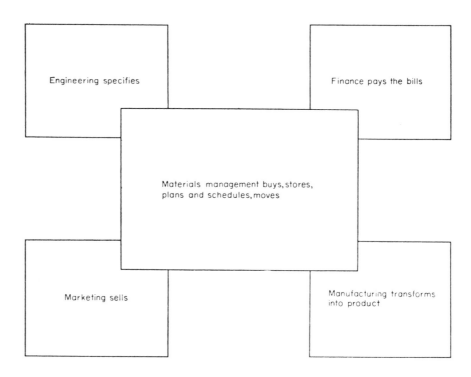

FIGURE 18:3   MATERIALS MANAGEMENT AS A SERVICE CENTRE
Adapted from Donald E Farr, "The Materials Management Concept", in Maynard, H B (Ed.),
Handbook of Business Administration, McGraw-Hill, 1967

design, which develops specifications; manufacturing which transforms materials and assembled parts into the product, marketing which sells and distributes it; and finance, which raises the money and pays the bills. Between these lies, according to Farr, a major service area in which material movement and availability is planned and balanced against needs. He stresses the service aspect heavily:

> materials management is basically a supporting or service function. It has an important role to fill. This role must be to serve – not dominate or control – because there is no profit-making end-product forthcoming, only service. The rewards for effective materials management must come from customer satisfaction in the end product and from good internal performance in specific areas such as inventory space usage, and handling costs. There may be even some merit in calling the materials management function "materials service" to give all concerned the proper connotation of its role. The term "service" is not meant to downgrade the importance of the function but rather to emphasise the support it must give if the company is to be strong.

Dean Ammer takes a different view. He argues that performance has often been distorted, in purchasing, stock control, and other areas, by the common practice of treating them as service areas. The natural tendency for the manager of a service area is to maximise the service within whatever cost constraints are laid down for him, instead of considering overall company profitability; and the restructuring of the organisation along materials management lines enables companies to set profit targets and apply return-on-assets criteria in the materials areas. Dr Ammer argues indeed, in an important and thoughtful paper, *"Materials Management as a Profit Centre" (Harvard Business Review,* January-February 1969), that this is itself a powerful argument for adopting MM.

The notion that purchasing is a profit-making activity as well as a service activity is well established in purchasing circles and is beginning to win acceptance with general management. Why not put these two ideas together, asks Ammer, and require the materials manager to earn his keep by making profits?

Criteria for a profit centre

Any part of an organisation which is to be treated as a profit centre must meet four basic criteria. Materials management departments meet three of these: they incur costs, employ capital and add value (by distribution). The fourth, pricing, can be readily supplied, just as is done in the case of subsidiary companies which act as captive suppliers. If the latter supply the whole of their products to other companies in the group *at cost,* then they are treated as pure service arms of other manufacturing associates. A common practice nowadays is to negotiate transfer prices which allow them to earn a profit – and enable group managment to assess them by the universal profitability yardstick. But standard practice for materials management is to charge out purchases to manufacturing at purchase cost.

And this is not, strictly speaking, even accurate. Purchasing and storage incur overhead and tie up capital. Goods bought for £100 delivered are likely to have cost the business at least £105, perhaps £110 or more, by the time they are fed into the manufacturing process. There is no reason why materials management should not charge internal transfer prices which cover these costs and give a reasonable return on capital employed, just as associated suppliers in the group charge transfer prices which enable them to be treated as profit centres. This is, after all, more or less what industrial distributors and stockholders do. Like them, materials management makes goods available at the point they are wanted, thus adding value.

We cannot run purchasing and stores without incurring costs and tying up capital. Suppose a materials manager is responsible for the following capital investment:

Fixed assets	
stores, warehouses and related equipment	£150 000
office equipment and floor-space	100 000
Current assets	
stock of purchased parts and materials	500 000
	————
Capital employed	£750 000
	————

His company earns 20 per cent before tax on capital employed. Does it not sound reasonable that the materials manager should be assessed on (among other things) his ability to earn 20 per cent (=£150 000) profit before tax on the £750 000 of capital he is employing?

"A MARKED DEPARTURE FROM PRESENT PRACTICE"

One difficulty strikes one immediately: how to tell what profit the materials manager is in fact generating. But Ammer argues that this is not important. The object of treating materials management as a profit centre is not academic accuracy, but motivation, the enforcement of a businesslike outlook, as with the accepted practice of treating subsidiary companies as profit centres. We can start with the simple assumption that all profit centres earn the same rate of return.

If the above-mentioned concern spends £5 million a year on purchases, and incurs costs of £100 000 a year in running its materials management operation, the total cost including "profit" (the opportunity cost of capital), for materials management would be:

Purchases	£5 000 000
Operating expenses	100 000
Return on capital (20 per cent on £750 000)	150 000
	————
Total "sales" to manufacturing	£5 250 000
	————

The value added by materials management on purchases costing £5 million is £250 000, and the purchased parts and materials should be transferred to manufacturing at a total cost of £5 250 000; that is, at an average mark-up of 5 per cent on cost price, to cover expenses and achieve the target return on capital. But this is only the start of the story.

Rules for running the new system

Once the transfer prices have been fixed, they have to stay fixed until the business changes selling prices for its own end-products. *So if materials management negotiates a lower price, or finds a cheaper supplier, it "keeps" the saving.* If goods formerly bought for £100, and charged out to manufacturing at £105, start coming in from a new supplier at £99, they are still charged out at £105, and materials management gets credited with an extra profit of £1.

But if, on the other hand, the materials manager approves salary increases for his staff, or if the supplier puts up his price, then profit margins are squeezed. Goods are still charged out at £105 even though the buying price goes up to £101; the MM gross margin is cut by £1. Relief comes when the company increases its selling prices. A 5 per cent rise in selling prices would increase the MM margin by adding 5 per cent to its internal transfer prices.

Furthermore the materials manager would be charged with the full cost shortages and other supply failures. If a casting turns out to be defective after considerable machining, the total cost is charged to the materials management budget, not to manufacturing. Only the cost of materials will normally be recoverable from outside sources. If late delivery leads customers to cancel their order, not marketing but materials management will be debited with the resultant loss of profit.

This forces the materials manager to behave like a businessman rather than a service department manager. Ammer gives a striking example of this, which may be adapted as below.

Do you choose to have shortages?

It appears that supply managers at present never admit to being responsible for shortages. Shortages always result from unreasonable demands by other departments, insufficient notice, market upheavals or natural disasters. Obviously any shortage at all reduces the service; but never to have any shortages is not business-like, since the cost of a 100 per cent service level is ruinous. Maximising the service instead of the return on capital is a service department attitude. But if no one is looking at the materials manager's return on capital and a lot of people are looking out for shortages this is the attitude one can expect.

Suppose the materials manager in our previous example decides to cut stocks back by £50 000, knowing full well that this will increase shortages and saddle him with chargebacks from manufacturing due to hold-ups amounting to £5000. His profit-and-loss account will look like this, assuming purchases at the same £5 million level:

"Sales" (including 5% mark-up)	£5 250 000
Less cost of purchases	5 000 000
Gross margin (or "value added")	250 000
Less expenses	150 000
Profit	£145 000

Because of the extra costs due to shortages, profit has been reduced from £150 000 to £145 000. A service centre approach would strive to avoid this. But with the profit centre approach it can make sense, since profit is seen as a return on assets employed rather than as an absolute figure. The materials manager reduced his asset base when he cut back on stock. He now employs only £700 000 capital instead of £750 000. Instead of earning 20 per cent on assets he is now earning 20.7 per cent, a $3\frac{1}{2}$ per cent increase in rate of return.

In boom years the materials manager will be impelled not to let stock move up as fast as sales, so as to keep his return on assets in line with the rest of the company. This is indeed what theory tells us he ought to do. But what actually happens in most stores, without the pressure of a profit centre approach, is that stocks increase at least as fast as sales in boom times, and the business gets caught with excess stocks when the boom flattens out. This is one cause of the downturn which tends to follow.

Failure-oriented or success-oriented?

The profit centre approach thus makes materials management people work for the company objective of profitability, and shows how effectively they are using the resources for which they are responsible. Dr Ammer points out that assessment of purchasing in particular tends to be failure-oriented, while the assessment of marketing, for instance, is success-oriented. Salesmen are praised for winning an order, but little is heard of the orders they do not win. Buyers are blamed for failing to get stuff in on time, but no mention is made of the large proportion of requirements which do arrive on time – that's just routine.

This makes purchasing chiefs extremely unwilling to take any chances. Is this why top management is drawn from marketing or manufacturing more often than from purchasing? A profit centre approach to purchasing could change this situation.

A simplified approach is also suggested, to cut out long hours of interdepartmental price haggling and extra paperwork. A purchase price index based on 10 per cent of purchases could be used to adjust overall figures, without altering the traditional cost-price method of charging out and recording goods. Thus if the second year's accounts show that issues to manufacturing have gone up from £5 million to £6 million, the price index can be used to sort out which part of this 20 per cent increase results from increased volume and which part results from increased prices. The price index might have gone up from 100 to 102, a 2 per cent increase. A few minutes calculation will give profit and return on investment on the lines outlined previously.

This is a simulation of the profit centre approach rather than the whole hog itself. But it can still have similar effects, of making materials management profit-minded rather than service-minded, of stimulating executive development by making the materials manager act like a businessman.

Part Five

Strategic planning

Chapter 19

Strategic planning and supply

Herbert Simon's famous precept:[1] "Don't let the urgent take priority over the important" is particularly relevant to the supply of materials. If a business is heavily reliant on the security of economic supply, a long-term view should be taken. Nevertheless, while businesses often spend a lot of time and thought on strategic issues in sales markets and marketing policy, the focus in supply markets and materials policy tends to be operational.

This chapter examines some arguments for including aspects of supply in the development of business strategy, considers some pertinent factors, and reviews approaches to the implementation of such strategic action. In doing this, the fundamental questions for managers concerned with any aspects of business should be borne in mind: Are we only doing things right? Or are we doing the right things?

Example of strategy

Business strategy may be concerned with survival, growth, the attainment of sustainable economic advantage over competitors. In all these areas supply markets may be relevant. It is clear that a successful strategy requires effective balance and integration between the various elements in the company system. If supply market aspects are disregarded, there may be imbalance; exploitable opportunities may be disregarded; and the impact of threats may be increased. The following example illustrates this.

A US company, Savin Business Machines, wished to enter the office copier market, which was dominated by the Xerox company. Savin needed to obtain an advantage over Xerox if it was going to win a share of the market. In three years the company took a major share of the low to medium, plain paper, copying market as a direct result of a balanced, integrated business strategy. The elements of that strategy related to the key areas of the Savin business system. For example, they sold their copiers outright instead of leasing or renting; they used a dealer network instead of selling direct; and they opted to be assemblers instead of manufacturers. This latter element was the basic thrust of their supply market strategy. The extension of it was that they opted to buy standard components from a small number of low-cost suppliers. And the design of their product was based upon these competitive, potentially high volume components.

The application of this strategy meant that they were able to reduce their costs to such a degree that, at one stage, they were able to sell their copier at a price 50 per cent below that of the equivalent Xerox model.

It is important to note here, that the Savin business strategy was integrated. Any of the elements in themselves need not have resulted in successful market penetration. But together they represented a formidable difference which gave the Savin company a competitive advantage.

Strategic planning and change

Why, in the light of such examples, should businesses appear reluctant to involve materials management in strategic planning?

There is little doubt that there is a traditional operational view of the supply function in many businesses. Thus, a perception of the supply function as pertaining to strategy, often necessitates a change of view and change of role not only of supply people, but of others in the system also. Because there is a tendency to resist change in most of us, such a re-alignment can be difficult. And that difficulty is exacerbated when for example the past experience of the managers involved; their professional training; the past experience of the company; and the views of the managers concerned regarding the professionalism of their peers, reinforce the perception of an operational role for the supply aspect of the business.

The interest of businessman in planning of any kind has fluctuated over the last two decades over a spectrum from enthusiasm to cynicism. In the process, corporate strategic planners themselves have been obliged to be agents of change as they have striven to get their approaches accepted. Where early planning efforts have failed, their problems have been exacerbated. But even where the company concerned has readily accepted the need for a formalised planning approach, the kind of problems discussed earlier still prevailed.

For example, one change frequently necessary where planning is introduced is to persuade key managers to recognise their responsibility for the next time frame. Frequently this requires an attitudinal change of some magnitude. Another involves the perception of the manager as operating in a business system as part of a team rather than in a departmentalised organisation. A third, seeks to increase his flexibility as regards alternative ways to achieve desired objectives and, indeed, the form and quality of those goals. Yet another seeks to ensure that the manager is better prepared for change. And in a business environment in which the pace of change has been increasing, this latter adjustment may be regarded as extremely important.

Another common problem relates to managers perceiving planning as being "control", suggesting "lack of freedom to act" and "lack of flexibility". Indeed the disciplines of planning require many people to re-orientate their behaviour. And when that is coupled with a concern about unfamiliar activities (e.g. considering the future) the difficulties involved may be greater.

Yet another, is the concern some managers have as they begin to become involved in planning, and the realisation that their progress against objectives can now be measured. Even where the manager is setting his own criteria, he may feel that he is committing himself.

Implementation

Without doubt an important requirement of a manager who seeks to successfully involve himself in any activity, is an understanding of the process and appropriate "technology". In many areas of business strategy the available literature to assist this process is fairly extensive. From the supply viewpoint that is not so. However, some material does exist which, when used in conjunction with the more general planning literature, can be helpful.

Another necessity is to consider the problems of individuals within the functional area as regards the change. This might necessitate development of new skills, attitudes and knowledge. It may require fears to be dealt with as individuals feel threatened by the proposed change. All people have a limited ability and/or motivation to change and each case needs to be carefully considered.

Another aspect of this is the "face-saving" behaviour of people who feel that they may not be able to cope with the proposed change. As a result they may, actively, oppose the change on grounds discussed earlier. Face-saving behaviour might appear too, if the person concerned perceives of the change as implying previous failure on his part. In cases of this nature, counselling and training can be helpful.

Having considered the circumstances within the department, the next task is to assess problems in promoting the change within the business as a whole. This analysis would then lead to selecting the best method to overcome the particular problems. A plan and related strategy should then emerge, including consideration of how to create the right environment within which the proposed change might be enacted.

Methods include:

1 Communication of benefits to various parties as a result of the change, while overcoming fears.
2 The development of pertinent information. In addition to the straightforward benefits, this would serve to support the improvement in perception of the supply function.
3 Involving for example planners and product development staff in discussions on supply markets.
4 Developing understanding of the potential benefits through providing examples (successes as well as failures) of supply market impact on strategy department.

Whatever methods are used should suit the particular circumstance. It is important to choose the right time to apply any method. Remember do not try to do too much too soon.

Having discussed the need for supply involvement in strategic planning, we now proceed to a consideration of some of the factors which need to be included in the planning process.

One of the key requirements of any planning process is to develop an awareness of the environment. The management process should be concerned with matching resources to opportunities.

The areas for consideration, from the materials point of view, may vary in detail from company to company. However, there are key considerations which apply to most businesses. Among these are the need to monitor changes in the environment; assess the level of risk attached to perceived trends; identify the strengths and weaknesses of the company's present position; identify the challenges in the environment; specify the objectives for the business; and develop and evaluate the alternative methods of achieving those objectives. From this analysis the materials plan should emerge as a key element of an integrated plan for the business as a whole. This should result in the establishment of priorities and the allocation of resources.

Review of the environment

As suggested earlier, the specific factors in the environment which will affect the materials element of the strategic plan, will vary from company to company. However, there are elements which are common in most cases. These include:

  Competitors activities and plans
  Changes in the social aspects of the environment
  Changes in the legal aspects
  Technological changes
  Economic developments
  Political developments

It will be a matter of judgement to ascertain the importance to a particular business of any one of these elements. However, it is likely that all businesses will be affected in some measure by each of these factors. The following examples illustrate this.

The impact of social changes on supply markets in recent years has been considerable. Some of these changes have resulted from pressure from labour unions, others from the enactment of laws and others from the unwillingness of better educated people to undertake certain types of work. Whatever the reason, and despite political shifts, an analysis of the last twenty years reveals a trend. Luc De Cock[2] gave examples of such changes in a talk in London at the end of 1980. Among those which he cited were:

1 In most countries there are difficulties attached to working overtime, and shift work
2 The concept of "unsocial hours" is being used, increasingly, as a means of increasing the premiums for overtime and shift working. This makes overtime working economically less justifiable

3 It has become more difficult and more expensive to make any employee redundant. In consequence employers are much more cautious about increasing the size of their work-force.
4 Safety, ecology and health protection regulations have been increasing both in scope and number.

One important aspect of this from the buying company's viewpoint, is that suppliers may be less able to adjust output to demand. This will be particularly true when such change is requested at short notice.

Availability of material

Among the factors which should be considered in the development of supply strategy concerned with material availability, is the current and future supply/demand balance. In many corporate strategic plans there has been either an explicit or implicit assumption that the relevant material/components will be available over the period of the plan. However, this can be a dangerous assumption for a variety of reasons.

Oil was the classic example of such an assumption and, if we are to take note of many authorities in the field, similar problems may arise with other materials. Roy Wright,[3] writing in late 1975, had this to say:

The industrial countries, but especially the United Kingdom, will face similar problems . . . unless we plan our future supplies. Unfortunately, we do not yet seem ready to accept the changes that have taken place and are taking place. Once the present recession is over, it is unlikely that there will ever again be "cheap" raw materials to feed our industries . . . we have to learn that we must work out a *modus vivendi* with the raw material producing countries . . . otherwise we will face ever increasing shortages, ever increasing prices and disruption of our industries.

Wright argued that the prices which the producers were receiving for their minerals were insufficient either to stimulate or fund the necessary investment. He pointed out that:

Fifteen years ago a mining company could build in eighteen months what was then a reasonably sized mine to produce, say 25 000 tpa of copper at a capital cost of $1,000 per annual ton. Today it is unlikely to contemplate building a . . . complex of less than 50 000 tpa . . . The increase in scale is necessary to offset the effects of declining ore grades . . .

The impact of this trend, and of an increasing awareness by countries with raw materials supplies and energy sources of the potential of adding value themselves, could result in considerable supply difficulties in the future. Even those manufacturing concerns which are secondary users need to be aware of the implications.

Example of planning involvement

Clearly, strategic action has to be based upon informéd awareness of relevant long-term supply market issues. The following example of involvement in strategic planning illustrates both the importance of such awareness and the potential impact upon a business.

British Aerospace, Aircraft Group,[4] along with other airframe manufacturers have used light alloy plate for some twenty-five years. However, the trend since the mid-sixties has been for consumption to increase enormously both in respect of quantity and thickness. Over that period supply lead times for the material tended to be a barometer of aircraft industry activity, varying from five to thirty months. For example, from late 1974/early 1975 through to mid-1977 the material was freely available on a six month lead time. By the end of 1977, however, confidence was returning to the industry and orders for new aircraft were being received and new projects launched. One result of this was that the lead time for light alloy plate had extended to fifteen months.

The long-term projection by the company's supply staff suggested that whilst the future supply position would be tight, it would be adequate. The thinking behind this forecast was that suppliers were increasing their output progressively through a) improvements in productivity, and b) relatively minor investment in ancillary plant.

By the third quarter of 1978 the British Aerospace Board were considering a revision to their trading forecast involving a major production-rate increase on a particular product over a 5–6 year period. The British Aerospace supply market forecast for the period in question indicated that material supply would be a problem unless substantial increases in tonnage were available. At the time of the forecast, suppliers were receiving encouraging information about their markets. However, their tentative plans would not have resulted in sufficient material becoming available within the period British Aerospace had in mind. Since British Aerospace's forecast of material requirement suggested a doubling of demand by 1982/83 this necessitated an overall investment in excess of £30m at 1978 prices.

In the face of this situation, British Aerospace's supply team set out to ensure that there would be material available to meet their needs. Initially the British Aerospace Board were briefed as to the position, as were the members of the composite Board involved in the project. (The project was international and involved several companies in a number of countries.) The relevant UK industry association was briefed as was its European counterpart. Through this connection British Aerospace's projection of total European requirement up to 1985 was confirmed. Subsequently, support was given to applications by suppliers for Investment Support Grants.

The application of this strategy resulted in the European airframe industry putting pressure on its suppliers to make major investments. In turn, the European industry was to be assured of its supply requirements at the expense of other customers; and suppliers were encouraged to increase output from existing plant to maximum levels, while bringing new investment on line in accordance with the forecast requirements of the European airframe industry.

By the end of 1980, two of the industry's key suppliers were well ahead with their investment programme to meet the projected demand. In addition, both had invested in new equipment in order to make plate to British Aerospace's specification.

A major lesson from this case is the importance of projecting supply/demand balance over a period on an *industry* basis. In the case in question, without such consideration, it would appear that there would have been a considerable shortfall in supply. It is true that the European airframe industry is involved in joint projects, thus facilitating the kind of collaboration described. While this might not be possible to the same extent in other industries, there are opportunities for buyer collaboration in respect of supply/demand forecasting in most major industrial situations.

Supply market analysis

Considerations include

1 The size of the market and the proportion "held" by the buying company
2 The level of efficiency in the supply market related to the company's own needs (eg quality, service levels)
3 The extent of purchase competition and the relationship to the company's own purchasing power
4 The pace of technological development in the market place against that of the buying company
5 The supply market price/cost structure as against the company's own requirements
6 Channel developments/"captaincy"
7 Supplier order book position relating to own (projected as well as present)
8 Supply industry capacity against own requirements (projected as well as present)
9 Supplier profitability/break-even levels
10 Relevant currency relationships

Through this process the strengths and weaknesses of the company's position in its supply markets will begin to emerge. The next stage is to establish priorities for strategic action. Given that every business has limited resources some kind of systematic approach needs to be taken.

One approach involves classifying materials for example:

CATEGORY ONE

"Pareto" majors with the highest level of risk attached to them. The process required the computer to classify the company's major production purchases. From this list, low-risk materials/components were extracted and levels of probability of failure attached to all others. Those items with the highest level of risk attached to them were then extracted for more detailed analysis.

Typical requirements for this kind of analysis included:

1   Detailed market date
2   Demand forecasts
    a) from production/marketing
    b) from the supply market
3   Collaborative/liaison with suppliers to obtain the necessary data
4   Where pertinent – buy or make analysis
5   Knowledge of logistic and process development
6   Information on buying competitors' activity
    (direct and indirect)

CATEGORY TWO: Key items which, though they might have been of relatively small value, involved potentially high risk.
   Typical approaches with this group involved

   1   Collaborative arrangements with suppliers
   2   "Strategic" stock
   3   Clear contingency plans

CATEGORY THREE: "Leverage items". Items which were readily available but involved the company in considerable expenditure, and which the company could use as a "lever" to promote some aspect of its strategy.
   For this type the following information was thought to be essential:

1   A clear analysis of the company's purchasing power
2   A careful analysis of the supply market and its inter-relationships
3   Awareness of the alternatives
4   Price/cost data
5   Demand planning
6   A good image in the supply market (as an attractive customer in other respects as well as volume)

Apart from the relatively straightforward approaches in respect of category two, none of the foregoing defines what strategic approach ought to be taken. However, thorough analysis will suggest alternative approaches. The buying company has then to select the most suitable strategy based upon that analysis and the objectives which are proposed. That selection should include careful consideration of for example the assumption upon which objectives, strategy and plan are based and, as importantly, upon the buying company's ability to manage the strategy.

Conclusion

In this chapter we have emphasised the importance of strategic longer-term thinking and action relating to supply markets. Clearly the degree of that importance will vary from company to company. We have not attempted to put forward a "cook-book" approach. Rather we have emphasised some of the basic concepts; indicated some of the reasons why involvement can be difficult; given some examples of application of the ideas being put forward; and suggested some questions for consideration.

In our experience, where supply managers have become involved in this kind of activity, both they and their businesses have benefitted. For instance:

1 The manager perceives his job in greater depth and as part of the business as a whole. Benefits here include improved liaison, greater job satisfaction and greater involvement in decision-making e.g. in new product development
2 It improves coordination (teamwork) within the business system regarding (e.g.) objective setting and related tactical planning
3 It improves policy development
4 It stretches the thinking of other key managers in the system as well as the supply specialist. This helps ensure that key assumptions are tested to a greater degree; that a wider range of alternatives is perceived; and the business team as a whole is better prepared to deal with changes in the environment.

In turn this has resulted in the business avoiding problems and taking advantage of opportunities which lack of such involvement would have rendered impossible.

However, in closing, it is worth emphasising that such advantages do not come about simply as a result of procedural or organisational change. Strategic planning is a process, it involves an attitude of mind which is positive, creative and committed. Certainly, it is a process which is a lot less comfortable than operational management.

References

1 Simon, H A *Administrative Behaviour*, MacMillan, 2nd Edition (1961)
2 De Cock, Luc in a paper to an IPS Seminar on Strategic Planning, Hilton Hotel, London 1980 (November)
3 Wright, R W *Planning Future Raw Material Supply*, Long Range Planning, February (1976)
4 Quoted by R W Townsend in a paper to an IPS Seminar, London 1980 (November)

Further reading

Kiser, G E "Elements of Purchasing Strategy", *Journal of Purchasing & Materials Management,* Fall (1976)
Farmer, D H "Developing Purchasing Strategies", *Journal of Purchasing & Materials Management*, Fall (1978)
Gluck, F W "Strategic Choice & Resource Allocation", *The McKinsey Quarterly*, Winter (1980)

Part Six

Case studies

1 Eden Foods Limited*

Eden Foods Limited produced a variety of food products sold both under the Eden brand name and as "own brands" by major supermarket chains. The company operated seven factories throughout Great Britain. This case describes the central purchasing department located at the Company's London Head Office, adjacent to its North London factory, and responsible for all buying activities relating to over 1000 items of food and packaging, plus common general supplies such as stationery and office equipment. Central purchasing was not responsible for buying manufacturing equipment, tools or maintenance items, which were bought by each factory individually, nor for transport which was handled by the Group transport manager. The finance director (who also acted as the company secretary) dealt with all buying and leasing of property, and advertising was bought by the marketing department. Nevertheless, because of the nature of Eden's business, purchased foodstuffs and packaging materials accounted for just over half of manufacturing costs. Sales reached a new peak of over £35 million last year.

COMPANY BACKGROUND

The company had its origins as a family owned food importer. It had grown fairly rapidly in the late 1950s and 1960s when it had foreseen the trend towards packaged foods, and had moved into processing and packing. Growth had been achieved by building new factories for some products and by acquisition of existing manufacturers when this provided a suitable means of entering a new segment of the market. The company went public in 1963, and this boosted the funds available for growth. The acquisition of a canned vegetable and soup manufacturing company near Aberdeen extended Eden's operations into Scotland in 1968. The opening of a large new cereal processing factory in Manchester a year later was a major step in its expansion programme, taking it into specialist breakfast foods – and into a highly competitive market dominated by companies such as Kellogg's and Quakers. Largely as a result

* This case was adapted by R Wagstaff from another prepared by Professor William Rotch, Colgate Darden Graduate Business School, University of Virginia, U.S.A., and Copyright 1974 by l'Institut pour l'Etude des Méthodes de Direction de l'Entreprise (IMEDE), Lausanne, Switzerland. Adapted and reproduced by permission.

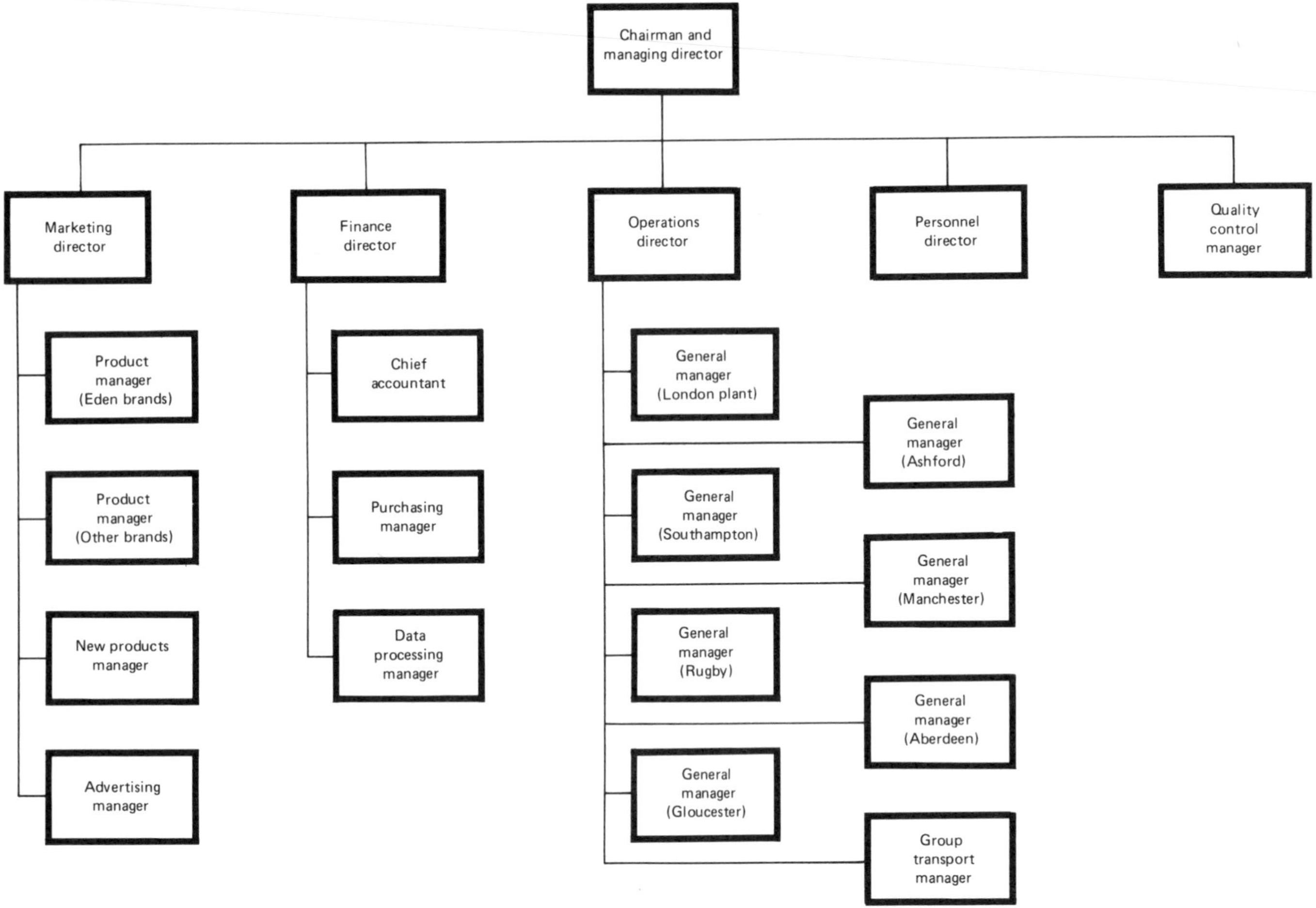

FIGURE 1. PARTIAL ORGANISATION CHART

The chart shows the following structure:

- Chairman and managing director (top)
  - Marketing director
    - Product manager (Eden brands)
    - Product manager (Other brands)
    - New products manager
    - Advertising manager
  - Finance director
    - Chief accountant
    - Purchasing manager
    - Data processing manager
  - Operations director
    - General manager (London plant)
    - General manager (Ashford)
    - General manager (Southampton)
    - General manager (Manchester)
    - General manager (Rugby)
    - General manager (Aberdeen)
    - General manager (Gloucester)
    - Group transport manager
  - Personnel director
  - Quality control manager

of its mixed pattern of growth, there was no particular dominant company philosophy or management style. In many cases companies which had been taken over tended to run much as before, often under essentially the same management teams. Factories which had been newly built were, perhaps, rather more closely controlled from head office.

Each of the seven factories was controlled by a general manager, who reported to the operations director. Control of production and of personnel was left largely to the appropriate general manager. Marketing and finance were controlled centrally. A partial organisation chart is shown in Figure 1.

MATERIALS PURCHASED

The items purchased were in two main categories: foodstuffs and packaging. The foodstuffs were classified into eleven families of items such as fresh fruit and vegetables: flavourings and spices; cereals; preservatives and colourings; juices and purees; fish, meat and poultry; etc. The few most important items in terms of value of purchases were handled by the purchasing manager. Other food items were handled by the senior buyers and the buyer responsible for sugars, except for a few dairy items (mainly cheese and dried and fresh milk) which were still bought by the assistant purchasing manager who had considerable previous experience with these items.

The packaging materials were divided into four groups under the control of a senior buyer, plus labels and printing under another senior buyer. Materials were bought all over the world. Some foodstuffs came only from certain areas or countries, and because of the changing political and economic conditions prices were not as predictable as they used to be.

None of the seven plants used all of the materials since no single factory produced all of Eden's full range of products. A few products were produced in more than one plant. Some plants were quite specialised, others produced a very wide range. One plant at Gloucester used a limited range of fresh fruit and vegetables which were mainly grown locally, plus bought-in sugar and syrups, and a small range of packagings such as tins, jars and caps, labels and cartons. In this plant production was highly seasonal. A specialised, modern factory in Manchester produced a narrow range of breakfast cereals using imported grain, sugar and flavourings, plus about 30 packaging materials such as plastic film, paper and cartons. On the other hand the oldest factory in North London produced a very wide product range calling for over 200 food items and about 650 packaging items.

The plants all had purchasing staff who had line responsibility to the general manager of the plant and functional responsibility to the central purchasing manager. The central and plant purchasing departments divided their buying responsibility as follows:

Central	Plant
All items with high total value	Items with low total value
Most items used in more than one plant.	Items purchased locally
	Items used only in that plant.

For the items which were bought centrally, the central purchasing department negotiated the price and quantity contract and the plants arranged delivery schedules to meet their production plans. Details of all items which were purchased locally were reported to central purchasing monthly.

The quality of purchased materials was particularly important because Eden prided itself on maintenance of very high standards. Each purchase contract defined the quality specifications which the supplied material should meet. Quality requirements were determined by consultation between Eden's quality control department, the product manager and the plant production people, with advice as needed from the purchasing department. Each delivery was inspected upon arrival at the plant, and any sub-standard supplies were rejected.

THE CENTRAL PURCHASING DEPARTMENT

There were about 30 people in the central purchasing department, as shown in Figure 2. In addition there were typically two or three staff at each factory who dealt with plant purchases. Each factory also had stock control and warehouse staff who reported to the plant general manager.

John Hagan, the purchasing manager, had joined the company in sales and marketing and had moved into buying when the company opened its Ashford factory. He took charge of central purchasing ten years ago.

The assistant purchasing manager was functionally responsible for buying all foodstuffs, as shown by the dotted lines in Figure 2, although in other respects the two foodstuffs senior buyers reported to Mr Hagan.

Like both Mr Hagan and the assistant purchasing manager, the purchasing staff concerned with foodstuffs had considerable experience in the food industry, but few, if any, formal qualifications. The buyers and senior buyers of packaging materials, on the other hand, tended to be technically qualified in a relevant subject to at least HNC level. Two, at least, were also known to be completing part-time courses for membership of the IPS. When asked what he thought were the most important capabilities and qualities of a buyer in a department such as his, Mr Hagan thought carefully and listed four, in order of importance:

First, honesty and integrity – the *sine qua non,* in my view.

Second, curiosity, interest in learning about new trends, new products, new sources.

Third, I look for initiative and the ability to organise one's own work. I like to be able to give my people a job to do, and not to have to keep checking up on them to see if they've done it.

Fourth, they must have a sound technical knowledge of the products they're buying, the manufacturing processes used, and so on. In fact, the last two people we've recruited as assistant buyers have both got technical degrees, one in metallurgy and one in plastics technology.

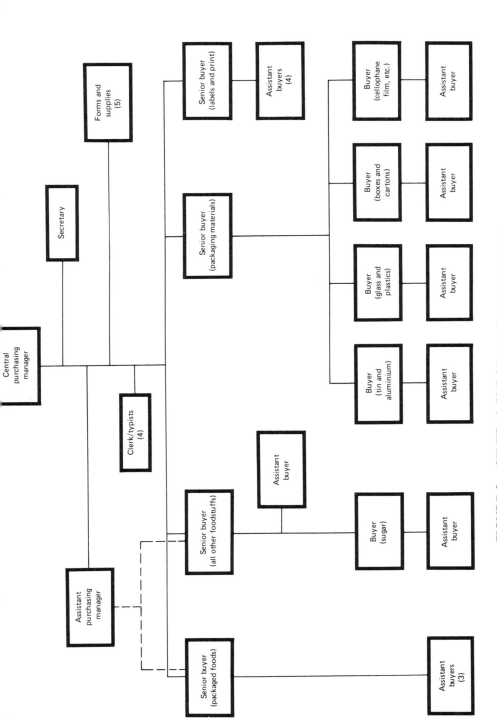

FIGURE 2: CENTRAL PURCHASING DEPARTMENT

THE PLANNING AND BUDGETING PROCEDURE
The planning and budgeting procedure followed a series of steps throughout the year.

1   In September the central purchasing department made a price forecast for the following year. A revised price forecast was normally made in June. Modified price forecasts for individual materials were made at any time, whenever price changes were large enough to warrant a new price standard. The annual forecast made in September showed an expected price for each purchased material for January, July and October. This forecast also listed the "coverage" required for each material. Coverage was a period of time which would normally elapse between placement of an order for the material and delivery. It was influenced by expectations of the supplier's stocking practices, the location of supply sources and transportation and processing speed. Coverage varied from six days on items which nearby suppliers regularly stocked to six months on some items from Africa or South America. The annual forecast made in September provided an average price for the year, considering the anticipated purchase price changes, as well as the purchase volume and timing, the last two factors reflecting planned inventory levels.

2   After the purchase price forecasts had been made in September, the sales department made a forecast of sales volume for each product.

3   Production requirements for end products, based on the sales expectations, were then assigned by headquarters to the plants.

4   At about the same time the plant purchasing departments converted planned production volumes of each end product into raw material requirements. These amounts were adjusted for the estimated beginning inventory as well as an ending inventory requirement for adequate coverage. The resulting quantities were the basis for the monthly plant reports indicating the amounts which would have to be bought.

5   The actual purchase contracts were negotiated throughout the year, at times determined by seasonality, type of material and required coverage. Purchase contracts usually specified the currency to be used in payment for the delivered goods. The finance department was responsible for paying the invoices and consequently the availability of currency other than Sterling was their responsibility. However, the purchasing department made particular efforts to let the finance department know when large amounts of foreign currency would be needed, and to incorporate in contracts any currency provisions suggested by the finance department. Since currency coverage was usually not permitted beyond three months, there were occasions when the actual Sterling amount paid would differ from the amount recorded by the purchasing department at the time of purchase using the exchange rate of that day.

REPORTS
Among the many reports prepared by the seven plants were two which were regularly used by the headquarters purchasing department.

1   Each month the plants prepared a report showing, month by month, for the next
    year, a forecast for each material:
    Inventory at the beginning of the month
    The amount needed to carry out the production schedule
    The amount ordered but not delivered
    Shortages, if any.
2   The same information, by weeks, for four months into the future

These two reports enabled the purchasing department at headquarters to keep track
of usage and purchases of each material, and to see whether the actual coverage was
expected to drop below that which was required for that item. Most of these reports
were prepared by plant computers.

There was also a report which appeared every two months comparing actual
material costs with standard costs, by groups of products. The variance shown could
be caused by either a price or a quantity variation or both. Quantity variations could
be caused by changes in the formula or in the method, or by the substitution of an
alternative material. Price variance could be affected by variations in certain handling costs included in the material cost, also by stock valuation at the beginning and
end of the period, since stock was shown at cost price. The report did not show price
variation separately, and consequently was not much use to the headquarters buyers
in following price behaviour. Instead the buyers used their own methods to keep
track of prices. These included informal records and an intuitive feel for the situation.
In general the price trends in major items for which they were responsible were well
known to them.

The cost variance report was used internally by the plants as a performance
measure. However, if the variance exceeded one per cent the standard would be
reviewed and possibly revised. (The latest report from one plant showed favourable
cost variances for some product groups, unfavourable variances for others, and a net
variance for the plant of minus 0.2 per cent, i.e. 0.2 per cent below standard budget
cost for the previous two months.)

SOME CURRENT ACTIVITIES IN CPD

In addition to negotiating price and quantity contracts, and preparing price forecasts,
central purchasing department had a number of other concerns, for instance:

1   *Materials substitution:* research was under way on alternatives to plastics
packaging materials, used in film coverings, bags, caps to jars, boxes and other
containers. Plastics were getting increasingly expensive, mainly because of their
petroleum base, and in some cases there was a threat of shortage. Tinplate, paper and
cardboard were possible substitutes which were being evaluated for availability, cost
and effect on marketing.

2   *Price relationships:* selling prices for most end products were fixed for a
considerable period, mainly for marketing reasons, yet the raw materials from which
the products were made could vary sharply in price within the same period.

3   *Currency fluctuations:* for instance a large shipment of a certain commodity was delivered one Friday just before the French presidential election, to be held on Sunday. Payment was due immediately (ie within 24 hours) in French francs. There was still time on Friday to buy francs; or the finance department could wait till Monday. But the outcome of the election would undoubtedly influence the exchange rate, perhaps by one per cent either way. This would increase or decrease by £5000 the amount due to be paid for the commodity. Sterling had risen 0.56 per cent against the franc in the previous two days.

Points for discussion

1   The general manager of the Gloucester plant recently sent to members of the management committee a memo recommending a change to materials management organisation structure in his plant. The monthly management committee meetings have discussed the related question of purchasing centralisation or decentralisation on several occasions over the past two years without reaching a conclusion. As central purchasing manager, write a memo to members of the management committee recommending with reasons either:
a   The adoption of a materials management structure at each factory, or
b   Further centralisation of purchasing with suitable changes to factory structures, or
c   The retention of existing arrangements with any modifications you consider desirable.
2   John Hagan, Central Purchasing Manager, was suddenly taken ill and had to retire early; and the assistant purchasing manager was appointed as his replacement. As the newly appointed central purchasing manager, explain what changes you would wish to make in the organisation of central purchasing department, assuming that the role of the department is to continue essentially as before.
3   Still as newly appointed central purchasing manager, write a memo to the finance director reviewing the usefulness of the reports currently submitted by plant purchasing staff, and advocating any other reports you would like to see to cover key result areas or to assist in assessing the efficiency of purchasing.
4   Consider the case for setting up a small purchase research section in central purchasing. Outline the major areas for research, suggest six topics for investigation, and briefly indicate how the cost of taking this step would be related to the benefits.
5   What kind of programme for staff development and training would you propose for central and plant purchasing staff, and staff in related functions?
6   What procedure would you adopt for coping with currency fluctuations between the date at which contract price is agreed and the date at which payment is to be made?

2 Materials mismanagement

KW Electronics Ltd manufactured a variety of electronic equipment at their main factory in Bristol, with feeder factories in Bath and Gloucester. Their head office in London issued revised master production schedules every six weeks. These schedules showed planned output of each product week by week for three months ahead, and probable output month by month for a further three months.

When the Bristol buying office received a revised master production schedule, the extension to the production schedule of products was immediately exploded into requirements for parts from outside suppliers. Purchase orders were promptly placed with suppliers for the total extra quality required. Orders were marked: delivery to be in accordance with demand schedules to be supplied shortly.

Meanwhile, the materials controller was preparing the demand schedules. The gross requirement for sub-assemblies, parts and materials was regenerated by exploding the revised and extended master production schedule through the parts lists. To arrive at the net requirement, stock on hand was deducted from the gross requirement. Demand schedules for purchased components were sent to suppliers in similar format to the master production schedule itself: week by week net requirements for three months ahead, with a further three months projection of probable requirements for use in planning.

There were, however, a few problems. The three thousand items of stock were thought too numerous to pick production requirements day-by-day, so two weeks requirements would be issued at a time for each item required. When preparing a new demand schedule the materials controller would find stock of some items to be very low because two weeks supply had just been issued. Once items had been issued to manufacturing, they were outside the materials controller's jurisdiction and he had no information on them.

Additionally, some components were required weeks earlier than others used on the same product, to enable feeder factories to complete their operations or for the manufacture of sub-assemblies which had to be ready before work could start on final assembly of the product.

Demand schedules were also affected when work was switched from a first preference supplier to a second or third source because of availability problems or performance ratings.

Also new orders were continually arriving from customers, some of them regarded as urgent, and existing orders were being amended or cancelled. The materials controller would immediately amend his demand schedules by telex and telephone when he received word of these changes. It was difficult for suppliers to cope with the changes if they arrived in the middle of the month or later, by which time most of the month's production would be complete.

The new master production schedules which were issued every six weeks did not just add another six weeks output plan; figures for the current month were revised as well.

The result of all this was that the timing and quantities called for on demand schedules was quite different, and out of sequence, with the purchase orders placed by the buying office. Often there was no order cover to authorise deliveries called for on the demand schedule; often there was no demand schedule to call for components which had been ordered. When new demand schedules were sent to suppliers, it usually appeared that in the light of the latest figures some components had already been over delivered and some had been under delivered.

Over delivered components were returned to the supplier, involving double handling and transport costs. Under delivered components led to continuous and energetic chasing, again at disproportionate cost.

Points for discussion

1   Assume you have just taken over as materials controller at the Bristol factory of KW Electronics Ltd. What actions would you take: (a) as first priority; (b) in the longer term?

2   Assume you are the sales and technical representative for a major supplier to KW Electronics Ltd. What actions would you take: (a) as first priority; (b) in the longer term?

3   Now think about your actual working environment. What lessons can you learn from this case which might have applications in the business you work for?

3 Browns Industries Limited

"Well, Mr. Saunders, that is about all I can tell you about the company. You've been recommended to us as someone who can have a considerable influence on our business. I have been told that your approach to materials management resulted in your last employer turning around a loss-making business within two years.

As you have heard, we are not losing money, at the moment, but there are tough times ahead. We've asked you to join us in order to increase our efficiency and effectiveness in order that we can survive in an increasingly competitive world."

Fred Saunders reflected on his new MDs comments. It was a huge task. Browns Industries Ltd had four divisions and twenty-six plants. Their product range covered motor vehicle components, small domestic appliances and military equipment. The plants were located all over the UK. He pondered on how he should tackle his task. At 10.30 a.m. on his first day it seemed immense.

Nonetheless, being an advocate of planning, he reached for a note pad in order to make a first draft of how he was going to approach the job.

Points for discussion

1   If you were Fred Saunders, what headings would appear in your plan?
2   To which items would you give priority?
3   Having explored these questions, assume that you have been appointed to a new job at a level appropriate to your present experiences. Write a check list outlining your own broad plan.

4 Atlas Incorporated

Mike Hunt was group coordinator for European purchasing for a large American-based multinational, Atlas Inc. Atlas manufactured drugs and other chemical products and had plants in most West European countries. Each plant was either a subsidiary company or a profit centre within such a company. Atlas adopted a highly decentralised approach to production and purchasing. However, about three years ago it was decided to appoint a group coordinator for purchasing in Europe to investigate commonality in material requirements and the scope for joint purchase arrangements.

Operating from the corporate headquarters in New England, Mike Hunt's predecessor had spent some time with the purchasing staff in each of the European plants and had collected a fair amount of data on common requirements. In his final report he stressed that he had only been able to scratch the surface. He recommended that his successor should operate from Brussels, sharing office accommodation with the European sales coordination staff, and that he be supported by a small staff of European nationals. After his promotion to a higher position at corporate headquarters, Mike Hunt had been appointed coordinator, had moved to Brussels, and had appointed his small staff.

That was over two years ago, and Mike Hunt felt that he had now arrived at a point where he needed to take some new approach. He'd had successes, but there were also instances where plants had simply stuck to their guns and insisted on their traditional independence. He'd discussed this with a vice-president over on one of his periodical visits, and got the following reply: "Mike, Rome wasn't built in a day. Sure we want to improve profitability; but we also want to improve relationships over here in Europe. I want this to be a team job, and it doesn't seem to me that plant managers are going to obtruct any proposals from you which are commercially advantageous to them."

"Sounds okay," thought Mike. "But human nature is a funny thing, some of these guys just won't let go."

One of his first group contracts had been signed with Bauer GmbH, a three year contract for the supply of raw materials to six different Atlas plants in various parts of Europe. A few months ago a French concern, Pan-monde, had offered to supply the same material at a price almost 30 per cent lower than Bauer's. Of course a contract is a contract, and there was no question of cancelling the agreement with Bauer. But there was the possibility of re-negotiation. A key point was that the contract mentioned a total requirement over three years of about 3.5 million units, and actually in two years 3.75 million units had been taken. It was likely that the requirement would continue to increase, because of a new product coming on stream at two of the plants. After a fairly lengthy negotiation, Bauer agreed to reduce contract price by 24 per cent for the last ten months of the three year contract period. Mike Hunt received complete cooperation from the six plants affected and felt that this was a successful instance of group negotiation for common requirements.

An unsuccessful instance occurred recently where three plants were using the same material but were buying it to different specifications. Because of foreseeable cost trends Mike felt it important that a standard specification should be agreed and a joint contract arranged. But he had not been able to persuade any of the plants to agree.

Mike Hunt subscribed fully to the corporate policy of decentralisation and what was referred to as the "folly" of centralised purchasing. What was needed, in his view, was more cooperation without dictation: joint purchasing where appropriate and where requirements could be grouped, by persuasion and teamwork rather than by edicts from on high.

Points for discussion

1   What do you think could account for the reluctance to cooperate by some plants on some occasions?
2   How could plant purchase departments help the group coordinator to help them?
3   What new approach could Mike Hunt adopt?

5 X Y Z Excavator Company

Bill Treadwell, purchasing director of XYZ Excavators, finished his talk to a gathering of suppliers with these words:

> Gentlemen, let me reiterate. As we move into the Eighties we are faced with a problem of survival. One of our Japanese competitors is coming into our markets with selling prices equal to our variable costs. We cannot sit back and let them take our markets, so we must fight back! Since purchase costs represent more than 65 per cent of our selling price we must look for savings there. Quite frankly gentlemen, not only are we saying that we will not accept *any* price increases; we are also asking for price reductions. And I must say, in fairness to both your companies and ourselves, unless we get reductions we will be forced to source abroad. We don't wish to do that, but if it comes to a matter of survival or buy British, then I am afraid that there is only one answer.'

As the delegates to the XYZ supplier workshop at Henley moved out of the conference room the buzz of conversation was intense. Bill Treadwell, who was gathering his papers together was approached by a grim faced supplier.

> Look, Bill, we hear what you say and we sympathise. But, how can you expect us to hold prices, let alone reduce them, when we are faced with double figure inflation and crippling interest rates? If you really mean what you have said I'm afraid we couldn't live with it. What happens then, if we go to the wall? You will not have a home based supplier of our product, since we are the only one. Will your overseas suppliers work with you like we have? Will they give you the credit you have taken off us? Will they give you the kind of "breakdown" service we have provided? You can be sure they won't be messed about like we have with your constant schedule changes!

Points for discussion

1 Do you agree with Bill Treadwell's approach to his suppliers?
2 What credence do you give to the suppliers' warnings?
3 Name the key strategic implications in this case.
4 How would you deal with the situation in Bill's place?

6 Colourtone Cosmetics Limited

Bernard Hammond, general manager of Colourtone Cosmetics (contract division) banged his desk.

"Look, Harry, this business operates on a fast response basis. Impossible is not a word which our customers recognise!"

Harry Slater, who was responsible for all materials management matters for the Colourtone division, sighed as he left his boss' office.

"Fantastic", he thought to himself, "Able and Willing (the retail stores giant which was the division's largest client) were at it again."

As he walked back to his office, he thought over the events of the last eight weeks. Colourtone Cosmetics (contract division) was a division of a leading manufacturer of a middle-market range of cosmetics. The division was concerned with producing own brand cosmetics for several stores. Able and Willing accounted for just under 30 per cent of the division's business. Thus they were of considerable importance to the business.

The particular event which had resulted in Harry's present dilemma, had its origins more than six months before. At that time, an Able and Willing director had asked the division to quote for a run of 2000 units of a face cream dispenser with refill packs and contents. The dispenser was designed to be mounted on a bathroom wall. The initial order was for a market test quantity. Able and Willing said, that, if it went well, they would order more. Since this was a regular Able and Willing approach with new products, which, for the four years they had been working together had failed to produce a significant second order, no one queried the implications.

In due course Harry had bought tooling for the dispenser capable of producing 5000 units. With money as tight as it was at the end of 1980 that was a reasonable thing to do. However, it turned out otherwise. Within two weeks of the initial delivery hitting the Able and Willing counters, they were back with an order for a further 3500 for "immediate delivery". The division responded quickly and Hammond had immediately questioned Able and Willing on further needs. Whilst reluctant to commit themselves the stores people had said that they were excited at the prospects. The second run finished the tooling for there was an unacceptable amount of rejects in the last batch.

279

Bernard Hammond asked Harry what the position would be if they came back again. Harry had told him that long run tooling had a lead time of twelve weeks – the softer tools could be lined up in about six. Bernard suggested that they should discuss the matter at a meeting which was to take place the following day.

An hour before the meeting was due to take place Harry had been called to Bernard Hammond's office.

"Harry, Able and Willing have come back with an order for 75 000 units, delivery to commence within twenty-one days, with completion in twenty-eight!"

That was when Harry had said "Impossible". But the economics of the order were extremely attractive to Colourtone. Not only were Able and Willing prepared to pay the price agreed for the initial run (indeed they hadn't even questioned Colourtone on a reduction for the increased volume), they were talking about a sales bonanza.

When Harry arrived back at his office he knew he was about to perform the impossible yet again.

Points for discussion

   1   In Harry's place how would you set about the task?

   2   Given the nature of the business and the power of Able and Willing how would you attempt to reduce the extent of the problem on future occasions?

7 Two weeks' supply

"Look Mr. Curtis, we've tried hard with your base casting. It's a pig, if I may use that expression! On average 35 per cent of the castings we pour are rejected by your inspectors. And, what's more, you're screwing us on a price we quoted on the assumption that we would get at least a 90 per cent yield."

The Manager of Lloyds Foundry was, clearly, serious as he responded to Ken Curtis's complaints. Ken was chief buyer of Deboard Equipment Ltd, and was in trouble with his own production people because of Lloyds failure to deliver to schedule. The base casting involved was a key item in one of Deboard's major products and had given considerable trouble for the three years of its life. Despite Ken's personal attention, Lloyds were unable to meet schedules. In the process Curtis was having a rough time with his own colleagues.

As the conversation escalated to an argument, both parties began to raise their voices. And in due course Ken finally lost his temper and yelled at the Lloyds man.

"If you can't give us the castings we want after all this time, you'd better give me our pattern equipment here and now. I'd better find a decent supplier to meet our needs!"

The response was swift and sharp.

"You can have your damn pattern! We'll be glad to see the back of it!"

As a result of the contretemps at the Lloyds foundry, Ken Curtis found himself, with the pattern equipment, back in his office.

His first check showed that Depoards had two weeks' supply of acceptable castings in stock. Lloyds had been a single source, so no other existed. He realised then, that he'd been too long in that situation and wasn't in touch with the market. Grey-iron foundries were far fewer than ever before. And when he looked for the precision and quality which he was after, only two alternatives suggested themselves.

Within three days he had established that neither was interested in the job. Indeed only one would quote and at a price almost double Lloyds' price. In desperation he swallowed his pride and rang the Lloyds Manager, only to find that his former supplier was adamant. He was no longer interested in the base casting business.

Points for discussion

1 What should Ken Curtis do?
   a) in the short term
   b) in the longer term
2 What lessons should be learned from Ken's experience?

8   Double delivery dilemma

Brian Bevan was the general maintenance foreman for Associated Glassware Ltd. His responsibilities included preventative maintenance of making machinery and he was well thought of by Stuart Ferguson, the AGW Works Engineer to whom he reported. Ferguson thought well of Bevan, among other things, because he was prepared to work on his own initiative and "got things done while others were still talking about it."

Despite the preventative work which was being done, the pressures of the twenty-four-hour AGW operation resulted, on occasions, in the breakdown of key machinery Brian Bevan and his team then had to work around the clock to get the relevant machine back on line. It was on these occasions that his boss thought he was seen at his best, and Stuart Ferguson had told his own chief that Brian was promotable material on the strength of consistently good performances under such pressure.

BUYING SOME TIMBER

Early one Friday morning, the making foreman on the ten-till-six shift rang through to confirm that the number 3 machine would be available as arranged, first thing on Monday morning for its major overhaul under the preventative maintenance scheme.

In order to do this overhaul, it was necessary to shore up with timber and Brian's calculations suggested that he would need two standards of spruce to do this. Taking down his requisition pad, he made out the form to cover his need, carefully filling in the coding data. Brian knew that the last timber he'd requisitioned had come from Mantle & Boston, a large local importer who had supplied timber to AGW for many years. Consequently, he filled in this firm's name in the "preferred suppliers" box on the form.

The AGW requisition system required Brian's signature to be first countersigned by his boss, the works engineer, and then by the chief engineer. So, in order to save time, since he wanted the timber first thing on the Monday, he took the requisition himself to Stuart Ferguson's office. As Stuart was on the telephone when he went in, Brian put the requisition in front of him, pointing with a stabbing motion to the words, "Urgent must have Monday a.m.," which he had printed in large capitals at the base of the form. While carrying on his telephone conversation, Stuart nodded and gave Brian a "thumbs up." At that point Brian left his boss's office and proceeded with the many other arrangements which he had to make.

As soon as Ferguson had finished his telephone conversation he picked up his internal 'phone and rang Terry Price, AGW's purchasing manager.

"Terry, I'd like you to get cracking and get two standards of spruce in by Monday 8 a.m. Brian Bevan wants it for shoring up on the number 3 machine overhaul. I thought that I'd let you know on the 'phone, for by the time the chief engineer countersigns the requisition and it's cleared, it'll be Monday before you get it."

After checking on accounting code numbers and the requistion reference, Terry said that he would make sure that the timber would be there on the Monday.

As it happened, Terry had been doing a survey of timber suppliers only recently, for he felt that Mantle and Boston were getting too complacent about AGW orders. In addition, their prices seemed to be creeping up on every order placed. Thus, armed with an urgent need, he rang Coslett Timbers Ltd. Cosletts had been trying to get AGW orders for some time and he thought that this would give them a chance to perform against a tight delivery and would give him an opportunity to judge their ability. Terry was pleased to see that they quoted what he considered to be a keen price, and guaranteed delivery to meet his needs. Thus satisfied, he placed a verbal order, and then reserved the purchase order number, which he had quoted as was his custom, against receipt of the requisition.

As soon as he had finished speaking to Cosletts he rang Stuart Ferguson and told him that the timber would be in, as requested, at 8 a.m. on the Monday.

At 3 p.m. Brian Bevan called his chargehand into his office.

"Right then, we've got everything organised for the number 3 machine job on Monday. The only thing we have to make sure of is the timber. You'd better get on to Mantle and Boston and check that everything is laid on. If we don't get that we'll be jiggered."

When the chargehand had spoken to Mantle and Boston and they had denied all knowledge of any order, Brian took the 'phone himself.

"Ah, is that you, Mr Waring. Look, I've put a requisition up for two standards of spruce. We must have it by 8 a.m. on Monday. I expect those bloody purchasing people are sitting on the note. Yes, it's all approved. Many thanks. I'll look forward to getting it."

In the ensuing conversation between Bevan and his chargehand, purchasing didn't come off too well. Indeed, Brian was just on the point of going up to Stuart Ferguson to gripe about their inefficiency, when a further urgent job was reported. Cursing the day he ever got involved in maintenance, he dashed off to sort out the new problem.

On Monday, Terry Price found that his 'phone was ringing when he arrived at his office at 8.30 a.m.

"Gate here, Mr Price, Brian Bevan says to tell you that he's got two lots of timber and will you sort it out."

Points for discussion

1 In Terry Price's place, how would you deal with the immediate problem?
2 How would you deal with the overall problem?

9   Leader Chemical Limited

The largest amount of money which Adam Ferguson spent per year on one raw material was approximately £1 million. As purchasing controller of the Leader Chemical and Pharmaceutical Company Ltd (LCP), this represented about 12 per cent of his total spend. Adam had contracted for a material called Chlorane in 1978 and 1979 and there was every indication that, in 1980, his requirements and, hence, expenditure, were likely to be slightly greater.

Chlorane was one of Ferguson's success stories in what he called dynamic sourcing. Five years ago, it had replaced a natural raw material which was both inconsistent in quality and declining in availability.

In conjunction with the LCP chief chemist, he had scoured the country looking for an alternative. His efforts had appeared to be in vain until the chemist had developed a process which changed the properties of Chlorane to the stage that it was a more controlled product than the raw which it had replaced.

In 1974, Ferguson had placed orders for £100 000 worth of the material, which was converted by the new process into a series of three intermediates, Hypo-Chlorane 1, 2 and 3. These were subsequently used in the manufacture of a key group of LCP products, called the "Amphile Range" (see chart), which was a market leader in its field.

INCREASING REQUIREMENTS FOR CHLORANE

During 1975, LCP marketing department found that other manufacturers wished to purchase Hypo-Chlorane as an intermediate for non-competitive products. Thus, Ferguson's requirements for Chlorane increased, not only in line with the needs of Amphile, but also with regard to the increasing market requirements of Hypo-Chlorane.

By 1977, Ferguson was beginning to get concerned about supplies of Chlorane, for he was now spending about £600 000 a year with two suppliers, Zemph International and Bauer Chemicals. Bauer were supplying slightly more than Zemph, but there was not a great deal in the split. His only other source was a smaller company called Danielson with whom he spent £70 000 a year. Danielson had been his original supplier of Chlorane, but had now resorted to reselling Zemph material. Ferguson kept them on, however, for their material appeared to be slightly more tightly controlled than either of his other suppliers. The LCP chief chemist had put this down to the fact that Danielson's used Chlorane as an intermediate for one of their